AT THE EDGE OF
THE UNIVERSE

THE ELLIS HORWOOD LIBRARY OF SPACE SCIENCE AND SPACE TECHNOLOGY

SERIES IN ASTRONOMY

Series Editor: JOHN MASON
Consultant Editor: PATRICK MOORE

This series aims to coordinate a team of international authors of the highest reputation, integrity and expertise in all aspects of astronomy. It makes valuable contributions to the existing literature, encompassing all areas of astronomical research. The titles will be illustrated with both black and white and colour photographs, and will include many line drawings and diagrams, with tabular data and extensive bibliographies. Aimed at a wide readership, the books will appeal to the professional astronomer, undergraduate students, the high-flying 'A' level student, and the non-scientist with a keen interest in astronomy.

PLANETARY VOLCANISM: A Study of Volcanic Activity in the Solar System
Peter Cattermole, formerly Lecturer in Geology, Department of Geology, Sheffield University, UK, now Freelance Writer and Consultant and Principal Investigator with NASA's Planetary Geology and Geophysics Programme
DIVIDING THE CIRCLE: The development of critical angular measurement in astronomy 1500–1850
Allan Chapman, Centre for Medieval and Renaissance Studies, Oxford, UK
SATELLITE ASTRONOMY: The Principles and Practice of Astronomy from Space
John K. Davies, Royal Observatory, Edinburgh, UK
THE ORIGIN OF THE SOLAR SYSTEM: The Capture Theory
John R. Dormand, Department of Mathematics and Statistics, Teesside Polytechnic, Middlesbrough, UK, and Michael M. Woolfson, Department of Physics, University of York, UK
THE DUSTY UNIVERSE
Aneurin Evans, Department of Physics, University of Keele, UK
SPACE-TIME AND THEORETICAL COSMOLOGY
Michel Heller, Department of Philosophy, University of Cracow, Poland
ASTEROIDS: Their Nature and Utilization
Charles T. Kowal, Space Telescope Institute, Baltimore, Maryland, USA
COMET HALLEY — Investigations, Results, Interpretations
Volume 1: Organization, Plasma, Gas
Volume 2: Dust, Nucleus, Evolution
Editor: J. W. Mason, B.Sc., Ph.D.
ELECTRONIC AND COMPUTER-AIDED ASTRONOMY: From Eyes to Electronic Sensors
Ian S. McLean, Joint Astronomy Centre, Hilo, Hawaii, USA
URANUS: The Planet, Rings and Satellites
Ellis D. Miner, Jet Propulsion Laboratory, Pasadena, California, USA
THE PLANET NEPTUNE
Patrick Moore, CBE
ACTIVE GALACTIC NUCLEI
Ian Robson, Director of Observatories, Lancashire Polytechnic, Preston, UK
ASTRONOMICAL OBSERVATIONS FROM THE ANCIENT ORIENT
Richard F. Stephenson, Department of Physics, Durham University, Durham, UK
EXPLORATION OF TERRESTRIAL PLANETS FROM SPACECRAFT: Instrumentation, Investigation, Interpretation
Yuri A. Surkov, Chief of the Laboratory of Geochemistry of Planets, Vernandsky Institute of Geochemistry, USSR Academy of Sciences, Moscow, USSR
THE HIDDEN UNIVERSE
Roger J. Taylor, Astronomy Centre, University of Sussex, Brighton, UK
AT THE EDGE OF THE UNIVERSE
Alan Wright, Australian National Radio Astronomy Observatory, Parkes, New South Wales, Australia, and Hilary Wright

AT THE EDGE OF THE UNIVERSE

ALAN WRIGHT, B.Sc., Ph.D.
Australian National Radio Astronomy Observatory
New South Wales, Australia

and

HILARY WRIGHT, B.Sc., M.Sc.

ELLIS HORWOOD
NEW YORK   LONDON   TORONTO   SYDNEY   TOKYO   SINGAPORE

First published in 1989 and
Reprinted in 1991 by
ELLIS HORWOOD LIMITED
Market Cross House, Cooper Street,
Chichester, West Sussex, PO19 1EB, England

A division of
Simon & Schuster International Group
A Paramount Communications Company

Printed and bound in Great Britain
by Hartnolls, Bodmin, Cornwall

British Library Cataloguing in Publication Data

Wright, Alan
At the edge of the universe.
1. Universe
I. Title II. Wright, Hilary
523.1
ISBN 0–13–050626–5

Library of Congress Cataloging-in-Publication Data

Wright, Alan, 1943–
At the edge of the universe / Alan Wright and Hilary Wright.
p. cm. — (The Ellis Horwood library of space sciences and space technology.
Series in astronomy)
Includes bibliography and index.
ISBN 0–13–050626–5
1. Cosmology. 2. Astronomy — Technique. I. Wright, Hilary, 1942– . II. Title. III. Series.
QB981.W83   1988
523.1–dc19   88–34060
                                                                                                        CIP

For information about our audio products, write to us at:
Newbridge Book Clubs, 3000 Cindel Drive, Delran, NJ 08370

Acknowledgements

We would like to thank:

George Middleton for the drawings in Chapter 6,

Kluwer Academic Publishers for permission to reproduce the material from IAU Symposium 110,

A.W. Reed, Reed Books for permission to reproduce a paraphrase from *Aboriginal Legends,*

the Royal Astronomical Society for permission to reproduce material from Monthly Notices Vol 193,1980,

Halton Arp for his encouragement and permission to reproduce photographs from his book *The Redshift Controversey,*

the Anglo-Australian Observatory for permission to reproduce the photographs in Chapter 2,

and, finally, the CSIRO, Division of Radiophysics (now the Australia Telescope) for permission to use photographs and reproduction facilities.

To Iain

Table of Contents

Introduction

Judging from articles that frequently appear in the newspapers and magazines, astronomy is one of the most popular sciences. Whether it be a report of a new object farther from Earth than anything previously seen, an exploding star flashing into prominence temporarily in our skies or the search for life elsewhere in the universe, astronomy attracts a wide coverage. Far more, for example, than the esoteric subject of thermodynamics, fundamental particle theory, industrial chemistry or the love-life of the lesser-spotted fruit fly.

And when a scientist finds himself at a party and replies in answer to a casual enquiry that he is a physicist, the conversation will quickly turn to the prospects for the next Test Match or Maggie Smith's latest brilliant film. But let his colleague mention that she is an astronomer and the reply is predictable; within a few seconds she'll have to field a question along the lines of: "What *are* these black holes, then?" or "Does the universe go on for ever? And where does it end?"

Such popular interest has led many people to take an interest in astronomy, either as a profession or as a hobby. And while one automatically thinks of the large astronomical telescopes being used by professionals employed by universities or government research organizations, much valuable work is performed by amateur astronomers using homemade equipment in their back yards.

In most fields of human endeavour, however, a large gap separates the amateur and the professional. For example, when the Saturday golfer misses a short putt it may, at worst, cost him first place in the "monthly medal" competition. But, for the professional, it can mean the loss of several thousands of dollars. Again, when the amateur actor disagrees violently with his producer, no great issues are at stake. But, in the professional theatre, the actor may well be out of a job and possibly a good meal for many days to come. Under these circumstances it is no surprise that the attitudes of those who engage in an occupation as a career are fundamentally different from those whose motive is recreation and general interest.

So too with astronomy. Many amateur astronomers undoubtedly know more about many branches of the science than their professional colleagues. But they will rarely have the same grasp of the overall frame-work against which individual discoveries are made. The day to day (and night to night) business of observing, applying for more telescope time, battling with recalcitrant computers and apparently idiotic editors of the so-called "learned journals" brings a dedication to the professional's life which no amateur can easily hope to achieve. Particularly so since employment and promotion prospects are strongly linked to the outcome of these "battles"!

Unfortunately it isn't easy to convey this exciting — but often infuriating — world of the professional astronomer to print. For example, while there are several excellent books dealing with such subjects as galaxies, quasars and cosmology, there are few which try to reveal the way in which researchers actually think about the distant universe they study.

This book is such an attempt. We have tried to describe not only the factual material that forms the background to mankind's present view of the universe on the largest scale but also the opinions, hopes and prejudices of the astronomers which are an equally important part of it. However we have no illusions that we shall be completely successful.

For one thing, we have made no attempt to be comprehensive in our coverage of topics. Rather we have selected a few areas of the science and looked at them in sufficient detail to allow the non-professional reader to converse intelligently with "the experts" if, and when, the opportunity should arise. The topics this book *does* cover were chosen from those that actually occupy researchers at the moment and which are frequently reported on in the astronomical journals.

The first few chapters describe the background data and techniques which are fundamental to understanding the large scale structure of the universe. We then turn our attention to the "fabric" of the universe and consider the expansion and curvature of space. Later chapters introduce and describe the quasars, almost certainly the most distant material bodies discovered to date. And, finally, we discuss the discovery and implications of the cosmic microwave background.

At the beginning and end of this book we have placed a short account of a night's observing on the large Anglo-Australian telescope. This story is fictional as regards characters. But the places and events are completely typical of the experiences one of us (AEW) has had over many years. I should like to thank my colleagues for the many exciting and pleasant observing nights we have had during this time in search of the highest redshift quasars. In particular I owe an enormous debt to John Bolton with whom I had the deep satisfaction of working for many years and who introduced me to the fascinating world of big-telescope, optical observing.

Alan and Hilary Wright, Parkes, March 1989

Prologue

The dirty Ford Falcon station wagon sped swiftly northward along the dusty road in central New South Wales. The red dust ballooned up in the noonday sun to settle lazily in the adjoining paddocks. Inside the car sat three men. The driver concentrated on the road while his two companions ate hamburgers and took occasional sips from cans of soft drink.

A casual observer would have taken one look at the blue jeans and open-neck shirts of the men and dismissed them as farm hands or shearers. A more careful inquirer would have been puzzled by the computer tapes stacked on the half-empty back seat and the piles of books and files in the rear compartment. But it would have taken inspiration to guess the true purpose of their journey, for these were not station hands on their way to shear a thousand sheep — they were scientists in search of objects at the edge of the universe.

The car turned from the the dirt road onto a surfaced two-lane highway and, a few minutes later, entered the town of Coonabarabran. A small town of a few thousand inhabitants consisting, almost, of only one wide, long street. Shops lined each side of the street, which was split down the centre with dusty gum trees. A brief stop for petrol at a small supermarket and to stock up on some food and beer and then the car was under way again, turning west into the afternoon sun.

The road now wound gently upwards, degenerating into a dusty track. Slowly the trees were left behind to be replaced first by hills and, later, mountains of volcanic rock marking the beginning of the spectacular Warrumbungle Mountains National Park.

Twenty minutes out of Coonabarabran, the road took a sharp turn to the right and started to climb steeply up the side of a steep, tree-covered mountain. Five more minutes of twisting and turning and they were on the top. Here a glorious view of the surrounding countryside, an area the size of Scotland, met the astronomers.

The road along the top of the mountain was surfaced and crossed by occasional cattle grids. On the right loomed suddenly a telescope dome, stark white but with golden flashes from the sun's afternoon rays. This was the United Kingdom Schmidt Telescope, known by the almost unpronounceable acronym of UKSTU. A gigantic camera dedicated to surveying the whole of the southern skies, providing the basic information for use by other telescopes.

Further along still, a sign announced sternly that it was "strictly forbidden for visitors to proceed further". During the working night, the slightest gleam from an unshaded headlight could ruin hours of painstaking work. Beyond the sign stood the king of the mountain, the Anglo-Australian Telescope or AAT as it was more commonly known. As high as a six storey building and ten times as impressive. It was this monster that the men had come to use — the best optical telescope in the southern hemisphere.

The astronomers drove past the giant telescope and on along the road to check in at the Lodge. This small motel-style accommodation with its spectacular views would be "home" for the next few days. A quick shower to freshen up and wash off the dust and the observers drove back to the AAT to unload their observing gear. First a key to unlock the front door had to be found. This was collected from the usual secret place. Then a ride up six floors in a small lift, almost too small to hold the men and all their files.

As the lift stopped, the smell of fresh-brewed coffee and the sound of chatter could be heard coming from a small kitchen a few steps down a corridor to the right. The astronomers made their greetings to local technical staff as they sipped on the strong, black brew. But several faces were frowning. The main question on everybody's lips was, "Would the telescope be ready for the start of tonight's observing?"

The telescope itself was fine as usual. But there were problems with the main instrument that the astronomers planned to use, an electronic spectrograph called the IPCS (standing for Image Photon Counting System). This instrument was needed to determine redshifts for the distant quasars the astronomers had come to observe. Deep inside this spectroscope lurked a special television camera; but the voltages on its focussing coils were all wrong. Could it be fixed in time? The engineering crew were not sure. Was there a replacement on site? No, the closest was in England! By chance, the normal stand-by instrument had also suffered a slight accident while undergoing preventative maintenance in the telescope's laboratory. This had rendered it too insensitive for tonight's observing.

The engineers suggested that the astronomers should go and have a quick bite to eat while they worked on. Then the observers would be ready to start when — and if — the fault was fixed. One of the astronomers, Dick, volunteered to stay back in case he could be of any use — he'd been involved in the development of the instrument a couple of years ago when it had been first put on the AAT. His colleagues, John and Peter, took the lift to the ground floor again and walked slowly back to the observing Lodge. They discussed what they could do if the IPCS couldn't be fixed. Would it be worth getting the alternate spectrograph system fired up? Could be — although it was several years old: almost an antique in the hi-tech world of astronomy. And it would take several hours at least. Perhaps a complete change of observing plans would be best. Peter had a programme he had wanted to do for several years now, of taking very sensitive pictures of some distant quasars to see if they showed any faint galaxies around them. Perhaps that was what they should do? It would need the "top end" of the telescope changed to mount the photographic camera, a job taking only about half an hour. But, as a project, it would be very much second best.

In the Lodge, other astronomers were gathered for the evening meal. These people were scheduled to work on the other, smaller telescopes on the mountain, such as the Schmidt and the telescopes of the Australian National University. For many of them an evening meal at 6 o'clock was a bit early: but the time was dictated by the imminent beginning of darkness and the observing night at 7 o'clock. Again there were greetings with colleagues and a chance to discuss problems and plans.

The two observers scheduled to use the mountain's second largest telescope were planning to study faint stars in a large southern-hemisphere globular cluster. They were trying to discover the age of the cluster and relate it to the age of our galaxy. This was a long-term project on which they had been working for years. It could provide vital clues as to how our galaxy was born. No major problems here, since this was their fourth night on the telescope. The only worry was whether the sky would stay clear — the slightest trace of cloud would ruin the programme.

The Schmidt observer was, as usual, working on her own. Preparing to load and unload massively heavy photographic plates in awkward places on the telescope many times during the 10 hours of her long, solitary night. Perhaps understandably, she was the keenest to chat with colleagues and catch up on the latest gossip.

John and Peter hurried through their delicious meal, not giving it the respect it deserved. They looked enviously at the three visitors from England who had just finished their stint on the telescope the previous night. They were staying on the mountain for a further two nights to look at the data they had collected and process it before returning to England. For them, the high pressure of observing was over: they could afford to linger over a tasty dinner helped down with a bottle of excellent Barossa Valley claret.

As they leaned back in their chairs, John and Peter looked down into the valley below where crows and currawongs wheeled about in the dying rays of the evening sun. In the far distance a small group of kangaroos was coming out to feed. The long observing night and the search for the edge of the universe was about to begin.

1

In the Beginning

It has been said that astronomy is the oldest science. But this is an unprovable assertion, since none of us were there at its beginnings. Who would have the temerity to say when the first crude observations and superstitious interpretations of primitive man turned into "science"? And how do we separate myth from method millenia ago?

Although this is a book primarily about modern astronomy and astronomers, it is important to gain some perspective of the events that preceded today's knowledge and speculations. We live in exciting times in which we have come to accept that new discoveries will be announced at frequent intervals in our morning papers. Against this background, it is difficult to remember that it was not always so. For centuries science stood still and even stagnated, although the intellectuals of the time did not feel its loss. Before the nineteenth century the modern word wasn't even used. It was referred to as "Natural Philosophy".

Did early man look up and perceive the stars and other heavenly bodies as far away and unattainable? We can have no definitive answer to this question. It appears from anthropological studies that many primitive tribes considered themselves so much a part of the world-scene that differences such as "self" and "cosmos" had no meaning. But legends about the heavens have abounded since long before the invention of writing. What we regard as myths were, to the peoples who told them, a completely convincing explanation.

The authors of this book live in Australia, a land eminently suited to astronomy with its clear skies and marvellous views of the fascinating southern heavens. It is also the home of the Australian Aborigine. They were a nomadic people who never achieved a written language. Only now are we beginning to discover just how rich their customs and legends were and still are. Stories of the Creation vary from tribe to tribe and all occur in the **"Dreamtime"**. This is the Aboriginal word for the time before this present world.

Unfortunately there are now no full-blooded Aborigines in our area and we have no direct knowledge of their folktales. But there are plenty of magpie birds, which feature largely in the story below. Considerably bigger than the European variety, in the breeding season they can be bold enough to fly at your head (bald or otherwise) ostensibly to collect hair for nests! Understandably some local farmers prefer to look at them through the sights of a rifle! Here is the magpies' story.

In the beginning there was no space between the Earth and the Sky;
they met together and touched at all places. It was dark and there was

no room for the magpies to fly. The birds grew tired of crawling around and being unable to take wing so they held a meeting and resolved to try and change things by raising the Sky. Each bird had a stick, either in beak or claw and, when told, all pushed together against the sky-roof. At first, nothing happened. Then, as they all pressed and pushed, the sky began to give a little. Light began to show all round the horizon. As the sky lifted up the magpies had to fly to keep pushing and their thousands of wings made strong winds. The sky moved yet further upwards, hesitated on the tree-tops and then became free and floated like an enormous cloud. Although there was now plenty of space, there was as yet little light and everything lay in dark shadows as on a dull day. But, as the birds watched, the sky split open and the light of the Sun flooded the world. For the first time trees and other land forms could be easily seen. The sky floated free and became a track for the Sun goddess, the Moon god and the star people. Clouds lay both under and over the sky. Never have the magpies forgotten their first experience of sunlight so that, every day at sunrise, they greet it once again with a chorus of song.

This legend has much in common with other stories of the creation of the universe (although, of course, early man would have called it the "sky" or "heavens"). Whatever the sky was, it was seen as being separate and different from the Earth. The Sun and Moon travelled over the vault of the heavens in daily progression while the stars appeared stationary moving only slowly with the seasons. The planets were noticed as "different" stars, much smaller than the Sun and Moon but, like them, changing their place from night to night. The patterns made by the fixed stars suggested animals, people and objects, giving rise to the constellations. What these were varied amongst cultures and also in the stars included. Bright objects in the sky were referred to as heavenly "beings", gods and goddesses, some beneficent, others malevolent. Man personified things he did not fully understand to help remove some of their mystery and terror.

A second aboriginal legend comes to us from Central Australia — an area of desert, scrub, stone and magnificent colours. The Central Australian tribes knew the sky as a great nothingness. Here is their story.

Once the sky was supported on three huge gum trees. At that time the land contained water, lakes, rivers and trees. In the sky lived horrible monsters who peered through the gum leaves and saw this beautiful land. To them, it looked much better than their sky home and they gazed at it enviously and for long periods of time. Maybe they became dizzy from looking too long or maybe the branches swayed too much in the breeze but, eventually, they all fell to the Earth, died and decayed leaving only dry bones to remind men of these fallen monsters.

*Ages passed, the three gum trees died and the lakes and rivers dried up. Where the trees had been, there were now only holes in the sky. These gradually enlarged as do the holes in a worn-out fishing net so that, in time, the sky became one vast hole. The land became parched and bare as there was no sky to shield the Earth from the heat of the Sun. But the bones of the ancient monsters remain as what Aboriginals call **kadimakara**but which the white man prefers to think of as dinosaurs.*

There are similarities and differences between such invented stories and the scientific approach. Both use observation and, sometimes, oral and written records. Both are examples of creative thinking. But the story will rarely take into account *all* the available evidence. In the history of astronomy we see time and again that people only saw what they wanted to see in the sky: that which would fit in with their previous conjectures and theories. And it is still the same today, even in our "scientific" age. People can and do bias the interpretations of their observations to correspond with preconceived ideas of what "ought to be". We shall see several examples of this in later chapters.

In many cultures science and storytelling continued side by side. The Egyptians were good engineers and keepers of calendars — you needed to be if you were dependent on the Nile flooding for irrigation. But they applied little of that science to observation of the heavens. They could align the Great Pyramid with their pole star and knew the connection of the rising of the "dog star", Sirius, with the annual Nile flooding. However, the picture of the zodiac we have from an Egyptian tomb dates from much later and is probably borrowed from another culture.

The Egyptians were a peculiar, isolated people with a difficult tongue. The majority of the population did not feel the need for associating with most of the rest of the known world. And even their diplomats used another, special language for dealing with "foreigners" on the occasions when they came into contact.

The Babylonians were contempories of the Egyptians but they had few interactions. Babylonian culture had two "flowerings" interspersed with the usual conquerings and sackings. The first started about 1900 BC. (For the Biblically minded; the Exile of the Jews to Babylon took place in about 600 BC in the second period of power.) The Babylonians believed that the sky was a bowl inverted over their heads through which the morning Sun entered via an eastern door and the evening Sun disappeared through a similar door in the west. Behind the bowl were the "upper waters" (which were released when it rained) and beyond lay the home of the heavenly beings. Beneath, the Earth was hollow, supported on pillars and the home of the dead. Much of this picture comes to us through the Hebrews of the Old Testament who journeyed in the Fertile Crescent and who used many of these ideas in Biblical teachings.

The Babylonians were great observers of the skies — romantic legend has their priests frequently peering up from the top of ziggurats. From their clay tablets we are sure they had accurate records of the risings and settings of Jupiter and Venus together with an efficient calendar. Their year had 360 days and, indeed, much of our modern system of timekeeping comes to us from the Babylonians, since they were preoccupied with the numbers 6 and 60. Unfortunately the Babylonian calendar, like that of the Egyptians, gradually got out of kilter with the seasons over the centuries because the Earth, most inconsiderately, does not circle the Sun in a exact whole number of days.

The second Babylonian Empire in 600 BC was also interested in astronomy, though for a very different purpose. Magic and mysticism played a large part in this culture and the Babylonians tended to use their inherited knowledge of the constellations and wanderings of the planets purely for astrology. The primitive ideas of the gods and goddesses having no direct influence on mankind had progressed to them being heavenly bodies whose tendrils reached into all aspects of everyday life[1]. Despite its suspect motivations, astrology was crucial in increasing the body of "scientific" knowledge of the heavens at this time because accurate observational results were needed for predictions. Furthermore, astrology was to provide this useful function for many centuries.

Next in our history we turn to the Greeks. No-one knows for sure why these fascinating people should suddenly start to flourish in the 6th Century BC. But the results of their culture permeate our ideas in science, in philosophy and in the arts even today. They inherited much astronomical information about star positions from the Babylonians But they had the sense to ignore the trappings of astrological ideas that came with them. To the Greek "natural philosophers", the universe was something to be understood and explained.

Thales was the first Greek scientist whose record remains. This cosmological theorist thought the earth was "a flat plate floating in an infinite sea of water". On the other hand, Anaximander, who was somewhat younger than Thales, put forward a completely different theory. He postulated a cylinder floating in space with the human race inhabiting one end. Strange though this may sound today, his theory deserves underlining as the first one that used the idea of a free-floating Earth. He also had other "modern" ideas; amongst these was that the Earth was only one of an infinite number of worlds which would eventually all come together again.

But, if one knows the name of only a single Greek scientist, it is likely to be Pythagoras: give your name to something and it will ensure immortality. He was undoubtedly a singular character and the schools he founded on the Greek island of Samos and in Italy gave science an enormous impetus. On the other hand, it is difficult to say now with certainty exactly which were the Master's original ideas, since only a portion of his work remains. We do know, though, that his followers believed in a universe which bordered on mysticism in that it was without a rational basis.

Unlike the Babylonians, who revered 6, the Greeks thought 10 was the perfect number. Therefore they postulated 10 heavenly bodies arranged in concentric circles on 10 celestial spheres and around a central fire. Actually they knew of only 9 bodies — Earth, Sun, Moon, Mercury, Venus, Mars, Jupiter and Saturn, even counting the dubious inclusion of the "Sphere of the Stars". So they invented one more! This was a "Counter-Earth" which circled the central fire and hid it from our view. Each sphere had a musical note, separated by harmonizing intervals. The idea of celestial music (which could only be heard by heavenly beings of course) persisted until the 1600s and was a concept used by the poet, Milton.

However strange it may seem, this is a fairly logical universe. The Earth is allowed to move freely, around a central fire, while the planets are recognized as closer objects with dissimilar motions to those of the stars. The outermost sphere was that of the fixed stars and never changed. Clearly the Greeks were on the right track — but later developments were to hold up astronomical thought for centuries.

Plato and Aristotle were to blame. Unfortunately we have little exact knowledge of what either wrote. Pupils "researched" for the Masters who then put their name to the work. These pupils were often glad of the fame even by proxy.

---

[1] The families of modern astronomers may feel at times that the stars have an undue influence on their lives. Particularly when the observations have to be made at a certain time of year also often during the "Dark of the Moon". But fortunately their destinies are not so inextricably intertwined with the heavens as those of the Babylonians!

Following the Masters' deaths, adoring editors gathered up every remaining fragment and published it under a common name[1].

The main idea troubling Plato and Aristotle was that of "Perfection". The world and the universe had obviously been created perfect — it was simply one's duty to find explanations for this perfection. Much time and ingenuity was expended in devising means of fitting the observed orbits of the planets into circles around the earth. The planets were difficult. They did not move evenly across the sky and, at times, even appeared to travel backwards. We now know that this is because we view them from the moving Earth, rather than from the centre of the solar system. But, in a perfect world, the Earth would naturally be at the centre, and so systems of circles-on-circles or **epicycles** of ever-increasing complexity were invoked to shore up this belief.

The lowest celestial sphere, between the Earth and the Moon, was the only changeable one. Thus all new events observed, such as comets and shooting stars, occurred at this level. Aristotle, who may have thought the spheres were solid and crystalline, pondered how they moved. He proposed that either the outermost sphere of stars (the "Prime Mover") controlled all the others or even that they were all placed in motion by an "Unmoved Mover" outside. Probably Aristotle was propounding a system of philosophical thought and never envisaged that it would be regarded as the exact truth for centuries to come. Certainly his ideas fitted in well with the emerging Christian beliefs some years later.

Whilst it may be all very well to sit on an Ionian island — or in a modern research lab — and ponder the Great Questions of the universe, the real world will impinge at intervals. To the Greeks this intervention came, as so often, with wars and rumours of wars. Alexander the Great went his conquering way across Eastern Europe, dying splendidly (and almost certainly rather younger than he'd intended) in 323 BC while his generals carved up his captured territories between them. Ptolemy Solar got Egypt, where the Pyramids were already tourist attractions, and, being a man who admired culture, set up a school of learning at Alexandria in which he established a famous library.

To this oasis of learning, exiled Greek scientists brought their ancient texts. Here one man, Aristarchus, proposed a Sun-centred (heliocentric) universe. But his idea was "obviously" so stupid when set against those of Plato and Aristotle that it was to receive no serious consideration for another 1,000 years[2].

In the first century AD, Ptolemy (who, rather confusingly, was no relation to the general who had founded the school) gathered up all the astronomical learning in a book he called *Mathematical Syntaxis,* after adding his own observations and theories. This work in 13 volumes is better known as *The Almagest* (meaning "The Greatest", which is an Arabic corruption of its Greek title). Unfortunately, in the following centuries, the Alexandrian library was sacked and burned more than once by conquerors with no use for anything other than religious learning. We will never know how much was lost. Fortunately for the progress of astronomy not all was consigned to the flames. In particular we next hear of *The Almagest* in Baghdad which was then under Islamic rule.

The remaining Alexandrian scholars had fled from Egypt towards the country which we now know as Turkey, where Islam proved more tolerant towards secular

---

[1] It is said that the poet Wordsworth suffered from the same problem – relatives taking things out of his wastepaper basket which he had never intended to survive!

[2] Astronomers have always been good at thinking up wild ideas and science has speeded up since Alexandrian days so it would be instructive to "listen in" in 100 years' time. What was discarded today may well be seriously considered then.

learning than did Christianity. A number of Islamic ceremonies, such as praying towards Mecca and the beginning of Ramadan, require a knowledge of the heavens and detailed astronomical calculations. Even so, Arabian astronomers still firmly believed in Ptolemy's Earth-centred cosmos and never seriously questioned the idea of what lay beyond the final solid sphere of the fixed stars. Although the Arabian observations and calculations broke little new ground, they helped keep astronomy alive for over a thousand years and thus played an important part in the progress of our knowledge. Another important facet was the adoption by Arabian astronomers of "Arabic" numerals. This system of nine digits that we use today actually came from the Hindus and greatly improved calculation methods after it came into use in the nineth Century AD.

It is difficult today, surrounded by computers, films, communications satellites and "Starwars" epics, to imagine the non-scientific world during the "Dark Period" centuries from 300 to 1400 AD. We should remember that "civilization" (and hence all written learning) had only ever existed in small pockets. With the collapse of the Roman empire in the fourth century AD, the veneer of civilization over the primitive peoples of Europe disappeared. Europe almost lapsed back into barbarism and things were not helped by the Black Death which decimated the population in many areas. In some ways the situation must have been similar to how advanced imported machinery falls into decay today in the "third-world" countries when no spare parts or knowledge of maintenance is available.

During the Dark Period, all learning reposed with the monasteries, and ideas about the universe were taught by the early Christian church. God had created the universe according to Genesis 1 & 2 and, as we on Earth were specially created, obviously we were at the centre of things. Plato's ideas of the unreality of the present world fitted in well with the Christian tenets. We lived in a sin-filled world which would be exchanged on death for the perfect world to come. All would be explained in heaven; so it seemed pointless to worry about it now. Life in those days was hard and short. Why ponder the problems of the universe when such immediate needs as food and shelter were pressing?

This remained the situation, with rare exceptions, until the 1400s. The celestial bodies had been mapped. And if the astronomical calculations and speculations didn't quite fit the observations, then perhaps the observations weren't that accurate after all? People saw what they were told to see, and if the outermost spheres were said to be unchanging then that is what they believed. It would certainly take more than the appearance of a few comets or supernovae to change their minds!

Into this world came five men who were to resurrect science from the Dark Period and launch the Scientific Revolution with their astronomical studies.

The first was an unlikely candidate. Nicolas Copernicus was a canon of the established church, learned in the disciplines of law and medicine but with an overriding interest in astronomy. Pictures of Copernicus show the typical mediaeval dress of tunic, fur–edged coat, flat headgear and long bobbed hair. His face is that narrow pinched one seen so often in stained glass windows. How then did this man challenge the established church by proposing that God's special creation, the Earth, was *not* at the centre of the universe?

Contrary to popular opinion, he did *not* directly confront the established church but only published reluctantly and after refusing to do so for 30 years. Rumour has it that he only saw the finished book on his deathbed. He appeared well aware of the problem he might be causing and hastened to propose good reasons for it. The Sun was the greatest light in the sky and so naturally should be at the centre of things. He likened it to a King in his temple though never went so far as to suggest that it should be worshipped as God. In fact the church was fairly tolerant of these writings — especially as the printer had added a preface saying that the heliocentric universe was only a theory and not to be taken as fact.

Copernicus himself realized that he had no proof of his heliocentric theory. If we on Earth travel in orbit around the Sun, then surely we should notice a change in the movements of the fixed stars? But this effect had not yet been observed (see Chapter 4). Copernicus explained the lack of changing positions of the stars by saying that the outermost shell of stars *was* fixed but was also very distant. This made it much farther away than anyone had ever previously imagined. The universe had suddenly become much bigger.

With the benefit of hindsight we can see that the implications of the heliocentric theory were quite shattering: not only was the universe far larger than previously thought, but also the Earth was no longer the most important thing in it. Not surprisingly, many people took refuge in the fact that Copernicus's notions *were* only speculation and had no basis in reality.

The second man was Tycho Brahe, an observer *par excellence* whose instruments were the finest ever built in the pre-telescope age. A wealthy man in his own right, he also enjoyed the patronage of the King of Denmark who gave him the island of Hven just off the Danish coast. There he built an observatory and made observations with instruments which were said to be five times more accurate than those of the Greeks. Brahe's picture of the cosmos, though, was not Copernican but geocentric, with the Sun and Moon orbiting the Earth and the other planets orbiting the Sun. Amongst Brahe's observations was that of the nova (exploding "new" star) in 1572. He could see that it was not in the so-called sub-lunary sphere between the Moon and the Earth. On the other hand, the Aristotelian view said that all other spheres were eternal and unchanging. Perhaps other things were also wrong with the older world picture?

The young Johannes Kepler met Brahe and, in fact, worked for him for the last 18 months of Brahe's life. Brahe was now established in Prague with another rich patron — the Emperor Rudolph. Kepler was no observer — in fact, childhood illnesses had left him with poor eyesight amongst several other disabilities. He believed in a pure form of astrology and was quite prepared to cast horoscopes in order to earn his living. On the other hand, he had exceptional mathematical abilities, an overriding passion for astronomy and was prepared to spend years working on a problem.

The problem Brahe gave this new assistant was the orbit of Mars. For centuries it had been known that the planets do not move steadily across the sky if observed over a period of time. They occasionally appear to stop and some, like Mars, even appear to "retrograde" or move backwards. Copernicus's ideas had made an explanation of these strange motions by putting the Sun at the centre of the universe. But his perfect circles — even if offset slightly from the Sun — were not good enough to explain the planetary "wanderings".

All previous measurements had been uncertain to at least 10 minutes of arc but Brahe's observations brought this uncertainty down to nearer 2 minutes. The improved data was an even worse fit to the perfect circles theory. Kepler, with the supreme confidence of a genuine young scientist, boasted he would solve the problem of Mars in eight days. Actually it was to take him nearly four years of tedious calculation. Eventually he produced the only orbit which accurately fitted the data — an ellipse — and formulated the laws of motion which are still the basis for all modern calculations of planetary motion.

The fourth man to usher in the scientific revolution was Galileo. Contrary to popular misconception, he did not invent the telescope. Nor was he even the first to point it at the heavens. He heard of this device when in 1608 Hans Lippershay, a Dutch optician, applied for a patent. Galileo was a talented instrument-maker besides being a mathematician and physicist and was able to make several of his own. In addition, he was concerned with the naming of this new instrument. Previously it had been called a "spyglass" or an "eyeglass perspective". The name *telescope* was suggested by the poet Johannes Demisiani at a banquet in Galileo's honour in 1611.

Of course what we remember today are Galileo's detailed observations of the heavens. The Moon was not perfect but was pitted with craters; Jupiter had four moons circling around it. He also saw and recorded Neptune, though he didn't recognize it was a new planet. Most importantly, though, when he turned his telescope on to the Milky Way it was revealed not as an amorphous cloud but instead as containing countless thousands of stars. Galileo certainly believed in the heliocentric theory although he was still convinced the planets moved in circles. This is surprising since he had corresponded with Kepler and had even received a copy of the latter's book describing the elliptical motions of the planets. Perhaps Galileo never read it — it was certainly not referenced in any letter he wrote to Kepler.

By now, the heliocentric system was becoming accepted as one possible view of the universe amongst many and, if it hadn't been "thrust down the Church's throat", may well have gradually become *the* accepted picture. Unfortunately Giordano Bruno had inflamed church circles with various wild ideas, the most sensible of which was the Copernican system. Furthermore Galileo, who until then had enjoyed court and papal favour, wrote a popular book strongly advocating the heliocentric theory. The arguments against this system were put into the mouth of a character called Simpliticus. Unfortunately they also happened to coincide with those of the Pope.

The heresy trial and recantation which followed broke Galileo and he spent the rest of his life under house arrest, going blind at the end. More importantly, it also broke the great thrust forward of Italian Renaissance science. All books advocating the Copernican system were put on the banned list and further progress in astronomy was only to take place in the Protestant countries of Northern Europe where speech was freer.

The work of the English scientist Isaac Newton marked the zenith of the scientific revolution. He explained the splitting of white light into its component colours, initiating the science of spectroscopy. He taught himself mathematics and went on to invent one form of that most important tool, the calculus. But, more importantly for our purposes, Newton solved the problem of why the planets moved as they did by formulating his inverse square law of universal gravitation.

Others had tackled this problem before him. Kepler had thought the planets were driven by invisible spokes stretching out from the Sun. Galileo, returning to the Greek ideas, thought the motion was driven by an eternal "prime mover". Descartes had thought that there were invisible vortices in the fluid of space which carried the planets along. Newton realized this was impossible as the friction would cause their orbits to decay and fall into the Sun. He showed that the force of gravity applied to everything both on Earth and in space. Unfortunately he was never able to calculate an exact example from the observed planetary motions since each planet influences the orbits of the others, making the problem tremendously complex. Even today these calculations require considerable time on a large computer. However he showed how new planets could be predicted from these secondary effects, which was eventually to lead to the discovery of Neptune in 1846.

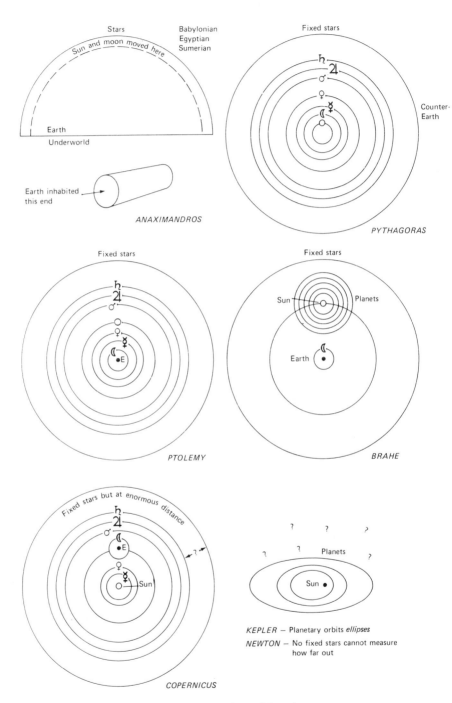

Fig. 1.1 — Early views of the universe

Newton was truly a great man though not one with an entirely pleasing personality. He was invariably furious when others made similar discoveries, even years after him, if they published first. This was despite the fact that he'd not bothered to publish himself! He lived for his work and was never very successful in his personal relationships. He insisted that, as his method of the calculus was the first to be invented, it should be preferred. This seriously delayed the progress of mathematics in England since the alternative method, proposed by the German Leibnitz, was much easier to use.

While Newton's private life was occupied by such petty problems, his scientific work forged ahead. He realized that the stars had to be extremely distant: if not, they would fall into the Sun. And, since they were so far away, they must be very luminous in their own right. If they were suns, did they have planets like ours orbiting around them? With Newton, mankind's picture of the cosmos had grown much bigger. At last we were beginning to comprehend the true scale of the universe.

2

The Cosmic Doorstep

Out in the countryside, on a clear night, it is quite easy to see over 2000 stars. Under the best possible conditions, a closer look will reveal nearer to 5000 or 6000 stars. With a pair of binoculars the number rises to several million; and the world's biggest telescopes are capable of showing thousands of millions. And these are just objects in our own galaxy. What of the rest of the universe? Modern astronomy has shown that the cosmos is populated with over 100 thousand million galaxies, each containing thousands of millions of stars.

In this chapter we shall attempt to provide an overview of the universe and its contents as revealed by modern astronomy. We shall return to discuss individual objects and ideas in more detail later.

On the doorstep

Most of the people on this planet have to use their legs as their only means of transport: to them, a journey of a few tens of kilometres is a long way. Many of us dread a long, intercontinental jet flight. Yet again, to date, only a handful of men have travelled to the Moon. But on the cosmic scale the Earth is very small. A modern 747 jet travels at about 1000 km/h. If we could imagine travelling to the Moon at this speed, the journey would take us around 10 days — even assuming we could bear the atrocious food! A trip by jet to the nearest planet, Venus, would take us over 10 *years* and the most direct route to the farthest planets in our solar system would occupy us for more than 500 years.

Enormous though these distances are, they are insignificant compared to the distances to the stars. Travelling at the speed of our 747, a trip to the nearest stars would take millions of years. Astronomers are often asked how far their telescopes can see: they find the question difficult to deal with. The answer, expressed in kilometres or miles, would be quite unimaginable. Because of this we use the speed of light as a standard. Light travels through space at almost exactly 300,000 kilometres per *second* which exceeds the speed of our 747 jet by almost one million times. If we were to restart our interstellar trip at the speed of light, we would leave the Moon behind after only 1 second. Venus would be a mere 5 minutes away, the Sun 8 minutes and Neptune less than 5 hours. Of course, travel at anything approaching the speed of light is quite impossible with our present technology. But let's imagine.

A voyage to the neighbouring α Centauri star system at the speed of light now requires a little over 4 years[1]. This number emphasizes a most important property of space: its extreme emptiness. We leave Neptune and the solar system behind in the first 5 *hours* of our journey — but it is over 4 *years* before we enter another stellar system.

Our star, the Sun, is just one amongst 100,000 million stars that make up our galaxy — or the **Milky Way** as it is sometimes called. This is an enormous number. To put it in perspective: 100,000 million is comparable with the number of grains of rice you could pack into one of the world's great concert venues, such as the Albert Hall in London or the Sydney Opera House. The grains would be packed floor to ceiling and wall to wall. However when we contemplate this enormous number, we could easily fall into the trap of supposing that the stars in our galaxy are crowded closely together: but they're not. The rice analogy would let you down badly in demonstrating the emptiness of space. To be more realistic we would have to find an opera house big enough to contain 100,000 million grains of rice but which would also allow each grain to be separated by many kilometres! In fact, it would have to be far bigger than the Earth!

At the speed of light, a trip across the whole of our galaxy would take an almost incomprehensible 60,000 years[2]. If the astronauts of the next century are going to find interstellar travel very difficult, they will surely find inter*galactic* travel impossible! Even an attempt to visualize these distances using a scale model is almost certainly doomed to failure: if we show the Sun as the size of a marble and the Earth as a tiny speck of dust a metre and a half away, we shall not find the nearest stars until we have travelled 1000 kilometres from "marble-Sun". And on the same scale, the whole galaxy would spread over a region of space larger than the distance of the Moon from the Earth.

Large though our galaxy is, we are still sitting on our own "back doorstep" in cosmic terms. This book is not about our own galaxy but the remotest regions of space and the objects they contain. So let us now turn our attention beyond the Milky Way and consider what objects we find out there in the universe at the largest distances.

Beyond the doorstep

Astronomers have estimated that the visible universe contains around 100,000 million galaxies, coincidentally the same sort of number as stars in our Galaxy. Most of these galaxies are not distributed evenly throughout the universe but are clustered together in groups.

Our nearest galactic neighbour is the **Large Magellanic Cloud (LMC)**. In fact we should probably call him one of our own family rather than a neighbour since a stream of gas (called the **Magellanic Stream**) connects us to the LMC, forming a sort of "family tie". The LMC is an example of an **irregular galaxy** and is much smaller than the Milky Way. It lies about 150 thousand

---

[1] The distance to the α Centauri system is 4.3 lightyears. A **lightyear** is the distance light travels in empty space during the course of one year. In more conventional units, one lightyear is close to 10 million million kilometres or 6 million million miles.

[2] This number refers to the visible stars and the hot, ionized gas we see in the vicinity of newborn stars. If we include the cool, neutral gas revealed to us by radiotelescopes, then the size increases to about 100 thousand lightyears. We shall use this larger figure in what follows.

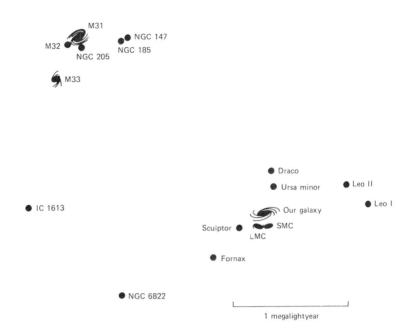

Fig. 2.1 — Positions of some of the galaxies in the Local Group

lightyears from the centre of our galaxy. It has a similar but smaller companion galaxy, appropriately called the **Small Magellanic Cloud (SMC)**.

Our own galaxy and the Magellanic Clouds are just three of several galaxies that comprise a system known as the **Local Group**. As well as the Milky Way, the Local Group contains the nearest large, spiral galaxy similar to our own, **M31** (also known as the **Andromeda Nebula**) at a distance of 1.8 million lightyears, the somewhat smaller spiral galaxy, **M33**, as well as many other smaller galaxies[1]. In the next section we shall look at these different sorts of galaxy in more detail. For the moment, however, we shall just try to put the size of the whole universe in perspective. Fig. 2.1 represents the positions in space of some of the galaxies making up the Local Group.

To find the nearest giant elliptical galaxy, we must leave the confines of the Local Group and travel 33 million lightyears to another nearby group. In the centre of the **Virgo Cluster** we find the violently exploding **M87** (see Chapter 14). One of the more distant clusters of galaxies, the **Hercules Cluster**, is about 10 times further still, and the **quasars** (which we shall talk about in later chapters) span a range of distance from somewhat less than 2000 million lightyears to around 15 thousand million lightyears.

---

[1] Incidentally, the names "M31" and "M33" are used because these are the 31st and 33rd objects respectively appearing in the French astronomer Messier's list of bright, "fuzzy" objects to be ignored when looking for comets!

When we were talking about the position and size of the Earth in the solar system or the position and size of the Sun in our galaxy, we were struck by the enormous "emptiness" of space. In fact, we had difficulty in conceiving of the overall size of the galaxy, even with a scale model. It therefore perhaps comes as a pleasant surprise to realize that we *can* easily build a scale model of the whole (observable) universe in which the size of our galaxy is represented by something considerably more than a vanishingly small "pin-head".

Let us show the Milky Way as a grain of rice, about 2 millimetres in length. On the same scale, M31 is a similar size and is found about 6 cm away from us. M87 in the Virgo cluster lies just over 1 metre away (and, again, has a similar diameter). The Hercules cluster of galaxies on our model has the diameter of a golf ball and lies about 10 metres from the Milky Way, while one of the nearest quasars, 3C273, is situated 60 metres away. Finally, the most distant quasars at the edge of the observable universe would be around 100 metres from the grain of rice we called our galaxy.

This is a large model but one that we can still easily understand. If we were to build it, we could view the whole "universe" at a glance and yet still comprehend the size of a galaxy within it. If we think in terms of galaxies rather than stars and planets, the universe becomes a much more imaginable place!

Unfortunately our simple model could be deficient in several important respects. Firstly, astronomers have shown that the whole universe is expanding, so that the separation of all the galaxies in our model should be increasing as time goes by. Secondly, it would appear as though all galaxies, quasars and other objects stopped at the edge of our model. In reality it is not only the matter but space itself that should stop. There is no edge because nothing lies "outside" our universe. Finally the "shape" of space itself may be different from the ordinary geometry we are familiar with and so apparent distances may be wrong. These are intriguing points that we shall return to in later chapters. For the moment, though, we must realize that our model gives us a view of the universe which is somewhat misleading. Nevertheless, it is useful, and serves to show that the galaxies occupy a significant part of all space. The universe may be a *small* place — but at least it is not an *empty* place!

The universe of galaxies

When reading descriptive books on astronomy, it is often difficult to put objects in their proper perspective. It is natural that the authors will stress the more exciting and spectacular objects in our universe at the expense of the mundane. But, if anything in this amazing universe of ours could be said to be "ordinary", it would be the galaxies. They link astronomical objects on the scale of our solar system, such as the Sun and planets, to cosmology and the fabric of the whole universe itself. While the galaxy in which we live is made up primarily of stars, the universe is made up primarily of galaxies.

Our galaxy is typical of many **spiral galaxies** we see throughout the universe. The name spiral derives from the fact that the few bright, blue, obvious stars such galaxies contain form a rough spiral pattern[1]. See Fig. 2.2. To a very

---

[1]To describe in detail why this is so would take us too far from the present discussion. Suffice it to say that astronomers believe that a compression wave is moving around the galaxy, rather like a massive tidal wave. A spiral galaxy contains material everywhere, not just where we see spiral arms, and the wave compresses gas causing new stars to form. Despite appearances, these arms will not get tangled up as time goes by even though the galaxy is rotating.

Fig. 2.2 — The spiral galaxy NGC 6744. (Photograph courtesy the Anglo-Australian Telescope Board.)

good first approximation, a typical spiral galaxy is made up of small, red stars having masses considerably less than those of our Sun and spread out in a thick disc with a diameter of about 20,000 lightyears.

Using **radiotelescopes**, we can see another important constituent of this typical galaxy. About one-tenth of its mass will not be stars at all but gas. The gas will not be distributed evenly throughout the galaxy, but will start about 30% of the way out from the centre and extend out at least twice as far as any of the stars we see. We believe about 90% of this gas is hydrogen and about 10% helium.

When we measure the velocities of the stars and gas by the **Doppler effect** (see Chapter 7), we find that they are rotating together around the centre of the galaxy. But we will also find that the velocity of gas in the outermost regions does not decrease in the way expected from Kepler's laws of motion of orbiting bodies. Instead, the velocity continues to increase as we move outwards. This leads us to suspect that there is even more "unseen" mass in the outermost regions of the galaxy, as yet undetected with our radiotelescopes.

Although we find it difficult to see the great majority of the small red stars that make up the bulk of our typical galaxy's mass, their *combined* light will exceed that from the few spectacular blue stars in the spiral arms. This will give the whole galaxy, as seen from a distance, a reddish colour. Only if the galaxy is fairly close to us do we see its spiral pattern and the individual blue stars. One part of the galaxy we shall find contains almost no blue stars at all, however. This is the central region, or **nucleus**, which we mentioned above was also devoid of gas. Astronomers believe that this is no coincidence. Gas is the material out of which the stars form. In the central regions of a typical spiral galaxy, the gas was used up in making stars many thousands of millions of years ago and only old stars now remain. Astronomers know that old stars must be red stars, since blue stars are massive, prodigal stars that burn up very quickly. Blue stars would have undoubtedly been born in the central regions of the spiral galaxy: but they would have long since burnt out. The only stars remaining today are the low-mass, red ones.

As we look closer at the nucleus of our typical galaxy, we find that it is surrounded by a swarm of **globular clusters,** ball-like objects consisting of hundreds of thousands, or even millions, of reddish stars — but virtually no gas. These clusters orbit about our galaxy in a way that causes them to dive directly in and out of the nucleus along almost randomly orientated lines, quite unlike the neat and orderly circular rotational motions of the bulk of the stars and gas.

So far we have been talking about a typical spiral galaxy such as our own. But there is a second important type: the **elliptical galaxy**. These objects derive their name from the fact that, when viewed through a telescope, they look like circles or ellipses ("flattened" circles) and have no spiral structure (see Fig. 2.3). Of course we don't believe that the ellipticals really *are* flat, two-dimensional objects. On the other hand, a truly spherical galaxy could not appear as an ellipse. The simplest assumption is that the ellipticals are actually *spheroidal* [1] in shape.

---

[1] The difference between **spherical** and **spheroidal** is is that a soccer or basket ball is spherical while a rugby or grid-iron football is spheroidal. Just to complete the picture: a rugby football that has been "sat on" is ellipsoidal. A mathematician would say that it depends whether or not there are two axes of symmetry (the sphere), one axis of symmetry (the spheroid), or no axes of symmetry (the ellipsoid). And to confuse matters, there are *two* distinct types of spheroid: a football is a **prolate** spheroid, while a pumpkin is an approximation to an **oblate** spheroid.

Fig. 2.3 — The elliptical galaxies NGC 1399 (larger) and NGC 1404 (smaller). Note that NGC 1399 is near-circular, while NGC 1404 is more elliptical. (Photograph courtesy the Anglo-Australian Telescope Board.)

On average, elliptical galaxies tend either to be either considerably *less* massive than the majority of the spirals or considerably *more* massive. These two types are called — with a sad lack of originality — **giant ellipticals** and **dwarf ellipticals**. The dwarf ellipticals have masses only a bit larger than the most massive globular clusters, and are very similar to them in many ways. On the other hand, the giant ellipticals are the most massive galaxies known, with masses ranging up to a million million (10^{12}) solar masses. The most important difference between the ellipticals and the spirals, though, is that the ellipticals contain almost no gas at all. As we mentioned above, this implies that they can no longer give birth to new stars and can contain only old, red stars.

Spirals and ellipticals occur in roughly equal numbers throughout the universe and account for the great majority of the galaxies we observe. There is, however, one more type which we mentioned earlier; the **irregular galaxies**. These often look like small spirals that have been "blown apart". The most famous examples — at least in the southern hemisphere — are the Magellanic Clouds. Certainly, in the case of the Magellanic Clouds, there is strong evidence that they have indeed been ripped apart by passing too close to our own galaxy.

As we gaze out far into the universe past the nearer spiral, elliptical and irregular galaxies, individual objects become harder to discern. The most obvious aggregations are the giant clusters of galaxies, many of them far larger and containing more galaxies than our own Local Group. Until the 1960s, this was our total picture of the universe — the clusters interspersed with a few individual galaxies filled the universe. But, with the discovery of the quasars, our concept of the universe expanded by a factor of 10. What these mysterious objects are is still not clear. Modern opinion tends to the view that they are an unusually violent stage in the life of some galaxies, perhaps related to the birth or death phases. Whatever their nature, they are almost certainly the most distant objects we have observed to date. If anything could be said to mark the edge of the universe, it would be these enigmatic objects. Because of their importance, we shall be looking at the quasars in much more detail starting in Chapter 11.

3

Tools of the Trade

A visitor to a modern astronomical observatory will see and hear some strange things. There will be talk of "correlators", "pointing", "CCDs", "chopping secondaries", and many other things. All, no doubt, very confusing to the layman — and, it must be admitted, often to the professional astronomer too! Despite this, however, the main job of an observatory is very simple: it is to help the astronomer collect photons or particles from the universe and to decode the message they contain.

Perhaps one of the most astounding facts in all science is that a careful analysis of the light from distant stars and galaxies can tell us what these heavenly bodies are made of, how fast they are moving, and how old and how distant they are. And if we sometimes make mistakes in our interpretations, it should not be a cause for pessimism — rather we should rejoice in how much we *have* learned in only a few hundred years of intensive research. After all, the universe is still young (a mere 10 thousand million years old, so we believe): we must leave something for future generations to discover!

Electromagnetic radiation

Light is one form of **electromagnetic radiation,** so called because the radiation is a strange mixture of electrical and magnetic fields produced by electrons in motion. We call the mixture "strange" because the magnetic and electrical fields are not the fields of influence we are accustomed to near such everyday objects as bar-magnets and static-laden underwear. Rather the radiation has become divorced from the moving electrons that produced it and moves freely through space with its electrical part "feeding" on its magnetic part and its magnetic component extracting energy from the electrical field in a see-saw-like way.

Strange indeed! And if the modern theory of electrodynamics was not so spectacularly successful, it would be hard to believe. Even so, at the deepest levels of modern physics many mysteries concerning electromagnetic radiation remain. For example, we are ignorant of the details of the electrodynamic forces very close to the electrons which produce them.

Despite these problems, the main features of electromagnetic radiation are clear. First, the radiation occurs with different wavelengths and frequencies[1]. If

---

[1] The wavelength and frequency of any electromagnetic radiation travelling in a vacuum are related by **wavelength   frequency** = c, where c is the fundamental velocity, or speed of light (very close to 300,000 km/s). Wavelength is normally shown by the Greek letter λ (lambda) and is measured in metres or centimetres (radioastronomy), microns (1 micron = 10^{-6} cm) or Ångstroms

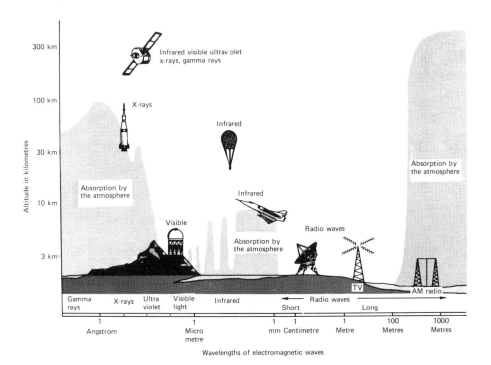

Wavelengths of electromagnetic waves

Fig. 3.1 — The electromagnetic spectrum from long radio waves to gamma rays. The wavelength and frequency are related by   wavelength x frequency = 3×10^{10} cm/s·

we find it convenient to think in terms of waves, then these different frequencies correspond to different repetition rates of energy maxima and minima. If, on the other hand, we consider electromagnetic radiation as small "packets" of energy, **photons** or **quanta** then the differing frequencies mean that the different packets have different energies. Both pictures are correct. If we have difficulties imagining something that can act like a wave one minute and like a particle the next, perhaps it is only to be expected. Photons are hard to picture simply because they behave totally unlike anything in our everyday experience: we have nothing even vaguely similar to compare them with in our macroscopic world.

Light is the form of electromagnetic radiation of which we have the most direct experience. Its different colours correspond to slightly different wavelengths of light. These colours appear different because, when the photons strike the back of our eyes, they cause the electrons in the atoms and molecules of the retina to oscillate at different rates. The differing electron oscillation rates are translated by our brain into differing psychological sensations. If we replace our eyes with a camera containing colour film or a television camera then very similar things happen, except that non-biological detectors capture the photons.

(optical astronomy). One Angstrom is 10^{-8} cm. The modern unit, the **nanometre** = 10^{-9} cm, which is used extensively in physics, is not yet in common use in astronomy. Frequency is shown by the Greek letter ν (nu) and is measured in **Hertz** (or megahertz or gigahertz), where 1 hertz is equal to one cycle of radiation per second.

Unfortunately our eyes are not sensitive to most of the great range of electromagnetic radiation that makes up the total **electromagnetic spectrum**. This is why astronomers must use different sorts of telescope to decipher the information contained in photons coming to us from objects throughout the universe. Fig. 3.1 shows the main forms of electromagnetic radiation, stretching from the Very Low Frequency (VLF) radio waves, through microwaves, infrared and optical radiation, and up to X-ray and gamma radiation.

Fig. 3.2 — The Anglo-Australian Telescope near Coonabarabran in New South Wales, Australia.

Telescopes

At the heart of any observatory is its telescope. This may be a large dome-enshrouded optical reflecting telescope; a giant radio dish exposed to the ravages of the elements; perhaps a cosmic ray or neutrino telescope buried deep underground; or even a satellite hurtling along its orbit in the depths of space.

The main part of any major *optical* telescope is almost invariably a reflecting mirror. Although glass lenses similar to those used in "pocket telescopes" can also be used to collect and focus light waves, large lenses above a metre in size are very difficult and expensive to build because they can be supported only around their rim. On the other hand, a glass mirror coated with reflecting aluminium can be supported from behind and made much stronger. This is important because the tolerance required is amazing: in order to be useful, the surface of any telescope mirror must not depart substantially from the shape of a perfect parabola by more than one-tenth of a wavelength of the radiation it is reflecting. This implies that the whole of a 4-metre optical mirror, for example, must have a shape perfect to less than one ten-thousandth of a millimetre. Perhaps even more amazing is that the mirror must still retain this accuracy when mounted in a telescope and tipped over towards any part of the sky. (See Fig. 3.2.)

The "mirrors" of radiotelescopes are quite different. No highly polished surfaces here: instead, perforated aluminium sheets or even "chicken wire" mesh (see Fig. 3.3). But at radio wavelengths such surfaces are just as reflective as solid metal. Since the radiation collected by these telescopes typically has a wavelength of around a few centimetres, a telescope surface containing holes a millimetre or so in size is just as good as a solid surface. More importantly, it is far less affected by the strong winds which are the bugbear of radio observatories.

Fig. 3.3 — The Parkes 64-m radiotelescope in New South Wales, Australia. (Photograph courtesy the CSIRO, Division of Radiophysics.)

Space telescopes are used to avoid one of the astronomer's greatest problems, the Earth's atmosphere. Without it, of course, we would die. But, to the astronomer, it is always a nuisance. It produces clouds and rain. Even when the weather is clear, it absorbs the short wavelength radio emissions, the long-wave infrared radiation and the less-energetic X-ray radiation. And when the photons *do* have the right wavelength to penetrate this blanket, turbulence in the atmosphere destroys the fine detail needed to produce the best astronomical photographs. Above the atmosphere, space telescopes may avoid most of these problems but still suffer from a new set of technological and communications difficulties.

Perhaps the strangest telescopes of all, though, are those used by neutrino astronomers. Deep underground in a disused mine in Deadwood Gulch, South Dakota, sits a large tank of dry-cleaning fluid. Highly energetic particles called **neutrinos** arriving from space may be stopped by this liquid while the great majority pass right through the Earth. Observing at this observatory necessitates analysing large amounts of the liquid to discern the faint ghosts of long-past events. So far, neutrino telescopes have provided us with astronomical information only about such relatively nearby bodies such as the Sun and supernovae. But, in the future, they will no doubt combine with Earthbound and space-born telescopes to detect the full gamut of radiation and particles arriving from the depths of space.

Eyes and photographs

Notwithstanding this bewildering variety of instruments, when most people think of astronomy, they think of **optical astronomy** and telescopes you can look through. But professional astronomers nowadays seldom put their eye to the end of an optical telescope. Perhaps this is a pity: the beautiful muted colours of the planet Saturn swimming in the black velvet of a clear night sky is surely one of the greatest sights of this universe. Even so, at the major observatories, eyes are normally used now only for staring at computer display screens or, in anguish, at a cloudy sky.

Why is this? Funnily enough, the obvious answer — that the human eye is not sensitive enough — is not true. In fact the eye *is* a very sensitive instrument capable of detecting very small quantities of energy per second, rates which compare favourably with those of the best, modern, "high-tech", astronomical light collection systems.

Part of the correct answer lies in the fact that human sight does not have the ability to add up or **integrate** light. When a photon is received by the eye, it stimulates the retina. The electrical impulses caused by this stimulation are passed on to the brain, their effects noted and then the impression lost except for a brief and often imperfect memory. This means that staring at an unchanging object for a few hours is no more useful than glancing at it for just a few seconds.

This is not true of the sensitive film used on a **photographic plate**. Modern astronomical film uses a thin molecular coating of chemicals on a supportive glass backing. When a photon hits one of these molecules, the odds are that nothing happens. But once in about every 20 times, a molecule has its structure changed so that later development shows an image contrasting with the surrounding part of the plate. The longer we expose the plate to the sky, the more molecules are put into this "developable state" and the developed image becomes darker[1].

Because of this "integrating advantage", modern optical astronomy makes extensive use of photographic plates. Furthermore they have the advantage, that the images can be examined in comfort and at leisure. But although such pictures reveal much more than can be seen with the eye, we are still far from being able to discern most of the distant and spectacular objects in the universe. We need to catch more photons! One way of proceeding would be to use a larger telescope mirror. However the largest telescopes cost many millions of dollars. There is a much cheaper way: we can make our photographic plates more effective at capturing photons.

---

[1] We say "darker" even though light has hit this part of the plate because astronomers normally prefer to work with negatives rather than the positive prints we are more familiar with in everyday photography. This sometimes comes as a surprise to the lay-person whose attention is directed to a "bright" centre of a galaxy —only to find that it is the blackest thing on the plate! But negatives have many advantages – the main one of which is that one less image-degrading photographic process is needed to produce them compared with a positive image.

In the early days of astro-photography, it was realized that better — i.e. shorter — exposure times could be used if the plates were "baked" first. You may picture a Victorian-age astronomer clad in his frock-coat taking a plate from the store and then placing it in an oven for a few hours. The temperature of the oven was carefully regulated not to get too hot, perhaps about 200 °F (around 100 °C). When the plate was removed he mounted it in the plate holder on the telescope and started his night's work. Using this method the required exposure times could be reduced from hours to minutes. Why this heat treatment worked, no-one was quite sure at the time. But work it did. Today we know that the baking process removes water vapour from the sensitive chemical emulsion on the plate. The water vapour slows down the exposing effect of the photons.

But even after baking, photographic plates remained devastatingly slow. The American astronomer Hubble, who discovered the expansion of the universe (see Chapter 7) had to expose his plates of the faintest galaxies for many hours each night in order to get enough photons to produce an image on the plate. At the end of the night, when he could expose no longer because the Sun was about to rise, he would remove his plates from the plate holder in the telescope, carefully wrap them up and store them away undeveloped. The next night the process would be reversed and the plate put back into the telescope which was brought back to exactly the same part of the sky as on the previous night and the exposure continued.

The (perhaps apocryphal!) story is told of the American astronomer who persevered with an exposure through the whole of four bitterly cold winter nights in this way. After this marathon observing session, he staggered into the dark room to develop his plate — only to plunge it into the fixer rather than the developer! The plate was, of course, completely ruined. His comments were not recorded.

Such techniques as baking were referred to as **sensitization**. They were particularly useful in reducing the exposure times needed for detecting the spectrum (see Chapter 12) of faint galaxies by factors of around 10: instead of spending nights at the telescope, only hours were needed. Modern techniques perfected in the last few years, known as **hyper-sensitization** are even better, producing similar results in only minutes.

Modern methods of hyper-sensitization "wash" the plate for many hours or days in an atmosphere of hydrogen gas. This process removes not only water vapour from amongst the grains on the plate but also most of the oxygen gas trapped on the plate. Oxygen, like water vapour, is known to slow down the exposure process. Of course, hydrogen is a very dangerous gas and will explode in air with devastating results if ignited. For this reason, most observatories keep the actual building where the "washing" is done as far as possible from the dome and other work-buildings.

Astronomers are some of the most demanding users of photographic plates. Actually the cost to companies like Eastman-Kodak of producing plates for astronomy is far greater than the profits. But they continue to be involved in producing special batches simply because the demanding astronomers push the technology and art of photography to extreme limits. Who else would demand a plate capable of receiving a mere handful of photons that have been travelling across space for thousands of millions of years?

One question that photographic astronomers are often asked is, "Are the colours in your pictures real?" Certainly if one looks through a telescope, then only rarely can any colour be seen. This is because the human eye contains two sorts of receptors: one set designed for normal light conditions which are colour sensitive; and one set which are designed for low light level conditions and which work only in monochrome or black and white. When we stare at the faint image of a star in a telescope, our eyes are receiving a mere few hundred photons each second. When we consider that each photon contains only about one million millionth of an erg of energy, we can easily calculate that we would have to receive energy at this rate for a thousand years to equal what we expend in blinking an eyelid! Certainly these light levels are so low that the eye operates only in monochrome.

But the colours in the universe *are* real. Hot stars are blue; cool stars are red; and certain sorts of gaseous nebulae are green. In order to see the colours, though, we must integrate the light for many minutes — perhaps hours. Astronomical photographers do not normally use ordinary colour film to record the colours because it is not sensitive enough. Instead three separate exposures are made of each object for which a picture is required using filters that pass only blue, red and green light. The reader may recognize these as being the additive primary colours from which other colours can be composed. To produce our final picture, negatives in the three colours are carefully aligned and have light shone through them onto ordinary colour film.

Photography plays a very important role in modern optical astronomy. A large photographic plate such as those used on the big Schmidt-type telescopes in America and Australia can record information from a region of sky 40 square degrees in area. This is far greater than any of the other detectors that we shall discuss later. Furthermore a large coloured photographic print has an emotional impact lacking in a pile of bits and bytes no matter how cunningly displayed on a computer screen.

Spectroscopy

Probably the most useful single instrument at any observatory (after the telescope itself) is a **spectrograph**. With it we can analyse light or radio waves arriving from distant celestial bodies, measure the relative amounts of elements they contain, tell how fast they are moving and, often, deduce their distances. Certainly the number of nights during which observations are made with a spectrograph at any major observatory will exceed those when any other instrument is used.

The earliest optical spectrographs used a glass prism. When a beam of light travels through any block of glass, it is bent when it enters the glass and re-bent when it leaves. This is the phenomenon known as **refraction.** In a glass prism, the surfaces are arranged so that the light suffers a considerable amount of net bending. More important for our purposes, though, is the fact that different colours of light are bent by different amounts. In a spectroscope, blue light is bent through a greater angle than red light, and yellow and green light are bent through intermediate angles. A similar effect occurs in a rainbow. Here, small droplets of water in the atmosphere act as prisms and spread out the different colours in the (nearly) white sunlight by differing amounts.

In the first practical spectrographs, the converging light from the main telescope mirror was focussed onto a slit cut in a metal plate in order to remove images of other objects from the telescope's field of view. The light was then collimated by lenses to make it into a parallel beam before hitting the prism. After passing through the prism, the diverging colours were focussed onto a photographic plate which recorded the spectrum.

Most modern optical spectroscopes work in a rather different way, although the result is the same. Instead of a glass prism, the modern spectrograph uses a **grating**. In essence, this is a plate ruled with extremely close parallel lines. These lines cause the collimated beam of light from the telescope to be split up into its component colours after reflection rather than refraction. The phenomenon is known as **diffraction.** The finer the lines are ruled, the more spread out — but also weaker — will the spectrum be. The diffracted light is focussed and usually recorded on some sort of electronic imaging device — either a television tube or a **charge coupled device array**(CCD).

Spectrographs are also in frequent use at radio observatories. Instead of prisms and gratings, complicated electronics is used to delay the incoming radio signals from the sky and mix them with themselves in a device called an **autocorrelator.** After further processing by computer the resulting signal represents the strengths of the radio signals at different frequencies exactly as if it had been "split apart" by a radio prism.

Other detectors

Until recently, astronomers wanting either to take direct pictures of objects in the sky or to record their spectra would have used photographic plates. Nowadays, however, by far the greatest amount of modern astronomical research is done with instruments called (rather unimaginatively, perhaps) **photon detectors**.

The main problem with photographic plates is the one we referred to previously: namely that the film can capture only about 1 in every 20 photons even after sensitization. More accurately, a physicist would say that photographic plates have a **detective quantum efficiency** (sometimes sarcastically called a "defective" quantum efficiency!) of only 5%.

Fig. 3.4 — Example of a waveguide used to transfer radio waves collected by a radiotelescope and convert them into electrical signals.

Electronic detectors can do far better. A modern charge coupled device array works rather like a very sensitive television camera and can detect more than half the photons which hit it. More importantly, such devices are extremely "linear", by which we mean that there is a very exact simple proportionality between the number of incident photons and the detected electron currents. This linearity permits very accurate subtraction of the faint night sky light and allows deep detail in the star or galaxy being studied to be revealed.

In radio astronomy the photon detectors are called **receivers**, since they operate in a manner similar to domestic radio receivers. The photons collected by a radiotelescope are focussed by the dish surface to a **waveguide** and probe whose job is to convert the electromagnetic energy into electrical signals. Fig. 3.4 shows an example. When the electromagnetic energy hits the probe, it cause electrons to move, thus creating electric currents. These currents are extremely weak and must be amplified to much higher levels by the receiver and amplifier system.

The trouble with all these electronic devices, in radio, optical and the other astronomies, is that the results are hard to interpret. While an optical photograph has an immediate impact and may stimulate a thousand thoughts, minute electric currents leave most astronomers in the dark.

The first stage of making some sense of the electrical signals is to use a computer to turn them into numbers so that they can be added together and permanently recorded on magnetic tape for later analysis. Unfortunately most people are not good at interpreting columns of hundreds or thousands of 10-digit numbers — and astronomers are no exception. And so the data may be displayed as a set of graphs on a TV screen or, alternately, the numbers are often turned into pictures by the computer. Lighter and darker shades of grey may be used to represent the smaller and larger numbers which, in turn, correspond to the lighter and darker areas of the original image from the sky.

And so we have come full circle. We start with an image from the sky, turn it into electronic signals, process it and finally turn it back into a picture we can see and use. Tedious though all these steps may seem, they are necessary. The radio astronomer can not see anything through his telescope: and even the optical astronomer must use these modern methods if he wants to make use of most of the photons collected by his telescope from the faintest and most distant objects in the universe.

4

How far?

One of the most staggering aspects of modern astronomy is the sizes and distances of the objects we study. And one of the questions most frequently asked of astronomers is, "How do you *know* that star or galaxy is so far away?"

Of course, judging distances in everyday life is no great problem. When we walk into a familiar room and see a chair, we can generally locate its whereabouts quite easily. Repeated experience has told us that it takes about three paces to get to the chair from the door. And we know from our schooldays that a pace is about a metre or yard.

Even in an unfamiliar room, we have few problems. Our eyes, working together, provide a stereoscopic picture to our brains and previous experience of similar situations again lets us estimate the distance quite accurately. Without two eyes, though, things are much more difficult. Car drivers with one eye must be particularly careful when overtaking and when distance estimation is critical. Nevertheless, for short distances of under a few hundred metres or so, our past experience normally serves us very well, as any professional golfer knows.

But what of situations where we have no direct experience: say, estimating the height of an unfamiliar building? The first approach of most people would be to reach for a long measuring tape. What we do then is compare the size of the building with the already-calibrated tape measure and read off the height. This is fine — but will only work for heights up to a few hundred metres. For larger distances, professional surveyors resort to **triangulation** and this technique is also used in astronomy.

Triangulation and parallax

Consider Fig. 4.1.

The problem here is that we have to measure the distance to the distant church spire. We can't get to it directly because the river is in the way — and, in any case, we certainly don't have a long enough tape measure! The approach used by surveyors is to measure two angles at the two positions (marked *A* and *B* in the diagram). We must also measure the distance between *A* and *B* but this can easily be done with an ordinary tape provided it is only a few hundred metres or so.

In order to see how the method of triangulation works, let's first assume that there are two surveyors, Alan and Bill, each equipped with a small angle-measuring telescope or **theodolite**. Alan turns his telescope to Bill and reads off an angle from his scale. Alan then turns the theodolite carefully to the distant spire and reads

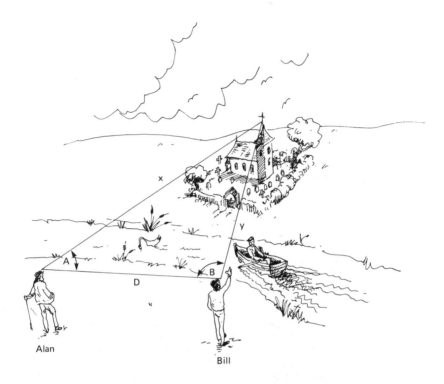

Fig. 4.1 — Determining the distance of an inaccessible church spire as an example of
triangulation.

off a second angle. He subtracts his two readings and gets a *difference* angle which
we shall call A.. Bill repeats the same procedure, turning first to Alan and then to
the spire. He finds a difference angle B. Finally Alan and Bill use their long
measuring tape to measure their distance apart — let's call that D.

There are now two ways of proceeding to get the distances of Alan and Bill
from the spire: the way surveyors *actually* use is to pull out their pocket calculators
and use some formulae from trigonometry. For example, the distance of the spire
from Alan (let's call it x, say) is given by the equation:

$$x = D \frac{sin(B)}{sin(A+B)}$$

and the distance y of the spire from Bill is

$$y = D \frac{sin(A)}{sin(A+B)}$$

However we must remember that our measurements were not perfectly accurate:
so perhaps we can be satisfied with a slightly less accurate answer. If so, we can
proceed as follows: take a large-ish piece of paper and draw the line between Alan
and Bill to scale. For example, if the distance D actually was measured as 271
metres, then draw the line between Alan and Bill on the paper as 271 millimetres.
Now, use a protractor to draw lines at the correct angles, A and B, from each of

the end points . Where the two lines cross corresponds to our best-guess for the point equivalent to the spire on our paper. By simply measuring the distances x and y in millimetres and converting them back to metres, we have the result we want. When we actually did this experiment, we measured angles of $84^1/_2$ degrees for A and 76 degrees for B. Our scale drawing gave us a distance of 770mm from Alan to the spire and 788mm from Bill to the spire. Trigonometry gave results of 787mm and 808mm respectively, which would be the "true" values *if* our angles had been measured perfectly accurately

The main difficulty in triangulation is in measuring the angles A and B. When the distances x and y are as big as a kilometre or so and D is only a few hundred metres, the angles A and B are very close to 90 degrees . A measurement error of a mere half a degree translates into an error in x or y of several tens of metres. And as x gets bigger, the situation becomes rapidly worse. This is why surveyors have to use very precise theodolites for accurate work. We shall encounter a similar problem when we describe how distances are measured elsewhere in the universe.

Almost exactly the same method as above is used by astronomers to measure distances to the Moon. On any given night, the position of the Moon against a background of the distant stars is different when seen from two different places on the Earth's surface. If we think of two observatories on the Earth — say, the old Royal Greenwich Observatory at Herstmonceux Castle in England and the Cape Observatory in South Africa — then we would find that their telescopes have to be aligned at angles differing by about 0.5 degrees[1] in order to focus on the same spot on the Moon. (See Fig. 4.2).

Our plotting method would be very inaccurate for angular differences this small. But trigonometry quickly gives the distance to the Moon as about 400, 000 km.

The triangulation method has also been used to measure the distance to several other bodies in the solar system, such as the Sun, some of the planets and the nearby asteroids. In astronomy it is known as the method of **parallax.** (As an aside we should perhaps comment that this name is rather strange, since it relies on the fact that the lines to the distant body from the two different observatories are *not* parallel! But then, astronomers often *are* strange!

Radar

For some objects within the solar system, we can use another and more recent method of measuring distances. It is known as the **radar method** and relies on the fact that the constancy of the velocity of radio waves in a vacuum (and, indeed, of all other forms of electromagnetic radiation) is one of the few absolutes of nature.

Imagine we use a radiotelescope to send out a sharp pulse of radio energy towards the distant planet Venus. The pulse travels to Venus at the velocity of light (almost 300,000 km per second) and is reflected back from its surface. Several minutes after transmitting, we may receive a faint "echo" of the original pulse from energy that has bounced off Venus and made the round-trip. By carefully timing the lag between transmission and echo, we can find the distance. For example, on 10 June 1988 the delay would have been 290 seconds. Since we know that the waves travelled at 299,792 km per second (the accurate value), we

---

[1] For the reader interested in details, we mention that we have used a distance between the two observatories of 5000 kilometres. Note, though, that this is not a distance over the Earth's surface but the direct distance *through* the Earth.

can quickly calculate that twice the distance to Venus on that day was 86,939,680 km and so its distance was 43,469,840 km.

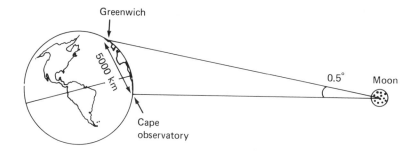

Fig. 4.2 — Determining the parallax distance of the Moon from observatories on Earth.

This method can be extremely accurate. So accurate, in fact, that it has been used to map geographical features on Venus using the fact that the tops of the Venusian mountains are just slightly closer to the Earth than the valleys! Fundamental to this technique is the fact that time is the quantity in physics that we can measure best of all. (For example, hydrogen maser clocks are in regular use at many radio observatories around the world. They can keep time accurate to a few seconds in thousands of millions of years[1].)

Accurate though the radar method of distance measurement is, it has severe limitations. In particular, for the more distant objects in the solar system, the returned echo signals are very weak. Even a strong radio transmitter, such as that on the American Voyager II spacecraft which has visited the planets Jupiter, Saturn and Uranus and will shortly visit Neptune, requires the world's largest radio telescopes to detect its feeble signals. When Voyager II passed by Uranus in January 1986, the energy received by the giant 64-m Parkes radiotelescope was millions of times weaker than that from a typical broadcast station. Unfortunately the radar method is not sensitive enough to accurately measure the distances to any astronomical bodies further than Jupiter.

---

[1]Funnily enough, although we can measure time very accurately, we really don't have the slightest idea what it actually *is*. But that's another story!

How then do we find the distances of the stars? Perhaps we might reconsider the triangulation method. Unfortunately the diameter of the Earth is only a few thousand kilometres. We can easily calculate that observing stars with this sort of baseline means that we have to measure angles with a precision of better than one thousand millionth of a degree (20 millionths of a second of arc), a feat which is quite impossible even using the best modern instruments. What we obviously need is a much bigger baseline. But we seem to be limited by the size of the Earth. Or are we?

Beyond the solar system

During the course of a year, the Earth makes one complete orbit around the Sun. This orbit is very nearly a circle with a radius of almost exactly 150 million km. This value was determined by triangulation from the Earth in the way we discussed above. Therefore, at dates separated by 6 months, the position of the Earth differs by about 300 million km. This is a tremendous baseline, nearly one hundred thousand times bigger than the size of the Earth, and it is just what we want to extend our triangulation to the stars.

In outline, the method of stellar parallax is as follows. First a photographic plate is mounted in a telescope and exposed on the region of sky containing the star whose position is required. The plate is then developed and carefully stored away. Six months later another plate is taken and the process repeated. A third plate is taken a further half-year after the second, at which time the Earth is back in roughly the same place as at first.

When the plates are compared, some stars will be found to have remained in the same place. These are likely to be quite distant, faint stars and we shall use them as a reference frame. A few objects will be seen to have moved small distances more or less in a straight line. These are stars that are moving rapidly through space: astronomers call them stars with large **proper motions**. They are always stars close to the Sun but which don't have exactly the same sort of motion as the Sun around our galaxy. Amongst these stars we will often notice a few for which the first and third positions are closer together than the second. These are the stars with large **parallactic shifts**[1]. It is the motion of the Earth around the Sun, during six months, that has caused the apparent angular shifts. And we can calculate the distances to the star using the size of the Earth's orbit in an exactly analogous way to our "church-spire" experiment.

In practice it is not necessary to expose the plates exactly six months apart — which is just as well since nights are often cloudy! Furthermore many observational inaccuracies have to be removed from the measurements. Nevertheless, the essence of the method is simply that of triangulation: we observe from two different positions whose separation we know and note the apparent angular shift. A bit of trigonometry then gives us the distance to the star.

It is the method of parallax that gives astronomers one of their units of distance. A star that shows parallactic shifts of plus and minus 1 arcsec when observed with a six-month baseline is said to be at a distance of 1 **parsec**. In more usual

---

[1] Actually this description is a gross simplification of the painstaking procedures that have to be followed in practice. In general, another effect called **aberration** has to be allowed for in the apparent shifts of the stars. It occurs because the Earth's velocity relative to the stars is different at different times of the year. Furthermore, normally not just three but many plates have to be taken to obtain an accurate parallax.

units this corresponds to a distance of around 3×10^{13} km. In this book we shall rarely use parsecs even though they are commonly used in professional astronomy. Instead we shall use **lightyears** — the distance travelled by light in 1 year — which are somewhat easier to understand and are more fundamental. To the accuracy we shall normally need, 1 parsec = 3 lightyears.

Effective though the method of parallaxes is for finding distances, it can only be used for the nearest few thousand stars, or so. This limits us to distances which are still very small compared with the size of our galaxy. Let us try to understand why the parallax method fails us.

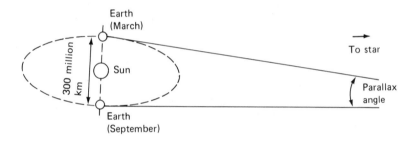

Fig. 4.3 — Determining the parallax of a distant star using the Earth's orbit as a baseline.

As we mentioned above, to produce a large parallax angle we need either a small distance or a large baseline. Of course we can't do much about the baseline — it is limited by the size of the Earth's orbit around the Sun[1]. This limited baseline means that parallax angles become smaller and smaller as we look at stars farther and farther away (see Fig. 4.3.) Eventually they become too small to measure. Why is this?

---

[1] It's interesting to ponder that Martians – if they exist – will be in a far better position to make parallax measurements because they live farther from the Sun. Their baseline will be about 50% bigger than that available to us poor Earthlings! Furthermore, their much thinner atmosphere will reduce the annoying effects of bad seeing which limits the smallest measurable angular sizes.

The apparent angular size of a star measured by any telescope depends on a number of things. Distance and the real size of the star are obviously two. But two other effects dictated by the laws of physics are even more important in practice.

The first is caused by the wavelength of the radiation being received and the limited diameter of the main mirror of the telescope. If we measure angles in radians, as mathematicians do, then the smallest size an image of a star can possibly show in a telescope — either as seen directly by the eye or on a photographic plate — is given by the approximate[1] relation:

$$\theta = \frac{wavelength}{diameter}$$

The reason for this **resolution limit** as it is known, is that the primary mirror of a telescope must bring light (or radio waves) arriving at different parts of the mirror to a single focus. Even if the mirror is a perfect parabola, the concentration of light at the focus can never be better than the wavelength divided by the diameter. It is as though the light gathering diameter of the mirror is uncertain to about one wavelength and so the precision of focussing of the radiation cannot be more accurate than the same relative amount. Table 4.1 shows some stellar angular sizes for typical-sized telescopes translated into the more usual units of seconds of arc.

Table 4.1 - Telescope resolution limits

Telescope mirror diameter	Resolution limit
5 cm	2".5
20 cm	0".62
1 m	0".12
4 m	0".031
10 m	0".012

The second and more important effect is caused by the Earth's atmosphere. The angular size of a star in an optical telescope is generally much worse than shown in Table 4.1. Light arriving at any telescope here on Earth must have passed through the Earth's atmosphere. The atmosphere is normally in a turbulent state, as is well known to all weather watchers. This turbulent atmosphere can be thought of as composed of many different refracting prisms of air and water vapour each causing our astronomical photons to take slightly different paths. These different paths

---

[1] The resolving power or resolution limit of a telescope is often more accurately quoted as

$$\theta = \frac{1.2\,\lambda}{D}$$

The small difference from the equation we give is unimportant in practice and is caused by a slightly different definition of size of image.

cause the photons arriving at the focus of our telescope to be smeared out a little, no matter how big or how well-figured our mirror is[1].

This degradation of a star's image by the atmosphere is known as the **seeing**. It varies from night to night and from telescope site to telescope site. Astronomers planning a new telescope facility search long and hard for the best possible site. At the best ground-based sites, such as in Chile and Hawaii — the seeing can often be better than 1 second of arc. But many astronomical observations, worldwide, have to be made with seeing as poor as 2 or 3 arcseconds.

We can now understand why the parallax method breaks down. In Fig. 4.4 we see a highly magnified photo of a star's image, taken when the seeing was several arcseconds.

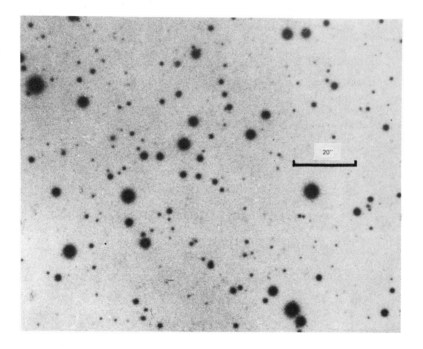

Fig. 4.4 — An example of "bad seeing" with an optical telescope. Note the large apparent sizes of the smallest star images, which are caused by turbulence in the Earth's atmosphere

If we had a similar photo taken about six months later, we would be hard-pressed to measure a change in position of the star smaller than about $1/2$ arcsecond. Even with the best telescopes and under the best seeing conditions, measurements more accurate than about 0.1 arcsecond are impossible. All of this

---

[1]It's both an amusing and depressing thought that photons arriving from a galaxy perhaps halfway across the universe, and having travelled for in excess of a thousand million years, get "messed up" in the last few kilometres and last few microseconds of that journey! It is, of course, for these reasons that astronomers desperately want to put large telescopes – such as the Hubble Space Telescope – into space to escape from the effects of the atmosphere.

means that we can't measure parallaxes smaller than 0.1 arcsecond — and so we are limited to distances of less than 30 lightyears.

How, then, do we find the distance to the more distant stars in our galaxy? And how do we find the distances of other galaxies?

Standard candles

When we look up at a clear night sky, we see many stars. We have been told that these are stars similar in many ways to our own Sun. But of course they don't look anywhere near as bright because they are much farther away. However, if we understand by exactly how much a star gets dimmer at different distances, we can estimate its distance from its apparent brightness. This is the principle of one of the most important methods of determining astronomical distances: the **standard candle**.

In what follows, we shall want to talk about both the "true" or *intrinsic* emission from objects and also we shall want to refer to how bright they *appear* to be. Because of this we must carefully define our terms. The two ideas are, of course, related by the distance of the object. Incidentally, professional astronomers are not always as careful as they should be and frequently refer to the "brightness" of an object without making it clear whether intrinsic or apparent is intended.

We shall try to avoid any confusion by using the following terms: where we want to mention how bright an object appears to be from here on Earth, we shall refer either to *apparent brightness* (in the optical region of the spectrum) or *apparent flux* (in the radio, and other, regions of the spectrum.) Where we mean the *true* or *intrinsic* levels of emission from an object, we shall use the word **luminosity** in optical astronomy or **power** in radioastronomy and for other parts of the electromagnetic spectrum[1], often adding the word "intrinsic" as well to remove all ambiguity. To the experts this may seem like "over-kill"; but we have suffered through too many confusing discussions simply because these ideas were not made clear at the start.

Unfortunately, optical astronomers still use a rather antiquated system of measuring apparent brightness in terms of **magnitudes**. Magnitudes are a logarithmic unit and fairly messy to use. Much more useful for our present purpose is the radio astronomer's (and infrared astronomer's) unit of apparent brightness, the **jansky**[2]. To tie the two methods of measurement together, we can use the approximate relation that a 9th magnitude star in the optical region of the spectrum is about 1 jansky and that its brightness decreases by a *factor* of about 2.5 times for every magnitude by which it is fainter than this.

Let's leave this annoying question of units and definitions aside and have some fun: we'll calculate the distance to the star Sirius just from how bright it looks and by assuming that it is a star similar to the Sun. This bright southern star has an apparent magnitude of about minus 1, corresponding to an apparent optical flux of

---

[1] Experts may also be aware that the word "brightness" is sometimes used in astrophysics to refer to the amount of apparent energy *per unit area* of a radiant body. We shall not make use of this meaning here, because we need the word to refer to "optical flux density".

[2] One jansky is equivalent to 10^{-26} watts per square metre per hertz of frequency bandwidth.

10,000 janskys. In contrast, the Sun has an apparent magnitude of *minus* 26, corresponding to about 10^{14} janskys. Thus Sirius appears to be about 10^{10} times fainter than the Sun.

Physics tells us that the brightness of an object decreases with distance in a manner inversely proportional to the square of that distance. This is the famous inverse square law of radiation. So we can calculate that Sirius must be about 10^5 times more distant than the Sun. And since we know the Sun is 150 million kilometres or about 8 light minutes from the Earth, we can estimate that the distance to Sirius as about 1.6 lightyears. Actually Sirius is one of the few stars close enough for us also to be able to measure a more accurate value by the parallax method. This method gives a distance of about 8 lightyears. So why didn't we get the right answer using the standard candle method?

The answer is that we have assumed that Sirius is a star of the same type as the Sun. But this is not true: Sirius is bigger and hotter. The different colours of stars indicate that they have different temperatures at their surfaces. Furthermore, some are big and some are small. Both of these properties affect the **intrinsic luminosity** or "true brightness" of a star. To determine this true brightness we have to calculate how bright the star would appear with the effects of distance removed.

Astronomers define a standard distance and imagine all stars "lined up" there. For historical reasons this standard distance was chosen as 10 parsecs or about 30 lightyears. The magnitude that a star would have at 10 parsecs is called its **absolute magnitude**. The absolute magnitude of the Sun is about +5 while that of Sirius is +1.4 or about 30 times brighter, which accounts for the above discrepancy in estimating its distance.

But how can we calculate distances from apparent magnitudes for other stars whose absolute magnitudes we don't know? We can't — at least until we find a separate method of deriving the absolute magnitudes or luminosities. Fortunately this turns out to be fairly easy for most stars. The optical spectrum of a star gives us a very good idea of its surface temperature. For example, we know that very blue stars are much hotter than very red stars. In a similar way, the spectral lines, which we shall discuss in Chapter 12, give us a good idea of the size of a star. Low-density giant stars will have narrow lines while the compact dwarf stars have such strong gravitational fields that their lines are broad.

Using these clues we can deduce the true brightness of a star and hence its distance simply by analysing the light coming from it. This method of distance determination is known as the method of **spectroscopic parallax**. Actually it has nothing to do with the previous method of parallax measurement we discussed above, but astronomers were so used to mixing up the words "parallax" and "distance" that this most inappropriate name stuck!

The method is useful for finding the distances to stars not only throughout our galaxy but also in other nearby galaxies. Of course, there are problems. First amongst these is that the light from the more distant stars in our galaxy suffers from being absorbed by dust contained in the clouds of gas lying between the stars. This means that the apparent brightnesses we measure are incorrect and so will be the distances we determine. Fortunately, dust imposes a characteristic "imprint" on the spectrum of the stars and careful spectroscopy can provide data that allows us to correct the measurements, at least for the stars within a few thousand lightyears of the Sun. Secondly, as we get farther away from home, we have to be very sure that the object we are measuring is in fact just *one* object and not a cluster of stars or — possibly — a region of ionized hydrogen surrounding several stars. Either of these possibilities would seriously affect our distance determinations.

Fortunately, as our spectroscopic distance methods begin to fail, radioastronomy comes to our aid. Radio waves are virtually unaffected by dust. Radioastronomers can determine the velocity of hydrogen gas in our galaxy by measuring the Doppler shift of the 21 cm spectral line produced by neutral hydrogen (see Chapter 12). A careful analysis of these velocities allows the distance to the gas to be derived. Using such methods, radioastronomers have shown that the Sun lies around 25,000 lightyears from the centre of our galaxy and have established the overall size of our galaxy as about 60,000 lightyears.

The net result of all these determinations is as follows: we are confident that we can determine distances in the solar system to a very high accuracy — to around one part in one hundred million. Within about 30 lightyears of the Sun, the parallax method using the Earth's orbit gives us distances accurate to a few per-cent. As we move farther away our distance determinations become increasingly poor until they are often uncertain to a factor of 2 or 3 or worse. Throughout most of the universe we have no *direct* way of determining distances at all, a topic we shall return to in Chapter 8 when we discuss the redshift.

Our biased view

As we gaze out into the universe, we must remember just how biased our view of it will be. It is the apparently brightest and biggest objects that force themselves on our attention: unfortunately these will rarely be the most important objects. Consider the Sun, for example: it blazes in the sky as a minus 26th magnitude star simply because it is so close. But on the universal scale, it is insignificant.

The equation which relates the apparent brightness of an astronomical object to how bright it really is, is the inverse square law:

$$S = \frac{P}{4\pi D^2}$$

where D is the distance to the object and P is its true power or luminosity.

Similarly, the apparent angular size of an astronomical body, θ, is given by:

$$\theta = \frac{Q}{D}$$

where Q is its true diameter and D is again the distance.

Obviously the largest values of both S and θ will come from the objects with the biggest values of P and Q and also with the smallest values of D. But which of these effects are the most important?

To answer this question, let's concentrate on just one example: the apparent brightness of stars in our galaxy. Astronomers have determined that the stars in our galaxy range in intrinsic luminosity from roughly 10,000 times fainter than the Sun to about 10,000 times brighter. Thus the total range of stellar luminosities covers a factor of about 100,000,000. *If* all the stars lay at the same distance from the Earth, then this is the range of apparent brightness we would see, too.

But they don't. Instead, they range in distance from about 4 lightyears for the closest object to about 50,000 lightyears for stars on the opposite side of the galaxy. Now, because the law relating apparent brightness and absolute luminosity contains the distance to a *square* power, this distance factor of around 10,000

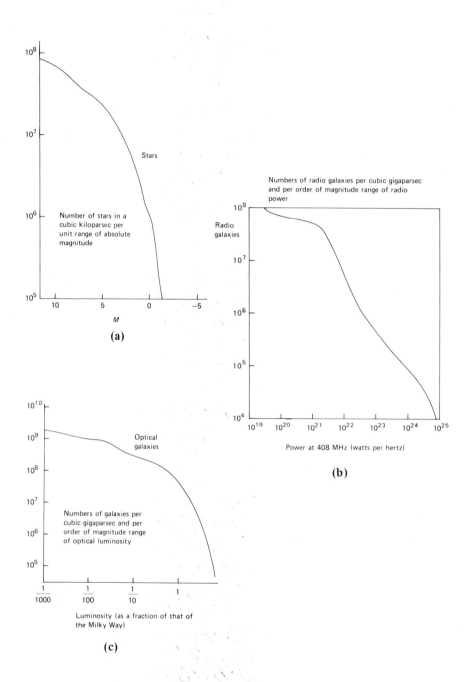

Figs. 4.5 (a), (b) and (c) — Examples of some "luminosity functions for stars (a), radio galaxies (b) and optical galaxies (c) showing the numbers of objects as a function of intrinsic luminosity or power.

implies a factor of around 100,000,000 in apparent brightness. Coincidentally this is just the same factor as the range in intrinsic luminosity. Thus one of the most intrinsically luminous known stars on the other side of our galaxy and one of the intrinsically least luminous stars very close to us will appear to have much the *same* apparent brightness.

Does this then mean that when we look up at the night sky we have an equal chance of seeing an intrinsically feeble star close by or a luminous star on the other side of the galaxy? Well, no — not necessarily. We have not yet considered the *relative numbers* of intrinsically powerful and feeble stars. The relation that describes how many stars have a particular luminosity is called by astronomers the **luminosity function**[1]. Luminosity functions have been determined for stars, galaxies and many other sorts of astronomical object, in the radio and other parts of the electromagnetic spectrum. For the moment, we shall skip over the painstaking observations and complex interpretation that went into deriving these functions and proceed just to make use of them.

For reasons that we don't fully understand, it seems that, in astronomy, nature always produces large numbers of feeble objects and very few intrinsically powerful objects. For example, there are many times more stars with luminosities one-half that of the Sun than there are with luminosities twice that of the Sun. It may be that there is an "equipartition" of energy: the smaller energy (per object) of the feeble objects being counterbalanced by their greater numbers. We show the luminosity functions of stars, radio galaxies and galaxies in Figs 4.5 (a),(b) and (c).

We said earlier that one of the most luminous known stars far across the galaxy and one of the feeblest stars close by would appear about equally bright to us. But we now notice from the luminosity functions that there are very few luminous stars compared with feeble stars. We might think, then, that the typical star we see in the night sky would be a relatively nearby, intrinsically feeble star and that we would have to search long and hard among the apparently faint stars for a truly luminous one.

Is this so? If we actually look at a list of the 100 apparently brightest[2] stars we can see at once that something seems to be wrong with our previous arguments. We expected the great majority of the stars to be intrinsically feeble objects. Instead most are very luminous stars, such as Rigel, with luminosities hundreds to thousands of times that of the Sun. So where did our argument go wrong?

We have forgotten one thing: there is far more *space* in our galaxy at large distances than at small distances. If we approximate our galaxy by a thin disc, then the amount of space lying between distances of 800 lightyears and 900 lightyears, for example, is roughly six times as great as that lying between 100 lightyears and 200 lightyears. Fig. 4.6 will make it clear why this is so.

---

[1]Of course, if you were to ask how many stars have *exactly* a luminosity 1.234 times that of the Sun, for example, the answer is none. The luminosity stated is too precise and no star is likely to have exactly that value. What we must do is state a small *range* of luminosities, perhaps from 1.2 to 1.3 solar luminosities, and ask how many stars fall within that range. An analogy may help explain this point: In a given school class, there are not likely to be any children who are exactly 10.000 years old. But there may be several who are between 9.9 and 10.1 years old. The size of the range – 0.2 years in this case – decides the number of people or objects that fall in the range. Roughly speaking, the number found is directly proportional to the size of the range.

[2]See, for example *Astrophysical Quantities* as mentioned in the Bibliography.

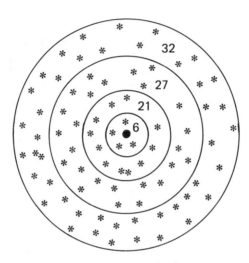

Fig. 4.6 — Schematic distribution of stars in the plane of our galaxy. If the stars were uniformly distributed (they're not), then shells at increasing distance would contain increasing numbers of stars in proportion to the square of the distance.

When we come to consider galaxies distributed in a sphere rather than in a disc, this effect will become even more important since the volume of space then scales as the *square* of the distance from us, rather than linearly.

Let us try to summarize so far: the number and appearance of the stars we see in our night sky gives us little direct information about the true properties of these stars or their relative frequency of occurrence in space. To understand the true importance of the objects we see we must carefully consider their distances, their relative numbers (the luminosity function) and how they are distributed in space.

As we shall see, understanding the stars in our own galaxy is a much simpler problem than that which faces us when we leave the Milky Way behind and look at the rest of the universe. For one thing, we have considerable confidence in our methods of measuring distances to the stars. For another, the spectra of the stars give us a very good (and independent) indicator of their true luminosities. Thirdly, the distribution of the majority of stars in our galaxy is well known to follow a disc pattern. Unfortunately, as we turn our attention to the rest of the universe we know neither the distances nor the true luminosities of the objects we shall find with any great degree of confidence.

5

Everywhere and all around

Astronomy is an observational rather than an experimental science. Astronomers can only look at and (hopefully) learn from the universe. They have no way of causing experiments to happen, unlike their physicist colleagues working in Earthbound laboratories. Probably because of this, astronomers are often forced to make sweeping assumptions based on the minute part of the universe they have observed. They then consider the implications of their assumptions and try to decide if these implications conflict with other observations.

Among astronomers, the group who make the most outlandish assumptions are the **cosmologists** who study the universe on the largest scale. It may come as a surprise to learn that almost all cosmologists assume the universe is exactly the same everywhere. To make this astounding assumption sound better, they say that the universe is **homogeneous**. Furthermore they argue that the universe looks exactly the same in all directions when viewed from the Earth. They call this the **isotropy** of the universe.

Well, clearly, in a very obvious sense they are wrong. On a sunny day, it will make a great difference to my suntan whether I face the Sun or not. And if I were to travel to the centre of the Sun (temperature estimated in excess of 10 million degrees Centigrade) it is a very different place from the South Pole! As another example, when we look up at the stars in the night sky, we see many more towards the centre of our galaxy than we do in other directions. The universe is definitely neither isotropic nor homogeneous, at least on the "small" scale. So what are the cosmologists talking about?

The blinking anthropologists

What they have in mind is a sort of "averaged" universe. Let's think about an analogy. We might consider taking a survey of the number of times each day people in different parts of the world blinked their eyes. In fact, let's imagine an exploring anthropologist who travels the world and determines the blink-rate for each country[1]. There would undoubtedly be differences in the survey between individual people, babies, old people etc. But the question that our peripatetic anthropologist would probably be interested in would be, "Are there any *systematic* differences

---

[1] This is the sort of work social scientists or anthropologists do all the time – who said astronomers were the only ones to study weird things?!

between countries? Do Australians as a whole, say, blink more than Americans?" To answer this question he would have to "smooth-out" the individual elements of the problem and just look at the averages. And this is the sort of thing we must do, too, when we discuss the universe.

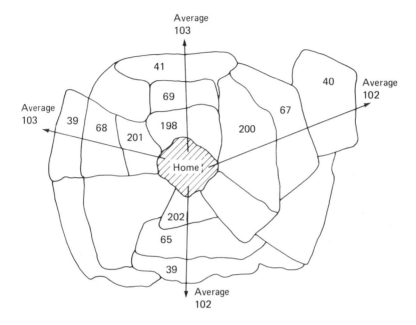

Fig. 5.1 — "Blink-rates" for countries in different directions as measured by a stay-at-home observer. Notice that the averages in each direction are very similar.

But first, let's imagine what our touring anthropologist may find. It is possible that after observing thousands of people in all countries, he discovers that the *average* blink-rate is much the same everywhere. If so, he would be able to say that, as regards blinking, the world is homogeneous. Of course these results might be criticized during the following few years in the erudite world of blinkologists so that, by the year 2000, it may be decided to repeat the whole experiment.

Our same explorer — no longer a mere post-doctoral student but a full Reader in Blinkology — sets off once again to repeat the survey. This time he finds that the blink-rate is still the same from country to country, but has dropped slightly overall from what it was previously. In this case, we would again say that the world was homogeneous as regards blink-rate. All that matters is that it be the same everywhere at one particular time.

Now let's think about the question of isotropy and consider a stay-at-home scientist who hates to travel. This anthropologist simply phones up different countries around the world and asks reputable local anthropologists to provide him with blink-rates. He draws a large map of the world with lines in different directions pointing straight away from his own country (see Fig. 5.1) and plots his blink-rates on this map. He finds that the blink-rate is different at different distances along any particular straight line. On the other hand, the average for every line is very much like that for every other line: *direction* doesn't seem to matter. He has found that the world is isotropic.

Clearly this is not the same sort of world that our exploring anthropologist found. But then, anthropologists rarely agree. Note, too, that all that matters for a view to be isotropic is that the blink-rate averaged along one particular direction is the same as the average rate in any other direction. It doesn't matter that there are variations *along* a particular direction at different distances. There may or may not be: but we would still call the world isotropic.

Now, there is one set of circumstances that would allow our two anthropologists to agree that the world was both isotropic *and* homogeneous: this would occur if our explorer was correct and the world's countries all had the same average blink-rate. Under these circumstances our stay-at-home anthropologist would still see the same rate in all directions and, as a bonus, would also see the same rates in all countries lying along a particular direction.

Isotropy and homogeneity in the universe

For the moment, we have probably had enough of anthropologists. So let's return to astronomy and the real universe. Instead of blink-rate, we can substitute any measurable physical value we like. Perhaps, to be concrete, you could think in terms of the average *shapes* of the spiral galaxies lying at a particular distance and in a particular direction. Let's consider the sort of scenario we might possibly see.

First, we take a series of photographic plates covering all directions from the Earth[1]. Next we measure the shapes of all the spiral galaxies on each plate and determine their average appearance. We encounter a slight complication because the plates taken in some directions are rather obscured by dusty gas clouds lying within our own galaxy. This is a nuisance, but can be allowed for. After we have made these allowances we find that the *average shape of the spirals on each plate is much the same as on any other plate* and we conclude that the universe is isotropic. But note we can *not* yet conclude that the universe is the same at all *distances* from us, at least on the basis of the observational programme we have just undertaken. It is quite possible that galaxies farther away from us have different shapes than those closer to us.

Now imagine that we have a wonderful spaceship which can instantaneously travel around the universe anywhere we like. (Don't tell Einstein about this!) This is obviously just what we need in order to sort out the unresolved question from above: "Are the galaxies the same at all distances?" Before we describe the results from this imaginary experiment, let's ponder what *might* happen.

One possibility is that the galaxies do indeed have different shapes at different distances. This wouldn't contradict what we found from our photographic experiment. But a little thought convinces us that it is a very peculiar result. It implies that we are in a very special place in the universe. Why? Because if we find that the galaxies have different shapes (on average) in different places (which means that the universe is not homogeneous) and yet we see the same shapes averaged along all directions as viewed from the Earth (which means that the universe *is* isotropic), then it must imply that the view from a galaxy other than our own could not also be isotropic.

Since this is perhaps a difficult point to grasp but is crucial to much of our understanding of the universe, let's consider one more analogy. The view from the

---

[1]This has actually been done during the large Schmidt telescope surveys that have mapped both the northern and southern celestial hemispheres.

top of a featureless hilltop down onto a featureless plain of grass may be the same in all directions and could thus be described as isotropic. But, if we move off the top of the hill, the view is no longer isotropic: the hilltop gets in the way and ruins the symmetry. A little thought should convince the reader that isotropy implies either that the world is homogeneous or that our viewpoint is very special.

The other possibility is that our explorer in his spaceship finds that the spiral galaxies have the same shape everywhere. Thus the universe is homogeneous (as regards these galaxies' shapes). In this case the situation is much simpler: the view from *any* part of the universe *must* be isotropic and we no longer have to inhabit a special place in the universe in order to explain our isotropic observational results. In terms of our analogy there *is* no hilltop and we are all standing on identical points of a smooth, featureless grass plain.

The real view

Well, so much for the theory: what happens in practice? We can *never* know with total confidence that the universe is homogeneous because we cannot travel to all places instantaneously. But we *can* make an important statement about isotropy. We shall summarize years of painstaking observational research astronomy by saying that we believe the universe is indeed isotropic as viewed from the Earth after the "appropriate" allowances have been made.

And what are these "allowances"? Well, one of them was mentioned above: we must correct for the obscuration caused by our galaxy's gas and dust. This correction is not too important if we are just talking about shapes; but it would be crucial if we were trying to measure the average *colours* of galaxies in different directions[1], since the obscuration also causes the galaxies to become redder. Secondly, we must be careful to average the universe over volumes considerably bigger than the size of a typical galaxy. Thirdly, if we are measuring velocities, we must allow for the fact that the Earth, the Sun and our galaxy itself are all moving relative to the fabric of space. This movement causes the velocities we measure for external galaxies to be "biased" in the direction towards which we are moving. We shall return to this point later, in Chapter 17, when we discuss the cosmic microwave background.

Well, the universe may be isotropic: but is it homogeneous? This is a much harder question to answer observationally. Unfortunately we *don't* have a spaceship capable of moving instantaneously around the universe. What we receive here on Earth is a series of "snapshots" of the universe coming from different distances. The snapshots close to home correspond to the way the universe looked only a few million years ago: those much farther away correspond to the universe as it was thousands of millions of years ago. This is an enormous complication. Of course, the time difference wouldn't matter if the universe didn't change during its lifetime. But we strongly suspect it does.

We have now encountered what is perhaps the hardest problem facing observational astronomers working in the field of cosmology. What we would *like* to do is compare different parts of the universe *at the same time* to see whether or not these different parts are identical. But because of the pathetically short lifetimes of human beings, all we *get* is this series of snapshots taken at different

---

[1] Incidentally, the colour of a galaxy is a more important property than you might think. We believe that the bluer galaxies are undergoing periods of much more active star formation than galaxies which are redder.

times. To make any sense of what we see, we must allow for the effects of evolution. Unfortunately, to do that would require a good knowledge of how the galaxies and quasars are formed and how they evolve. This we do not have.

It is a very daunting problem; perhaps impossible. But we should put what we are trying to do in perspective: we, a race of human beings, living on a second-rate planet, orbiting a third-rate star in the outer suburbs of a galaxy that is by no means the largest in the universe, we, are trying to understand how the whole universe evolved and how it is built! Perhaps we *should* expect the enquiry to take us a little time! In one sense, our question about whether the universe is homogeneous has been answered. It isn't. In fact, it can't be, because we view it at different times. But the sense in which the question is usually meant in modern astronomy is, "If allowance could be made for all the effects of evolution, *then* would it be homogeneous?"

We now have two options; fortunately, we can adopt them both at the same time. One is to try our hardest, by making deep surveys of the sky and by trying to understand how galaxies evolve, to answer observationally the question as to whether or not the universe is homogeneous. The other option is simply to say that we *believe* that we do not inhabit a special place in the universe, and thus we know it to be homogeneous *because we have proved it to be isotropic from our observations*.

This belief, assumption, or what have you, is referred to by the name of the **cosmological principle**. It may or may not be correct. It could perhaps better be termed the "Principle of Caution", since it affirms we live in a typical part of the universe: and history has shown that every time mankind *has* tried to put itself in a special place in the universe, it has been later proved wrong. Witness the revolution in thought initiated by Copernicus!

There is one further possibility that we should consider: it is just possible that we don't have to make allowances for evolution at all in trying to arrive at our true picture of the universe. This view was proposed by Hermann Bondi and Thomas Gold in 1948. They suggested that the universe was not only the same at all places (on average) but that it was *the same at all times*.

This is a very all-encompassing statement indeed. It was termed by Bondi and Gold the ***perfect* cosmological principle**. It implied that as galaxies grew old and (presumably) faded away, they were somehow replaced with new, adjacent, similar galaxies, thus maintaining the average number, shapes, colours and types of galaxy to be the same at all times. However, we know that the universe expands as time proceeds. (See Chapters 7 and 8.) Thus, if we have to keep everything the same, we must also keep the number of galaxies per unit volume (or space density) the same. To do that, requires not just that new galaxies are born to make up the numbers of those that are dying but also that additional galaxies be created as time goes on.

What are they being created from? Certainly not from already existing gas and dust: our arguments about the numbers of galaxies staying the same also applies equally to the amount of gas and dust too. No, the new galaxies must be created out of *nothing*! At the very least, the gas and dust from which the extra galaxies are to be born must be created out of nothing. This idea, originally propounded by Fred Hoyle, continuing the line of thought started by Gold and Bondi, is called the theory of **continuous creation of matter**.

If such an idea revolts the senses, as some astronomers have argued, let it be said that the **Big Bang** theory, which we shall mention in Chapter 17, does much the same. The Big Bang creates the whole universe in an instant out of nothing: in

Continuous Creation, the universe is created a bit at a time. It is hard to decide which is the more acceptable *a priori*. Fortunately we don't have to ponder the question indefinitely, for astronomy is essentially an observational science. We can go and look! When we do, we shall see that the evidence strongly favours the Big Bang theory.

In summary, our observations *show* that the universe is isotropic on the large scale. We *believe* that our view of the cosmos is quite typical and in no way special. This allows us to *deduce* that the universe is also homogeneous. But we cannot prove that it is homogeneous directly, because we have no good theory of the evolution of the galaxies. In the following chapters we shall frequently refer to these important ideas of isotropy and homogeneity.

6

Relatively speaking

Relativity and bathtubs

Some modern books on cosmology dealing with such subjects as "The Edge of the Universe", "Redshifts" and "Gravity" give the impression that it can "all be explained by relativity". Actually that is not true. The Special Theory of Relativity has virtually nothing of importance to say about cosmology. And the General Theory of Relativity differs from the "normal" law of gravity discovered by Newton only when the gravitational fields are very strong: again, something that rarely happens in cosmology. On the other hand, the theories of relativity *are* the only satisfactory way of discussing space and time. And these two quantities are at the very basis of much of cosmology. Therefore it is worth spending a little time discussing some of the ideas here.

But when people hear the word "relativity", we get the impression that they "turn-off", thinking the ideas are much too hard for them. That's a pity because, although the theories of relativity are a spectacular departure from "ordinary" physics, they are really quite simple to explain and understand. Not necessarily easy to compute mathematical answers for — that needs a bit of fairly complex mathematics — but easy to really understand.

In case the last sentence seems a bit paradoxical, let us give an example. If we put some water in a bathtub, let it stand for a bit and then pull out the plug, the water runs out through the plug-hole. Now, to calculate exactly how long it will take the water to run out is a very difficult theoretical problem in the branch of applied mathematics called fluid dynamics: in fact, most modern theories would not get the answer right within 50%. But to *understand* what is happening — that the water is going down the plug-hole — can be comprehended by the youngest child.

This is the sort of approach we shall take in this chapter. We shall use only the simplest of mathematics and so we may not get exact answers: but we *shall* be able to understand what is going on. It will be more than enough for our needs; and it will also be the way most astronomers and cosmologists think the great majority of the time. In fact, if an astronomer can't get a "gut feel" for a particular research idea, he generally doesn't believe it. Nor, we would argue, can he claim he understands it!

In order to comprehend the enormous impact relativity had on the physics of the early twentieth century, it is necessary first to talk about the previous way of looking at things that resulted from the work of such people as Galileo and Newton.

Just as an aside though, we find it amusing when someone says "Newton's" dynamical theory or "Maxwell's" laws of radiation, as though these people were the *only* ones to dream up the ideas. Today, if you look around at the way physics is done, it is very, very rarely the work of one man or woman only. Instead, many people contribute to almost all our "breakthroughs". In the real world, one person may be working on a particular problem or experiment for several years, perhaps gathering data but with no clear understanding or brilliant insight. Left alone, he or she might go on for ever — or at least until the research grant runs out. But maybe this same person gives a paper at an international conference; a rather boring paper, perhaps, but it might elicit a comment from someone working on a different, but related, problem. Very likely our original researcher doesn't take it in much — he's basking in the relief of having delivered his paper and is thinking more about the conference lunch to follow. But yet another person in the audience may pick up the germs of an idea which he then passes on to a colleague when he gets back to his own country, etc. etc.

That is the way most real science is done nowadays, not with brilliant solo *tours de force* of experimental work and ideas but with slow dissemination of understanding and with many false starts and stops. Of course, in the end, someone will publish the paper that "explains it all" — and they'll get almost all the credit. Furthermore, once their name becomes associated with a particular piece of work, it's convenient and easier for others to ignore other contributors. You only have to think of all the apocryphal comments attributed to Oscar Wilde or Winston Churchill — no doubt they were intelligent and witty men — but life would have been too short for them to say all they are supposed to have said!

But perhaps it was very different in the days of Newton and Kepler? Because there were so many fewer researchers, and because there were no international conferences, and because the amount of funding per active researcher was so much greater (in real terms) then than now: perhaps, for all these reasons, researchers really *were* the brilliant young scientists beloved by the modern press. Perhaps; but we doubt it. Although there seems little doubt that people such as Newton and Einstein were indeed great theoretical physicists, we think that they also owed a great deal to the (to us, unknown) colleagues with whom they came into contact. As Newton himself said, "If I have seen further than other men, it is because I have stood on the shoulders of giants".

So, while bearing in mind that we owe a great deal to the genius of Einstein, let us not be overawed by his theories of relativity. They are important and relevant. But they are also easy to understand.

Before Einstein

In the late years of the last century, physicists believed that all speeds were relative. That is, it only made sense to talk about the velocity of a body — say, a golf ball — *relative* to something else: for example, the head of the golf club or the hole. To say anything else, leads to awkward questions. If we just mention that the golf ball is moving at 80 km/h, it makes a great deal of difference whether that 80 km/h is directly away from you, sideways, or coming straight at your nose!

Of course, in everyday language, saying that something has a speed of 80 km/h generally means 80 km/h *relative to the Earth*: what the ball's speed is relative to is understood. This is because the Earth is stationary enough for most people, and direction can be picked up from the context of the sentence. But the Earth is really *not* stationary. For one thing, it is rotating. For another, it is whizzing around the Sun at about 30 km/s. Yet again, the Sun has a speed of more than 200 km/s relative to the centre of our galaxy, and so on. In fact the speed of any Earthbound golf ball — even one nestling safely in the hole — is more than 500 km/s relative to the rest of the universe!

This idea of all speeds being relative really seemed self-evident to our late-nineteenth century physicists. And so it is: we still believe that all speeds *except one* are relative. But the way in which we believe they are relative has changed slightly since the Theory of Special Relativity came along.

Before continuing with our discussion let's just be clear what we mean by "special" theory. Imagine we were trying to propose a theory to explain why Australian caterpillars always have an odd number of legs[1]. At first we may only work with purple caterpillars — perhaps because they are easy to catch. Eventually we might come up with a good theory that fitted all the observational evidence. But this would only be a restricted or specialized theory — in fact, a *special* theory — since it would only apply to purple caterpillars. Of course, a few years — and many munched nasturtium leaves — later we might have a theory that applies to *all* Australian caterpillars. A scientist could call this the *general* theory of Odd-Pod-Austral-caterpillology. The previous special theory is not better than the general theory — in fact, it is less so, since it applies only to purple caterpillars. The general theory incorporates the special theory and is better and more powerful.

It is the same with Einstein's theories of relativity. There are two: the Special and the General theories. The Special came first and talks only about objects moving at constant velocity, which means in straight lines and with no accelerations or decelerations. The other is the General Theory. It came later and has to do with accelerated bodies and gravity. (How did gravity get into this? Hang on and you'll see!)

The Special Theory is simple to understand, both at the "gut" level and at the mathematical level. It has been confirmed beyond all reasonable doubt. Any modern physicist ignores it at his peril. The essentials of the General Theory can be grasped easily enough but the mathematics is considerably more tricky. Perhaps this is why it is open to far more doubt than the Special Theory. It is probably correct — but many physicists are looking for a still better theory.

The Special Theory

First let us turn to the Special Theory. If we had to summarize the essence of this theory in one sentence, it would be as follows:

All velocities are relative, with the one exception of the velocity of light: that velocity is absolute.

Unfortunately the most compact way of putting a point is not necessarily the clearest way. And so we will have to look at what it means in more detail.

Imagine that you are careering along on one of the trains so often featured in the movies of the "Wild West". You are chasing the "baddies" who have, of course, just robbed the local bank and are making good their escape. In your chase

---

[1] Incidentally, this is not the case!

you have to climb out of the window and onto the top of the train. (Do we hear you say you've seen this one?)

Now for the physics. We'll say that the train is puffing along at 100 km/h. (Yes, we know that they really used miles per hour in the Wild West, but this is physics where metric units are used by everybody.) You, as the chief "goody", are running along the train roof at 10 km/h in the same direction as the train is moving — no doubt jumping from carriage to carriage clutching your six-shooter. Now, the question is this: if you were to forget that just down the track there was a bridge approaching, at what speed would you slam into the top of the bridge?(See Fig. 6.1).

Fig. 6.1 — Relative velocities as measured by a moving train and a stationary observer.

The answer seems to be easy; and, in everyday life, it is. You would clearly hit the bridge harder if you were running up the train (toward the engine) than if you were sitting still on the train top. Also you would hit the bridge a lot harder than if the train were not moving at all and you were just walking along it. In fact, it's "obvious" that the speed at which you would hit the bridge is 110 km/h, just the sum of the train's speed (100 km/h) and your speed relative to the train (10 km/h). In everyday life, this is indeed the right answer — or, at least, so close to it that it make no difference.

The previous example is so obvious that it immediately suggests how we might calculate what would happen if the conditions were somewhat different. For example, consider the case where we are running the other way down the train, that is, towards the back of the train. It's pretty obvious that you would slam into the bridge not quite so hard. In fact, your speed would only be 90 km/h relative to the bridge. And if the train were to slow down to a mere 10 km/h before it got to the bridge (can't you just hear those squealing brakes!?) then you would escape from hitting the bridge altogether. You'd just be keeping pace with it by running at the same speed in the opposite direction to which the train is moving. (Until, of course, you fell off the back of the train!)

Let's summarize these ideas in a mathematical form. If the velocity of the train (relative to the ground) is T and the velocity of you relative to the train is Y, then the speed, H, with which you hit the bridge is given by the simple equation:

$$H = T + Y$$

Let's check that: if T is 100 and Y is (plus)10 then H is 110 (the plus means the same way the train is going). If T is 100 and Y is minus 10 (the opposite way to which the train is going), then H is only 90. Correct!

Now all this is so reasonable that it is hard to think of any way in which it could be wrong. But it is — at least for large velocities.

In the early years of this century, a physics experiment was performed that showed that the above formula was not quite right. In fact, for very large speeds (comparable with the speed of light), it was badly wrong. To put things in perspective, let us remind ourselves just how fast light travels: its velocity is a staggering 300,000 kilometres per second. Not per hour, but per *second* ! At this speed the time taken from turning on an electric light in your home to the time you see the light is a mere one fifth of a millionth of a second[1].

The enormous speed with which light travels is the reason that we are not aware of light travel effects in most of everyday life. Only when you make an overseas telephone call via satellite and the signal has to go an appreciable fraction of the way to the Moon and back, do you realize from the slight delays that light and radio waves really *do* take time to travel.

The experiment we referred to above was called the **Michelson-Morley experiment** after the two American physicists that first performed it. The were attempting to show whether or not the Earth was moving relative to a fundamental, tenuous reference frame called the *aether* that pervaded the whole of space. We won't discuss the details of it here: it's described well in many books (for example, see Einstein's *Relativity – the Special and General Theories*). Suffice it to say, though, that the results were so staggering that many physicists didn't believe the original experimenters. And so they did the experiment themselves. Whenever they did, they confirmed the original results. So, what we are about to say is right beyond all doubt....even if it does seem strange!

Let us return to our Wild West train and see what the Michelson-Morley experiment said in terms of a **thought-experiment**. (A thought-experiment is something that astronomers do all the time. They imagine themselves in different parts of the universe and imagine what would happen on the basis of the known laws of physics.)

This time we don't run up or down the train holding our gun: instead, we sit down on the roof holding a nice powerful electric torch. On the bridge (standing

---

[1] For readers interested in the details, we've assumed that you are standing about 3 metres from the light. And remember that the electric signals to turn on the light also take the same time to travel from the switch to the light. Actually, though, this calculation is quite wrong. It really takes far longer to see the light, because the time taken by the filament to warm up in a standard tungsten lamp is much, much longer than the light travel time. However, for the moment, let's think like real physicists often have to do and concentrate on the problem we would *like* to solve, rather than the real problem!

still) is friend of ours who has equipment for measuring the speed at which light waves arrive. (That's easy to say but, in real life, such equipment would fill an appreciable fraction of a large physics laboratory!) To start with, we ask the engine driver to stop the train several hundreds of metres from the bridge. We turn on our torch and point it at our friend. After using his complex equipment, he shouts to us that the speed at which he is measuring our light arriving is 300,000 km/s. (Well, 299,792 km/s actually; but to keep the numbers manageable we shall assume that the speed of light is *exactly* 300,000 km/s: it won't affect our understanding at all.) So far, so good: that is the same speed we would measure in an ordinary laboratory.

Now let's move the train back a few kilometres and start it running towards the bridge at 100 km/h. When we are at about the same distance from the bridge as before, we turn on the torch and repeat the experiment. Ducking quickly as we zoom under the bridge, we ask the engine driver to stop and call out for the results of this second experiment to our friend on the bridge. Of course what we *expect* him to say is that the velocity of light he has measured is 300,000 km/s *plus* 100 km/h, just as it was in the first experiment we discussed above. But that isn't the answer we get. Instead, he tells us that he measured exactly 300,000 km/s again — just as if we hadn't been moving! We don't believe him; and we repeat the experiment several times. But the answer is always the same. This was the essential result in the Michelson-Morely experiment[1] that staggered physicists in the early part of this century.

Perhaps we should suggest a different experiment. This time, let's start at the bridge and run the train backwards. We would expect to measure a velocity of 300,000 km/s *minus* the 100 km/h as we recede from the bridge. But we don't. Once more, we find that the speed at which our colleague receives our light is exactly 300,000 km/s. So, we have a situation in which, if we use fairly slow velocities for our experiment (such as the speed at which we can run), then we get the sort of intuitive result we expect. But if we use the speed of light, we get very strange results indeed. Why?

The answer is stunning. It was stunning to Einstein and it has been stunning to generations of physics students. It is this: in one sense at least, an inch is not an inch; a kilometre is not a kilometre; and a second is not a second . To put it more accurately, what we *measure* as an inch or a second depends on the speed with which you are moving. The deep reason that a moving body, such as our train, measures an invariable velocity for the speed of light is because the "working values" of what we mean by a metre and a second change when the emitting body and the receiving body are in relative motion.

Surely this is ridiculous? How can a ruler, for example, change its length depending on who's watching it? That's *not* what we mean — nor is it what Einstein showed. What we mean is that the *apparent* length of the ruler changes if we and the ruler are moving relative to each other. Well yes, we may say, but what is the ruler's "real" length? Einstein was able to show that that question had no meaning because no experiment could ever be designed to answer it. The simple concepts of length and time disappear in Special Relativity to be replaced by a new, rather strange quantity that is a sort of "union" of the two. With a sad lack of originality, it was called **space-time**[1]. Mathematically it is related to space

---

[1] Note carefully that this is a single word. Many books fail to make it clear that in writing "space-time" they do not mean space or time – or both. Space-time is not space and it is not time. It is something different. Also, some authors prefer to define space-time as the negative of the way we use the word here. It doesn't matter at all to the physics.

and time by an equation we shall discuss in Chapter 8:

$$s^2 = x^2 + y^2 + z^2 - c^2.t^2$$

where x, y and z are the space coordinates, c is the speed of light and t is the time. For quantities in relative motion, x, y, z and t may change but the space-time, s, remains invariant.

Einstein maintained that all our knowledge of the universe could only come from *relative* experiments. That is why his two theories are called theories of relativity. All that matters is how the body we are observing behaves relative to us. In one sense, a theory of relativity was nothing new. After all, the simple expression for the velocities we gave above is a relative formula (sometimes referred to as the Galileian Theory of Relativity). It says that the apparent velocity we measure for a moving body depends on how the body is moving relative to ourselves and it gives the mathematical formula to do the calculation. It is almost a trivial statement: all we are saying is that the relative motion we measure depends on the relative motion! In fact it was so obvious that no-one thought to question it — until Einstein. And even he did not question the *qualitative* form of the statement — in fact, he confirmed it. But his important contribution was to replace the above formula for relative velocities with another that holds good for all velocities, both small and large.

So as not to hold the reader in suspense, we will state at once Einstein's new formula. In the terms of our first train problems it is:

$$H = \frac{(T+Y)}{(1+TY/c^2)}$$

Note that the speed of light, c, appears in this expression even though neither the train, nor you running along the train, had a velocity anywhere near the speed of light. Unfortunately we don't have space to thoroughly discuss why this happens. But we'll mention the reason here so that the reader does not feel that we are hiding anything. The quantity c should not really be thought of as the speed of light in the above equation. Instead, it is better termed the **fundamental velocity**. The fact that the speed (in a vacuum) of light, radio waves and all other forms of electromagnetic radiation happens to be equal to the Fundamental Velocity, is secondary. The quantity c is better thought of as a conversion factor. It relates space and time and, in particular, the square of c gives us the conversion factor between mass and energy according to Einstein's famous $E = m.c^2$ equation.

What is of the first importance is that there is one velocity that is *not* relative, but is absolute. This being so, Einstein's theories of relativity should perhaps, paradoxically, be called the theories of the "Absolute", since his main contribution was to recognize that the Fundamental Velocity played the role of an absolute velocity in physics. Corresponding to the above formula giving the relative velocity of objects, there are two more formulae that relate how lengths and time change when observed by relatively moving bodies. These formulae — called the **Lorentz transformations** — are not complicated, but we won't bother with them here. Interested readers can find an excellent "horse's-mouth" account in Einstein's book which we mentioned previously.

Let's now return to the new velocity formula that we stated above and see what it has to tell us. First, we shall discuss what happens when the velocities of the train and of ourselves are both small, as in the first train experiment. It will turn out that what we mean by "small" is that our velocities are small *compared with the*

Fundamental Velocity. Since c has a value very close to 300,000 km/s, the velocities of just a few tens of kilometres per hour that we meet in everyday life certainly are "small".

For small velocities, the last bit of the formula, the TY/c^2, can be safely ignored compared with the "1" that has to be added to it. If T was 100 km/h and Y was 10 km/h, then the value of this last bit is only about 10^{-15}, or one part in a thousand million million. Certainly much smaller than 1!

Therefore, to a much higher accuracy than you could calculate on any 9-digit pocket calculator, we get the familiar expression

$$H = T + Y$$

just as we had before.

But now let's see what happens as one of our velocities becomes very big. Again by "big" we shall mean something similar to the speed of light. In fact, we might as well make life easy for ourselves and set the velocity exactly equal to c. This would correspond to our second experiment when we sat on the roof top of the train carriage and turned on our electric torch. The light clearly has a velocity of c relative to the train[1].

In this case we have

$$Y = c$$

and so

$$H = \frac{(T+c)}{(1+Tc/c^2)}$$

A bit of elementary algebra gives us

$$H = c \cdot \frac{(T+c)}{(T+c)}$$

which is just

$$H = c$$

This is an astonishing result! It means that light which is travelling relative to the train at speed c is received by our colleague also at speed c, even though the train is travelling at 100 km/h relative to the bridge. But there is something more amazing still: the result we have found does *not* depend on the speed of the train! No matter how fast the train is going, it has no effect on the speed with which our colleague receives the light. In particular, the train could be travelling at near the speed of light itself. (If you are a little dubious of this result — and you should be! — confirm it for yourself from Equation 6.1 by putting both T and Y equal to c.)

---

[1] Actually, that's slightly wrong: the light's velocity will be slightly less than c because it is travelling through air rather than a vacuum. But we won't worry about this slight complication which won't affect our argument in any important way.

Surely this must be one of the most unexpected results in the whole of physics. No wonder that many people took a long time to believe it. But believe it you must, since it is true. Every properly conducted experiment that has been performed by disbelievers has not shaken Einstein's theory.

Actually, the Special Theory of Relativity has considerably wider implications than we have discussed. The velocity of light is only one example of a physical parameter that remains the same during relative motion. Einstein showed that *all* physics experiments would give the same result when viewed from what he called "inertially moving frames of reference". That is, reference frames which move relative to each other at constant velocity. Furthermore he showed that mass and energy were different manifestations of the same basic physical reality and that both varied depending on the frame of reference. Unfortunately we don't have space (or time!) here to follow up more of these fascinating consequences. Instead, we shall conclude our introduction to the Special Theory of Relativity with a summary.

The Special Theory of Relativity differs from "ordinary" physics only when velocities close to the speed of light are being discussed. For example these velocities must exceed 10% of the speed of light (i.e. be greater than 30,000 km/s) for the predictions of the new and older theories to differ by more than 1%. Furthermore, the velocities involved must be the velocity of something *through* space. Not of space itself. There are very few applications of the Special Theory in cosmology since, in that subject, we are normally talking about the expansion of space itself. And the motions of material bodies, such as the galaxies, *through* space rarely exceed a few hundred kilometres per second.

The General Theory

After the success of his Special Theory, Einstein attempted to expand the theory to preserve the constancy of the velocity of light and other physical experiments under *any* sort of motion. In particular, he was concerned with accelerated motions. At first glance, though, it would seem that any such attempt is doomed to failure. Let's see why.

Consider an international traveller taking a long flight in a modern passenger jet. We shall assume that the jet is very quiet and smooth in flight and the window blinds are drawn down. Under these conditions, it is common experience that there is no easy way to tell how fast you are travelling. Now the Special Theory asserts that, provided the jet flies smoothly (no bumps) and only in a straight line (no turning accelerations), then it is quite *impossible* to tell whether you are moving or to deduce your speed. No experiment you can perform wholly inside the jet will give you the answer. The only way to check your speed is by observing motion *relative to* something else — the ground outside, say.

So far, so good. But when we are no longer flying at constant speed in a jet, it seems easy to tell if we are accelerating. There is a great deal of difference in trying to drink a gin and tonic in a plane in smooth flight compared with a plane which is accelerating for take-off or decelerating after landing. In the latter cases, the drink has a nasty habit of splashing all over your seat. Perhaps that's one reason why they don't serve drinks before you're up in the air!

Drinking a gin and tonic is a type of physics experiment — albeit a pleasant one. Thus it seems as though we cannot possibly get similar results for all physics experiments in accelerated situations as in constant-velocity situations. Are we then to completely dismiss the idea of a successful General Theory of Relativity? Perhaps not. Consider.

The forces which cause objects to move in an accelerating jet plane have an interesting property. They affect all bodies equally, quite independent of the masses of the objects involved, what they are made of, their colour or any other property. This is not true of almost all other forces we know of. For example, it *does* matter what a body is made of if we are trying to attract it with a magnet. And, if we blow on it, a 1 gram table-tennis ball lying on a table-top responds very differently from a 1 gram piece of lead shot. Of course, we are not surprised that the motions of objects in, and relative to, an accelerating plane are similar. We explain it by saying that it's *really* the plane that is accelerating and that the gin and tonic bottles are *really* trying to keep going in a straight line. Well, that seems reasonable enough. But there is just one other force in nature that behaves exactly like accelerations. It is gravity. And Einstein realized that if he were to have any success in formulating a more general theory of relativity, it would have to include gravity.

Let's consider gravity for a moment. Newton's realization that the fall of an apple, the rise of the tides and the motions of the planets could all be described by a single force obeying an inverse square distance law was the outstanding success of his distinguished career. But he failed in his attempt to understand the cause and nature of gravity. Was it a sort of magnetism — but one that could only attract? Was it a form of electrical attraction? Was it caused by some sort of extragalactic wind? No-one knew the answer. The main difficulty was that the way in which a body moved in a gravitational field of force did not depend on what the moving body was made of, but only the total amount of *stuff* — or **mass** — in it. It needed Einstein to realize that the effect of gravity actually *was* an acceleration.

Unfortunately we must pass over the mathematical details of his theory because they need to be couched in a rather esoteric form of coordinate geometry called **tensor calculus**. In essence, Einstein found a way to describe the mass and energy of a body in a single parameter called the **energy-momentum tensor**. He also found a way to describe the shape of space in a particular region by another **geometry tensor**. He then postulated a simple relation between the geometry tensor and the energy-momentum tensor so that the shape of space was "decided" by the amount of matter in it. The motion of a small body in the neighbourhood of the matter responsible for the energy-momentum tensor could be understood by it as moving as "straight as it could" (physicists would say along a **geodesic**), but responding to the "bent" shape of space. Einstein explained the effects of gravity by saying that we were simply seeing the natural response of objects to this distorted shape of space. And the "distortion" was, in turn, caused by all the material bodies in the universe.

Lest all of that sound rather confusing, let's consider a simple analogy. Imagine that we are out in the countryside. Far away we see a horse galloping round and round a circular field. Because the horse describes such perfect circles around the field we suspect that either it has a small, unseen rider on its back or that it is tethered to a central stake by a long rope. In either case, the horse describes the circles because there is an *active force* constraining it to do so. But we get a surprise as we walk towards the field. When we get close, we find that there is neither rider nor stake and tether. Instead we find that what we thought was a field is actually a narrow, circular race-track, fenced on both sides. The horse has been running round in circles, not because of any direct influence but, rather, because there was nowhere else for it to go!

This analogy is not perfect: but it helps to explain the pre- and post-Einstein views of gravity. Before Einstein, gravity was thought to be some sort of force that hadn't yet been understood, rather like the tether or rider we hypothesized in the analogy. After Einstein, we are to understand gravity not as a force but as an effect of the shape of space, just as the shape of the track dictated where the horse could go. The aspect of gravity missing from our analogy, unfortunately, is that the shape of the track is determined by all the other horses in the vicinity!

Actually we are still left with some unanswered questions: for example, *why* does matter cause space to "bend"? In fact, Einstein's postulated equation connecting the geometry of space and the matter it contains was rather arbitrary. He used one of the simplest possible formulations, but other equations are also permitted by the mathematics. In particular Einstein *forced* his equation to agree with Newton's inverse square law of attraction when the effects of gravity were "weak". What is meant by weak in this context is that, if we are at a distance R from a body of mass M, then the Newtonian gravitational potentialwhich is

$$\frac{GM}{R}$$

must be much less than the square of the velocity of light. In practice, essentially all gravitational fields of force are weak according to this definition. For example, on the surface of the Earth the potential has a value of only 6×10^{11} (in cgs units) which is much less than the value of c^2 (around 10^{21}).

Nevertheless, there *are* places in the universe where we encounter "strong" gravitational fields. One is near the surfaces of old, compact stars such as white dwarfs and pulsars. Another is in the vicinity of the **black holes** that may lurk near the centres of the **quasars** (see Chapter 15). Under such circumstances, Newton's simple inverse square law fails and Einstein's theory comes into its own. Paradoxically, too, while the gravitational fields of almost all objects *in* the universe are "weak", the universe *as a whole* has a "strong" field. In one sense, the whole is greater than the sum of the parts and the universe may be regarded as being close to a black hole. We shall discuss both gravity and black holes further in Chapter 15.

7

From Herschel to Hubble

The work of Newton marked the start of the modern scientific renaissance. By this time, science had moved from mere observation and speculation to experimentation. The Royal Society held regular meetings in London and, although we find the occasional "description of an oddity" in the proceedings, most of the papers would resemble those given at a scientific conference today. There was even a person appointed to carry out experiments suggested by the members. Telescopes were improving, the Greenwich Observatory was established in 1675, and more people than ever before were looking at the skies.

Over a century earlier, the Milky Way had been shown by Galileo to consist of numberless stars. But no-one could as yet compute their distances because of the very small angles involved. Even with the naked eye, though, many non-stellar "clouds" could be seen in the heavens and the new telescopes revealed hundreds more. In the Northern Hemisphere, the Andromeda nebula[1] was visible just by looking up on a clear night, while in the South the Magellanic Clouds glowed brightly in the night sky. Some thought these were simply clouds of gas within the Milky Way, while others believed they might be comets. Charles **Messier**, as we mentioned before, catalogued a number of these clouds to ensure that they didn't cause a nuisance during his cometary searches.

The man who really put "nebulae" on the map, both literally and figuratively, was **Herschel**. He was a professional musician, a German who made his home in England and who had an interest in astronomy which eventually dominated his life. His discoveries gained him a pension from the King (George III) so he had the eighteenth century equivalent of a generous modern-day, state research grant. Herschel found he had a talent for grinding mirrors[2]. He built a number of telescopes, culminating in a 40-ft (12-m) reflector with a 48-inch mirror, at that time the largest in the world. Unfortunately there wasn't the requisite engineering expertise to mount it successfully and so it never achieved its full potential. Despite this, he made thousands of useful observations with his 20-inch mirror telescope, assisted by his sister Caroline. Herschel plotted a map of our galaxy from his accurate star positions and made star counts, which he called "star gauges", in a given number of fields. He assumed all the stars were intrinsically of

---

[1] "nebula" is the latin for cloud.

[2] From speculum metal, which was an alloy of tin and copper. Glass coated with silver was not used until the mid-1800s.

the same luminosity and that they were uniformly distributed over the galaxy. Although he knew this to be incorrect, he had no means of making a better estimate of the galactic shape.

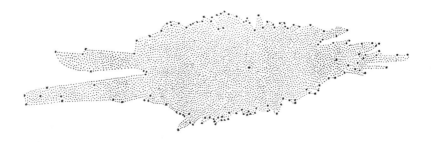

Fig. 7.1 — Herschel's map of our galaxy (as we now call it, though to Herschel it might as well have been the universe) in 1785. Our sun is the bigger star near the centre.

Herschel's map was published by *The Philosophical Transactions* (of the Royal Society) in 1785 (see Fig. 7.1).

He concluded that the galaxy was a flattened disc about five times bigger in diameter than in thickness. The Sun was near the centre of this disc with the numbers of fainter stars falling off sharply towards the rim. This was the first evidence that there was indeed an edge to the universe. We know today there are millions more stars than we can resolve even with our much bigger telescopes.

Herschel loved observing, and probably no other professional astronomer has ever spent so many nights at a telescope. Later he turned his attention to the nebulosities, a task continued by his son and finally published in 1864. They found over 5,000 of these clouds, many of them lying out of the well-populated stellar regions. What were they?

As early as 1755, the philosopher and scientist **Kant** had theorized that the nebulae were gigantic groups of stars, rather like our Milky Way. In fact he may have actually been the first to call them "island universes", a name that was later to become famous in the early twentieth century. Herschel wavered all his life between the "other galaxy" theory and the "cloud of gas" theory to explain these nebulosities. With the benefit of hindsight, we know that his catalogues indeed contained both sorts of object. But unfortunately even his "state of the art" telescopes were inadequate to resolve the nebulae and reveal their true nature. His telescope stood alone at the forefront of extragalactic research: nothing else had the required resolving power, so his announcements of discoveries went unchallenged and unchecked. His drawings were painstakingly made but show large differences from the corresponding images on today's photographic plates. This was not due to any lack of care but to the many subtle ways in which an observer's eye can deceive him at the telescope, as witnessed by the twentieth century discovery of the "canals" on Mars.

Amongst Herschel's many significant discoveries was his description of some nebulae as "planetary". These objects showed a star in the middle and cloud around the outside. He thought they represented a star being born. On the contrary, today we known that the **planetary nebulae** are in fact stars which have died and have blown off their outer layers. Even so, for the time, his drawings were outstanding. The next step in understanding our true position in space, however, had to await the development of spectroscopy.

The beginnings of spectroscopy

The art of glassmaking is an ancient one going back many thousands of years. The Egyptians would have known that any irregularities in the glass can split white light up into many different colours. The first telescopes suffered badly from this **chromatic aberration** and it was not until methods of combining two lenses to correct each other were invented that refracting telescopes could become really useful. Galileo must indeed have had good eyesight to see such detail in the blurred coloured edges of his objects! Despite these improvements, refracting telescope makers were always plagued by small residual chromatic effects and a long-term solution only came with the invention of the reflecting telescope, another product of Newton's fertile mind.

But chromatic aberration had its uses. As we said in Chapter 1, Newton is credited with first understanding the splitting of light into its component parts. He used a prism of glass to spread light from the Sun out into a **spectrum** and showed and understood how white light is composed of a mixture of, literally, "all the colours of the rainbow". Somewhat later, in the seventeenth century, William Herschel attempted to measure the strength of this solar spectrum in its various colours by using a thermometer. He found that his instrument still registered a temperature excess, even off the red end of the spectrum. He had discovered the invisible **infrared radiation** and probably suspected that there could be other spectral radiations not obvious to our eyes. And indeed there were — **ultraviolet** was discovered in 1802 by its ability to darken silver chloride.

That same year an English scientist, **William Wollaston**, produced another spectrum of the Sun and found that it contained some dark lines. **Frauenhofer**, a German optician and physicist, investigated these lines in much more detail some years later and counted 754 of them. More importantly, he looked at the spectra of other stars and found that their dark lines were often quite different from those of the Sun. Unfortunately these observations were made before 1840 when J.W. Draper took the first Daguerrotype of the Moon, marking the beginnings of astronomical photography. This meant that Frauenhofer and his contemporaries could only produce useful spectra of the Sun and the brighter stars — other objects were just too faint.

Side by side with the development of spectroscopy we find the last large telescope ever to be built with a speculum metal mirror. **William Parsons**

(Lord Rosse) cast and polished his massive 72-inch mirror in 1841, an age in which the wealthy amateur could afford to dabble in science and make important discoveries. The telescope was suspended between two thick stone walls and set up in the grounds of his castle in Ireland which, even then, was not a country noted for its clear skies. However Parsons, (whose name is still seen on telescopes all over the world today as "Grubb Parsons") looked at nebulae, made accurate drawings of them, and found that they often contained stars. Most significantly he was also able to show that many nebulae had a spiral structure and his drawing of M51 compares very favourably with photographs taken 100 years later. He suspected that all nebulae would turn out to be "island universes" of stars, but could not tell if the spirals were rotating.

Despite Rosse's excellent drawings, the future lay with photography and also with the emerging technique of astronomical spectroscopy which needed bigger and better mirrors and also a better recording device than the human eye. Both of these developments were not long in coming. New techniques in glassmaking were able to produce large pieces of unflawed glass. Furthermore Leibig found a method of putting a thin layer of silver onto glass. The large, accurate astronomical mirror was now a reality Anyone who has ever first looked at themselves in polished silver (which has roughly the same reflectivity as speculum metal) and then in an ordinary mirror will know the substantial difference in clarity.

John Herschel, son of the famous William and an astronomer in his own right, was responsible for the development of astronomical photography. He came back from four years observing at the Cape, after which his 20-ft telescope was never unpacked again. Instead he, like Galileo with the "spyglass", took the recent invention of "photography", which was a word he coined, and improved it. Originally the process had been very messy to use: the emulsions were fairly insensitive and the plates had to be wet. With Herschel's "dry" plates and his experimentation with emulsions it became possible to mount them in telescopes and, by 1875, **William Huggins** was photographing the spectra he had obtained of stars. Furthermore, objects of all types were photographed and hundreds of hapless employees gazed at photographic plates day after day to chart the positions of stars and nebulae taken the night before.

Meanwhile, Huggins had been looking at the Sun, the stars and nebulae. Some nebulae had spiral shapes and appeared to have the similar spectra to the stars. Others, like the one in Orion, had very different spectra and no spiral shape. Were these "spiral nebulae" actually other galaxies like ours but at enormous distances? Or were they something quite different?

One further discovery was needed before these questions could be answered. In 1842 Wolfgang Doppler had observed and explained the changed pitch of sound waves when a body is in motion. Huggins found that this "Doppler Shift" also applied to light. The spectra of his distant nebulae showed Frauenhofer lines shifted towards the red or blue end of the spectrum compared to those of the Sun. Huggins calculated that many of his nebulae were moving relative to us at 10 or 20 miles per second. He had discovered the phenomenon astronomers know as **radial velocity** for the nebulae. But he had no way of measuring their distances.

The method of parallax (see Chapter 4) provided the first accurate estimate of a stellar distance. In 1838 **Bessel** had found the distance to the close star 61 Cygni by making use of the earth's orbit and measuring an angle only $1/10,000$ of the diameter of the Moon. He determined that this star was 10 lightyears away, which is very close to the best modern value. By 1900, about 100 stars had had their distances determined using the method of parallax, and while these distances were not large, they were sufficient to begin to show the true size of our galaxy.

So, how did the universe look about 1900? Hundreds of stars had been catalogued by brightness, colour and spectra. It was known that apparent brightness was not the same as "luminosities" or intrinsic brightness. A classification of stars by spectral types had begun which was to prove important in the next decades.

(a) See Fig. 7.1

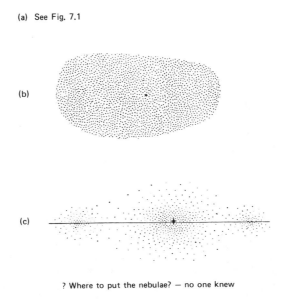

(b)

(c)

? Where to put the nebulae? — no one knew

Fig. 7.2 — Views of the Universe around 1900. (a) See Fig. 7.1, Herschel's early idea. (b) A flat disc of stars stretching to infinity. (c) A mass of stars in the centre and a ring of stars round the outside. (Reproduced from *Stellar Movements*, Eddington, 1912.)

As regards our galaxy, there were three ideas (see Fig. 7.2). Some thought it was a finite disc as Kant and Herschel had originally suggested. Others envisaged it as an unlimited slab of stars (as Herschel did in his later years). Thirdly, some considered it as a central cloud with a ring of stars around it. In all these models, the Sun was near the centre of the galaxy and our galaxy was the centre of everything. Only one man, C.**Easton** in 1900, suggested we could be a spiral galaxy with the Sun somewhere away from the centre. But even he admitted that he had no proof for his conjecture and thought it unlikely that the problem would be solved in the near future. Little did he know that within 50 years mankind's view of the universe would have been expanded by a factor of a million and our galaxy reduced to physical insignificance!

However the nature of the nebulae remained a mystery, although they had been extensively catalogued and were known to be unevenly distributed in the sky. The large irregular ones lay near the band of the Milky Way and often contained stars.

The smaller, more circular ones lay out of the galactic plane and appeared devoid of stars. But what were they? Some astronomers held they were clouds of gas and others that they were other "island universes", perhaps similar to our own. As to how far they stretched and the distance to the edge of the universe, no-one knew — or even hazarded a guess.

As we enter the twentieth century, we find Henrietta Leavitt at Harvard studying variable stars in the Magellanic clouds. Harvard by now had a telescope in Peru and had obtained good photographic plates of these Clouds which are only visible from the South. Astronomers know of many sorts of stars which vary. Those that interested Miss Leavitt were of a type known as **cepheids** which have a quick rise in brightness followed by a longer decline to faintness after which the whole process repeats. She looked at plates day after day for years (one wonders what it did for her eyes!) and eventually found that there was a direct relationship between the luminosity (i.e. intrinsic or true energy output) of each star and the time it took to vary through a whole bright-faint cycle — the brighter the star, the longer its period.

This was a crucial discovery because it meant that the true brightness of a star could be measured simply by timing its variations. More importantly, its distance could then be calculated from its *apparent* brightness using the inverse square law of radiation. Only one crucial piece of information was needed before the distance to the Magellanic Cloud nebulae could be obtained: just one Cepheid had to have a distance determined *by another, accurate method* in order to calibrate the whole of Miss Leavitt's relation. This information was available for one or two Cepheid variables in our galaxy — but were these stars similar to those in the Magellanic Clouds?

In 1914 **Harlow Shapley** came to the mountains of California and the new generation of big American telescopes. Originally trained in journalism, he had an outgoing lively personality and an enthusiasm which occasionally got the better of his judgement. Shapley had recently qualified in astronomy (from Princeton) and had been told the best place to search for Cepheid variable stars was in the globular clusters. Shapley made the sweeping assumption that all the Cepheids were of the same type, which allowed him to compute distances for the clusters. Using these distances, he plotted their positions. They lay both above and below the disc of our galaxy but were all grouped around one particular part of it which we cannot see because of large amounts of obscuring gas. Was Shapley's "cluster centre" the true centre of our galaxy? It seemed reasonable to assume so. If so, the Sun was no longer in the middle of things but relegated to the outer suburbs, thousands of lightyears from the centre of the galaxy.

Using the size Shapley had worked out for our galaxy and the calculated distance of the Magellanic Clouds, it seemed that our own system was so big that the Clouds lay totally within it. Could this be correct? If so, it certainly made our galaxy far bigger than any other nebula in the universe and went a long way to discrediting the "island universes" theory.

Debate on this topic raged for years and included a dramatic confrontation between Shapley and his contemporary **Curtis** ,which some report as being more vigorous than the 1860 debate between Huxley and Owen & Wilberforce on "the origin of species". We now know that Shapley was both right and wrong: he was right in that he had correctly placed the centre of our galaxy far from the Sun. But he had not realized the importance of the different types of variable star and had ignored the obscuring effects of interstellar material in calculating his distances and sizes. Our own galaxy was far more typical than he had supposed.

The person who was to make the observations which proved crucial to extragalactic astronomy was **Edwin Hubble**. In complete contrast to Shapley, Hubble had been at Oxford and had kept the accent and the sophistication. Except for a few close friends, he tended to distance himself from the rest of his astronomical colleagues. During his long career as an astronomer, Hubble was destined to make several important discoveries. But two were of crucial significance.

First, in 1923, he determined the distance to the Andromeda Nebula, M31, by identifying and accurately measuring a Cepheid variable and using Leavitt's period-luminosity relation. Shapley, in his determinations of the sizes and distances of the nebulae, had incorrectly mistaken a slightly different sort of variable called **RR Lyrae stars** for true Cepheids. RR Lyraes also have a period-luminosity relation — but it isn't the same as for the Cepheids. Hubble's distance[1] for M31 settled the dispute over the island universe theory: there could now be little doubt that many of the nebulae were actually separate galaxies similar to our own.

Hubble's other discovery showed that the whole universe was expanding. By now, obtaining spectra of stars was commonplace and astronomical spectroscopists had turned their attention to the far more difficult problem of the nebulae or galaxies. It was realized that here was a tool that not only could elucidate the composition of a nebula but also show us (through using the Doppler effect) how it was moving through space. Hubble used over 40 painstakingly gathered galaxy spectra, mostly from colleagues together with a few of his own and studied their **redshifts** from which he deduced their radial velocities. Andromeda and a few other galaxies were coming towards us but the majority were moving away. Furthermore there seemed to be a weak tendency for the more distant objects to be moving away more quickly. In 1929, on the basis of what many astronomers now regard as marginal evidence, Hubble proposed his famous relationship

$$Velocity \ = \ H_0 \ . \ Distance$$

in which the velocity of recession of a galaxy is directly proportional to its distance. The constant of proportionality in this relation, H_0, has come to be called the Hubble constant and, although our estimate of the value of H_0 has changed over the years with improving data, the form of the relation is not in question (at least for most galaxies). Simply by measuring the redshift of a galaxy, this equation allows astronomers to predict its distance[2]. Whatever may have been Hubble's evidence, time showed that he was right! His contribution to astronomy had a profound effect: not only was the universe immense but it was also expanding! Paradoxically, while Man had been looking further and further out towards the edge of the universe, that edge had been receding from him.

---

[1]Funnily enough, Hubble also had made a mistake in his distance determinations, which was not to be recognized until the early 1950s when Baade showed that the universe was much bigger still and relegated the size of our galaxy to being even "more average".

[2]The Hubble parameter constant H_0 is normally expressed in units of kilometres per second per megaparsec. The best modern estimates give it a value of between 40 and 100 km/s/Mpc. In this book we shall generally prefer to use mega*lightyears* (Mly) and adopt a value for H_0 of 20 km/s/Mly corresponding to about 60 km/s/Mpc.

8

The Shift to the Red

In Chapter 7 we described how the work of Hubble and others showed that our galaxy was only one of billions populating the universe. The overwhelming majority of these galaxies have redshifted spectra which showed them to be moving away from us. Based on this evidence, Hubble formulated his theory of the expanding universe.

But what is the cause of the redshifts of the galaxies? The reader may think the question trivial: surely they are produced by the Doppler[1] effect? Unfortunately this explanation is wrong, although it still appears in many books. The greatest part of the redshift of the distant galaxies has nothing to do with their motion through space towards or away from us. This idea is so important that we shall repeat it: *the redshift of a typical galaxy is not caused by its motion through space!*

Perhaps we should explain here that we are not talking about the so-called **non-cosmological redshifts** — redshifts caused by effects other than the expansion of the universe. Non-cosmological redshifts will be discussed in Chapter 16. No, we're merely stating a fact well-known to most astronomers working in the field of cosmology, but which is often misunderstood.

But if the redshift of a galaxy is not caused by its Doppler motion, what *is* it caused by? The answer is actually quite simple: the redshifts of the galaxies are caused directly by the expansion of the universe. Not by an expansion of the galaxies *through* the space of the universe: rather they are expanding *with* the universe. In the deepest sense, the galaxies are essentially not moving at all and yet their distances apart — and from us — *are* increasing!

If all of this sounds confusing, bear with us and we'll try to make it clearer! The common view of the universe is that galaxies far away are rushing through space away from us while we remain almost stationary. This is quite wrong: for one thing, on a simple view, it could imply that we somehow held a special position in the universe, which is highly unlikely to be the case, as we discussed in Chapter 5. A slightly more refined view of the universe is that all galaxies including our own are dashing away from each other. We could think of a flock of birds scattering in all directions, in which every bird is moving away from every other bird. But this idea wouldn't directly explain why the more distant objects are moving faster such that their speed is directly proportional to their distance. A slight modification improves the picture: the birds might have decided to scatter at different speeds *but starting at the same instant,* perhaps because we fired a gun. If so, after a few

---

[1] See Chapter 12.

seconds, the birds that were flying the fastest would have spread out the furthest, in direct proportion to their speed.

Where our analogy breaks down, however, is that there must be a "centre" from which the birds scatter and, as far as we know the universe has no special centre. If it had, it could not be truly homogeneous. To some extent this doesn't matter: although it may not be obvious, it turns out that our "scattering bird" model *can* produce a linear velocity-distance law no matter from where you view the action, providing you are not too close to the edge of the "bird-cloud".

None of these analogies, however, is useful for understanding the origin of redshifts in the universe, because they all assume that objects are moving through space. And, again, we state that the redshifts of the galaxies and quasars are not caused by their motions through space but *with* the space in which they are contained. Lest anyone think that this difference is merely one of semantics, consider the following example. If I am riding on a bus, I may well be sitting down taking it easy: a physicist would say "at rest" relative to the bus. On the other hand, the bus could be travelling at 100 km/h. In this example, the bus plays the part of space and I play the role of a galaxy. I am at rest in space but still moving.

In order to make some of these ideas clearer, we shall shortly turn to some useful two-dimensional models of the universe called "Two-lands". Before we study them, though, we must understand what we mean by dimensions.

Dimensions

We live in a universe which we perceive to be "three-dimensional". Three-dimensional means that three distances or numbers are necessary to specify the position of an object relative to any other position. For example, the position of a spider on the wall as this book is being written can be given relative to my nose by saying, "Go forward 120 cm, go right 205 cm and go up 110 cm". Again, the position of the top of Mt Everest relative to Trafalgar Square in London can be found by going South 2700 kilometres, East 7400 kilometres and vertically upwards 8800 metres. And a similar scheme can be used to fix the positions of all other objects in the universe. Note that in the first example the distances involved are in straight line while in the second case they are curved distances. But this doesn't matter: we always need three numbers; any fewer will not specify the position exactly.

Now, we said above that we "perceive" the universe to be three-dimensional. It may in fact be more complex. We may *see* it as three-dimensional simply because we are three-dimensional ourselves. Why three? We don't know. Certainly there are no mathematical problems in talking about more (or fewer) dimensions. For example (see Fig. 8.1), on a piece of ordinary (two-dimensional) paper, Pythagoras's theorem about the size of the diagonal hypotenuse, H is:

$$H^2 = x^2 + y^2$$

where x and y are the distances of the sides of the triangle.
In three-dimensions, we have:

$$H^2 = x^2 + y^2 + z^2$$

where x, y, and z are now the distances. This is the formula we could use to calculate the distance of the spider from the end of my nose.

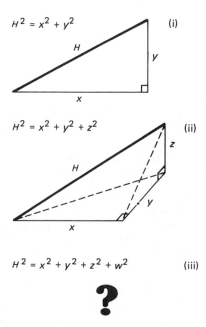

$H^2 = x^2 + y^2$ (i)

$H^2 = x^2 + y^2 + z^2$ (ii)

$H^2 = x^2 + y^2 + z^2 + w^2$ (iii)

?

Fig. 8.1 — Pythagoras' theorem in two, three and four dimensions.

Now let's take a bold step: it's quite easy to write down the expression for a four-dimensional universe, even though nobody has ever seen one — it is, of course:

$$H^2 = x^2 + y^2 + z^2 + w^2$$

where w is a new sort of distance in the fourth dimension, whatever that means. Incidentally, time is sometimes loosely referred to as a fourth dimension. But this is both wrong and misleading for our present purposes. In the restricted and general theories of relativity, which we discussed in Chapter 6, it is convenient to write down an equation similar to the above as:

$$s^2 = x^2 + y^2 + z^2 - c^2 \cdot t^2$$

where x, y and z are the same sort of space coordinates as above, where t is time, c the speed of light and where s is something called **space-time**. But notice that there is a minus sign in front of the $"ct"$ term. And this can't be "fixed" just by making time go backwards or any similar mathematical trick. In order to treat time similarly to Pythagoras's theorem, it's necessary to introduce what mathematicians call imaginary numbers, which emphasizes that time is quite different from spatial distances.

Two-lands

Earlier in this chapter we used the expression "expansion of space" and we must now discuss what we meant. The easiest way to envisage expansion of three-dimensional space such as our own is to view it in four dimensions. Unfortunately this is impossible since, as we said above, we are three-dimensional beings. But there is a neat trick we can use to help us: we can investigate what expansion of space means for a hypothetical two-dimensional world which we *can* easily envisage from our three-dimensional point of view.

Such two-dimensional worlds were called "Flatlands", first by the American novelist E. A. Abbot and, later, by the computer specialist A. K. Dewdney. We shall prefer to call them "Two-lands" to emphasis that they are two-dimensional and also because we shall want to use the word "flat" in another way.

Consider the simplest of Two-lands, one which is just a large flat plane stretching away in all directions and for ever. A mathematician would call it a "simple, Euclidian two-dimensional, infinite universe". The geometry on this plane is just the simple Euclidian geometry we are used to from schooldays. Two-landers who inhabit this two-dimensional universe don't live *on* the plane: they live *in* it. Most of their lives, they move around the rims of their circular disc planets which, in turn, orbit around their circular disc suns. Their galaxies are either flat spirals or ellipticals (which really *are* elliptical) stretching outward forever through their two-universe. From our privileged three-dimensional viewpoint, we can see that there is lots of space both above and beneath the two-universe plane. But, to the Two-landers, it doesn't exist. To them, two-universe is everything. And there is no need for a Pythagoras Theorem more complicated than

$$H^2 = x^2 + y^2$$

Let us suppose now that one day an astronomer called Two-Hubble finds that all the galaxies in the sky are moving away from his home galaxy. In addition, let's say that Two-Hubble finds that the more distant galaxies are receding at velocities in exact proportion to their distances. He realizes that one possible explanation is that there has been an enormous explosion at some time in the past, blasting all the galaxies apart (the flock of birds analogy). But there is another and much simpler possibility — the whole of Two-land may be expanding.

Imagine that at some particular time we draw a mesh of lines on the space of Two-land, rather like lines on an enormous piece of graph paper. Perhaps, to start with, these lines are separated by 1 million two-lightyears (1 megatly).

Now further imagine that the two-universe plane is made of rubber and consider what happens if the rubber is stretched, causing the whole two-universe to expand. Of course, our whole mesh of lines expands, just like the design that we might draw with felt-tip pen on the surface of a rubber balloon might expand. We shall imagine that the stretching continues until all the lines have become 2 megatlys apart.

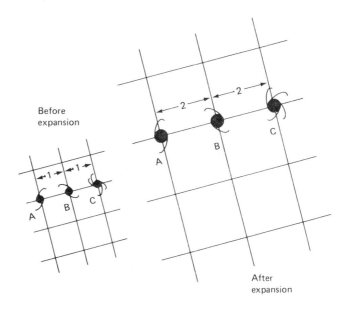

Fig. 8.2 — The positions of three galaxies in the universe before and after a twofold expansion of the scale length, R. Notice that the size of the galaxies stays the same while their distances apart increase and that the galaxy C has moved twice as far from A as the galaxy B in the same time.

So far, so good. But what of the two-galaxies in the two-universe? If they were not originally moving through the space of the two-universe, we would expect them to expand with the mesh lines. In this case, two galaxies, originally 1 megatly apart would now be 2 megatlys apart. And a pair of galaxies originally 2 megatlys apart would now be 4 megatlys apart[1] (see Fig. 8.2).

Now note a most important thing: galaxy C had travelled 2 megatlys from galaxy A in the same time that galaxy B has travelled 1 megatly from A, implying that galaxy C must have a recession velocity from A which is twice as big as that of B. This means that we predict a linear velocity-distance relation, just as Two-Hubble found.

In the example above, we postulated a mesh of grid-lines starting 1 megatly apart and expanding to 2 megatly. In general it is more convenient to refer to the spacing of this imaginary mesh as the **scale size** of space. We shall use the symbol R for the scale size and can think of it as being the distance apart of any two reference points fixed in space, rather like "trig" points in geodetic surveying. The main difference from terrestrial surveying, of course, is that these points are continually increasing their distance apart in an expanding universe. Note that the actual value of the scale size is arbitrary in Two-land — we could have picked two different points separated by a different distance. But the relative way in which R changes is determined by the rate of stretching and is a fundamental property of any universe, as we shall see.

If we attempt to relate the world of Two-land to the expansion of our real universe another question may suggest itself to the reader:"If the galaxies are expanding with the fabric of the universe, does this mean that the galaxies themselves are getting bigger too?" The answer is, "No". Although the distances separating the galaxies increases with time, the galaxies themselves are held together by their internal gravitational attraction and do *not* expand. We can think of space "expanding from under them".

In this regard the situation is different from a picture drawn on the surface of a piece of stretching rubber. Rather we must imagine the galaxies behaving more like flat coins lying on the rubber. The sheet expands and the coins move with it; but they don't change their size. In our own universe the situation becomes very delicately poised in the case of the large clusters of galaxies. Here, the net-stretching motion of universal expansion fights a near-equal battle with the weak inter-cluster gravitational attractions of the galaxies. In fact, it is difficult to see how some of the larger clusters can have formed at all in an expanding universe.

The cause of the redshift

Now let us try to put our fingers on the cause of the redshifts of the galaxies. Consider the small part of a two-universe shown in Fig. 8.3.

In the first picture, the scale size, R, of the universe was 10 units when light left the galaxy B. When it arrives at us (galaxy A) some time later, let R be 10% bigger. During the time that the light has been travelling, the universe has obviously been expanding. Because the light waves have been travelling through space, they have been expanding with it. Thus, light that started out with a wavelength of 1216 Ångstroms (corresponding to the Lyman α line) will be received by us with a wavelength 10% bigger, or around 1338 Ångstroms.

Because of the stretching, the wavelength at any intermediate time is

---

[1] Note that this really *is* 4 megatlys, not 3. Expansion of space is a stretching, *not* a simple movement. Unfortunately we don't have many examples of stretching in everyday life; most of our common experience is concerned with ordinary motion.

proportional to the scale size of the universe; and so we have

$$\frac{\lambda(when\ received)}{\lambda(when\ emitted)} = \frac{R(when\ received)}{R(when\ emitted)}$$

Also we define **redshift**[1] as,

$$z = \frac{\lambda(when\ received) - \lambda(when\ emitted)}{\lambda(when\ emitted)}$$

Thus the redshift that we measure for a galaxy is exactly equal to the *proportional* amount by which the universe has expanded since the time light left the parent object.

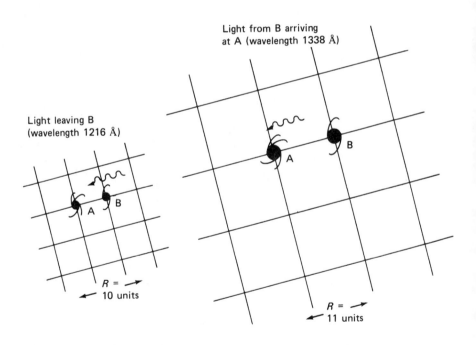

Fig. 8.3 — Light of wavelength 1216 Å is "stretched" by the expansion of the universe to a wavelength of 1338 Å between the time it is emitted and the time it arrives at galaxy A

---

[1] This is the definition of redshift used in optical astronomy. Radio astronomers prefer   to use frequencies

$$z = \frac{v_{received} - v_{emitted}}{v_{emitted}}$$

which is *not* the same as the above, especially for large redshifts.

Algebraically, we have

$$z = \frac{(R_{now} - R_{then})}{R_{then}}$$

or, alternatively,

$$(1+z) = \frac{R_{now}}{R_{then}}$$

and so, in our example, we would measure a redshift of 0.1.

This interpretation carries with it one very important corollary: it doesn't matter at all *how* the universe has expanded between the time of emission of light and its reception. All that matters is the total proportional increase of the scale size or, as it is often called, the "radius" of the universe.

Edward Harrison gives an excellent demonstration of this in his book *Cosmology*. Consider that, at the time light left galaxy B heading in our direction, the universe wasn't expanding at all. Cosmologists have constructed such model universes that have "quiet-times" when all expansion stops. Light leaves B and sets off. When it is well away from B, the universe begins to expand — perhaps slowly at first, then faster. After a while it slows down again and stops. Somewhat later still, the light arrives at our galaxy and we measure the redshift of B. If the total increase in R is the same as we considered earlier (10%), then we shall again measure a redshift of 0.1 for the galaxy B. But note something very important: both at the time light was emitted from B and at the time it was received by us, *neither* galaxy was moving! They were neither moving through space, nor was space itself expanding. Thus there is no possibility that the redshift can be due to any sort of "Doppler effect", since Doppler shifts require relative motion through space. This proves conclusively that redshift is not caused by Doppler shifts but is, instead, due to the expansion of space. Perhaps to be quite accurate we should say that the redshift is caused by the fact that space has expand*ed* between the time that light left the distant galaxy and the time that it arrived at the Earth

The effects of redshift in Two-land

Now let's look at some of the interesting results of the redshift in Two-land.

First, as we saw in Chapter 7, we can define a "Hubble" constant as the linear velocity increase with distance. That is,

$$v = H . d$$

Let's put some numbers into this relation similar to those applicable to our own universe. We shall assume that H is about 30 kilometres per second per each megalightyear. Thus, at a distance of 1000 megalightyears, we would see a galaxy receding at a speed of 30,000 km/s, or about one tenth the speed of light. So far, so good. But remember that we are postulating that our universe is *infinite* in size. What velocity would we measure for a galaxy at a distance of 20,000 or 30,000 megalightyears? If we used the equation above directly, we should get answers of two or three times the speed of light! Something seems to be a bit wrong.

To help resolve our problem, let's take a step backward and see where the Hubble constant comes from. At a particular time (t_1) say that the two-universe had a scale-size of R_1. As we mentioned earlier, by scale-size we simply mean that the distance between two fixed points (which could be two galaxies A and B) in the two-universe has a length R_1.

At a slightly later time (t_0) imagine that this length has expanded with the two-universe to a size R_0. Since t_0 is only slightly later than t_1, R_0 will be only slightly bigger than R_1. Let's assume that the times differ by an amount Δt ($= t_0 - t_1$) and the scale-sizes differ by an amount ΔR ($= R_0 - R_1$) respectively. During this small amount of time, B has been receding from A at a speed of

$$v = \frac{R_0 - R_1}{t_0 - t_1} = \frac{\Delta R}{\Delta t}$$

The distance of B from A at the later time is R_0 and so the Hubble constant H is given by the expression

$$v = H \cdot R_0$$

Actually we have to be a bit more precise; we have to specify what time our Hubble constant refers to, since it will normally be changing as time goes on. Fortunately this presents no problem. The distance between A and B was determined at time t_0 and so we get a Hubble constant for the same time. We shall call it H_0. So we have:

$$v = \frac{\Delta R}{\Delta t_0} = H_0 \cdot R_0$$

where we have put a "$_0$" on the $\Delta R / \Delta t$ term as well, to show that it refers to the rate of expansion of the reference points at time t_0 too. This rate of expansion is rather a clumsy expression. Modern mathematics has a shorthand notation for it which uses

$$R'_0 = \frac{\Delta R}{\Delta t_0}$$

(Note the "dash"[1] on the R.) So we have,

$$H_0 = \frac{R'_0}{R_0}$$

Notice that the actual sizes of neither R'_0 nor R_0 are fundamental properties of this two-universe. We could just as easily have taken two reference points twice as far

---

[1] Another notation for this is, of course, dR/dt, which will be familiar to calculus experts. For our present purposes, though, the dash notation is better and has the historical endorsement of being very close to the notation which Newton devised in his method of "fluxions".

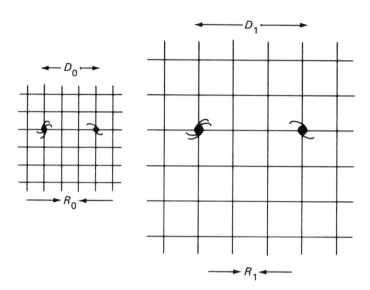

Fig. 8.4 — The expansion of space increases the distance, D , between any two galaxies in exact
proportion to the increase in the scale length, R.

apart, as we said before, and then we would have got a value for R_0 twice as big.
But the Hubble constant *is* the same everywhere and does not depend on which
points we choose. At any particular instant it is the same throughout the whole
universe[1]. It is for this reason that we refer to H_0 as being the Hubble *constant*. It
can (and we believe does) change with time: but at any particular time it is constant
throughout the whole universe.

Now consider galaxies which are separated by large distances and for which
long periods of time elapse between the light being emitted from one galaxy and
being received at the other. Think about the light being received by us now (time t_0)
from a distant galaxy whose *present* distance is D_0. See Fig. 8.4.

This light left its parent galaxy at a time t_1 when the universe had a scale-size R_1.
At that time, the distance apart of the two galaxies was smaller, let's say D_1.

Now, how fast was the galaxy B moving at the time light left B ? And how fast
is it moving now? Both questions are easy to answer. We have:

$$v_1 \text{ when light left} \quad = \quad H_1 . D_1 \quad = \quad \frac{R'_1 . D_1}{R_1}$$

---

[1]Provided that we assume the universe is everywhere similar in its properties, i.e. homogeneous (see
Chapter 5).

and

$$v_0 \text{ now, when light arrives} = H_0 . D_0 = \frac{R'_0 . D_0}{R_0}$$

On the other hand, the redshift we measure for this galaxy is given by,

$$(1+z) = \frac{R_0}{R_1}$$

Now we are in a position to answer the question we posed at the beginning of the section. Are the most distant galaxies really receding at speeds in excess of the speed of light? The amazing answer is ""*yes*," just as our simple Hubble relation would predict! A galaxy presently at a distance D_0 is presently receding from us at a speed v_0 given by

$$v_0 = H_0 . D_0$$

And if our universe is infinite and if H_0 has a value close to 30 km/s per megalightyear, then we shall get velocities that exceed the speed of light for distances greater than 10,000 megalightyears. There is no paradox in this nor any conflict with the theories of relativity because the galaxies are not moving through space but with space. What decides how fast a galaxy at a particular distance is receding is simply the value of H_0 and this, as we have seen, is equal to the fractional rate of change of the scale-size R.

As far as we are aware, H_0 could have any value at all. We shall see in Chapter 9 that the way in which it changes with time is governed by the amount of mass and energy in the universe. But its value at any particular time is decided by the initial "violence" of the Big Bang (see Chapter 17).

Note, too, in the example given above, that the *redshift* of a galaxy at a distance of 20,000 Mly is not infinitely great, even though its recession velocity is twice the speed of light. It is decided, as always, simply by the ratio of the scale-size, R, at the time light was received to the scale-size at the time light was emitted. The galaxy in question could be receding from us at twice the speed of light and yet only have a redshift of about 1.0 .

This may seem strange; and the reader may decide that the answer lies in the fact that the galaxy was perhaps *not* receding at a speed faster than c when the light *left* the distant galaxy. But no, this too is wrong. Any galaxy which we deduce is now moving at a speed greater than c is likely to have been receding even faster at the time that light left it! This point, perhaps more than any other, shows that the redshifts are caused by the overall expansion of space, which is not limited by the rules of relativity.

The question of whether or not we could actually *see* such galaxies, and the exact relation between redshift and and the recession velocities, depends on the precise way in which the universe is expanding: that is, on how R, and thus H_0, changes with time. We shall discuss these points in Chapter 9.

9

The Shape of Space

One of the most confusing ideas in cosmology is the apparent paradox that the universe can have a finite size and yet may not have an edge. This is often explained by talking about **curved space**. But what *is* curved space? And if it is curved, then what is it curved "around"? To tackle these questions, let us first understand what space is.

Space, lines and matter

Until early this century, space was thought of as a sort of "nothing-ness" in which objects existed and could move about. When they moved, however, nothing was pushed out of the way (as air would be if a jet plane moved through it) because space was just a vacuum — a complete "emptiness". Before Einstein, physicists had considered that matter (stars, say) simply *existed* in space without having any effect on it. Rather in the manner of several marbles lying on a large piece of paper. The marbles may or may not move over the paper, depending on the forces acting on them. They may bump into each other or be blown about by a wind. But even if they did move, they would not affect the paper in any appreciable way. This was the pre-Einstein view of matter in, but divorced from, space.

But, as we discussed in Chapter 6, Einstein showed that the presence of matter causes the space in its vicinity to become distorted. The greater the mass (and we include all forms of energy here together with mass), the greater the distortion. According to this view, it was not the Newtonian gravitational force that causes a planet in the vicinity of the Sun to move in an elliptical orbit. Rather, it is the "natural" motion of the planet in the "distorted" space caused by both the Sun and planet. According to Einstein, the whole of gravitational theory simply becomes one of taking into account all the important masses, calculating the net distortion and then describing how bodies move in this distorted space.

The motion always occurs in "straight lines". We put the words "straight lines" in quotes in the previous sentence because we mean something rather different than usual. In fact, Einstein didn't use the phrase "straight line": he preferred the more accurate, but more unfamiliar, term **geodesic**.

Let's consider an analogy: think about driving your car home through the centre of a city during the rush-hour. The shortest distance may be along the High St, turn left at the Park and then on home. However, long experience has taught you that this will take well over half an hour. Instead, you decide to turn right at the Hospital, do a wide circuit around the town and then turn left for home. This latter way saves over 10 minutes even though it is a couple of kilometres longer. In this

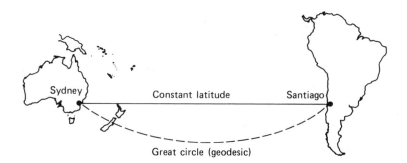

Fig. 9.1 — The shortest distance between two places on the Earth's surface is a great circle (space
geodesic) rather than the more-obvious line of constant latitude.

example, the direct route is the shorter in distance (or "space" as the mathematicians
would say!) but the circuitous route is shorter in time.

Of course, there may be still shorter routes in space, each taking a different time,
and shorter routes in time, each having a different distance. If we experiment for
several days and discover them, we can call the shortest route in distance a **space-
geodesic** and the route which gets us home quickest a **time-geodesic**.
Unfortunately the two are rarely the same, not only in terms of rush-hour traffic,
but also in the world of physics.

Let's consider another example. On the curved surface of a globe, the shortest
distance between two points is not what we might consider a true straight line. It's
a **great circle**: a curved circular path having the centre of the globe as its centre. In
particular, think about the Australian city of Sydney, situated at longitude 151
degrees East and latitude 34 degrees South. Let us say that we wanted to fly to the
Chilean city of Santiago, which is also at latitude 34 degrees (near enough!) and
lies 138 degrees of longitude to the East of Sydney, (see Fig. 9.1).After a few
calculations using a pocket calculator we find that the great circle distance turns out
to be 11,300 kilometres. On the other hand, the "obvious" line joining the two
places — the line of constant latitude of 34 degrees — would make us travel
12,736 kilometres, or 1444 kilometres *further*. The space-geodesic, great circle line
actually dips down to latitude 62 degrees South, halfway along the route.

Of course, the "real" straight line goes right through the surface of the Earth.
But there are constraints preventing us from taking that path! So too with physics:

the space-geodesic will differ from the "real" straight line whenever there are constraints of some sort operating.

Armed with the knowledge of what a geodesic is, we can re-phrase Einstein's theory of gravity. He showed that the presence of matter causes space to become distorted, as we mentioned above. A body such as a planet moving in this distorted space around the Sun takes the "path of least resistance" subject to the constraints. This path of least resistance is a geodesic, not in space nor time but in the **space-time** we discussed in Chapter 6. In general, the space-time geodesic is *not* a "real" straight line but a curved path, like the ellipse in our example of the Earth and Sun.

The post-Einstein view of the cosmos is that matter, space and time are distinct things but that they interact: the presence of matter causes space-time to become distorted while the distortion of space-time causes bodies to move in particular ways.

On the universal scale, this interaction between matter, space and time is very important. Consider a very simple universe, one in which space is everywhere described by the simple laws of Euclidean geometry and which is uniformly filled with galaxies. It is clear at once that such a universe cannot remain stationary. In conventional terms, the gravitational attractions of the galaxies cause them to fall together. Or, in post-Einsteinian terms, the matter causes space to distort in such a way that the more-distant galaxies try to fall towards the nearby galaxies. However, this is not the only effect: space, which we now know is inextricably linked to matter, must "fall" with it. Thus the whole of space contracts, presumably until there is a gigantic universal "crunch'.

This was the problem that confronted Einstein when he published his General Theory. According to the astronomical wisdom of the day, the universe *was* static. At that time, Hubble had not made his famous observations nor realized their implications. Einstein therefore attempted to "fix up" his theory of General Relativity by introducing a parameter into his equation relating the shape of space-time and the amount of matter it contained. This was the infamous "λ-term" or **cosmological constant** which acted like a repulsive form of gravitation.

It was repulsive in more ways than one, since only a few years later, the expansion of the universe was discovered and Einstein bitterly regretted introducing this "fix" to his theory. After Hubble's work, it was no longer necessary. Since then, the cosmological constant has been retained by some mathematical cosmologists and ignored by others. Of course, the fact that it is no longer *required* does not mean that it doesn't exist. Only observational astronomy can decide that question. It is a term *permitted* by the field equations of General Relativity; and Nature has a way of doing whatever it is permitted to do by its own laws!

For the moment, let's leave aside the question of how or why the universe contracts or expands and think about what the presence of matter does to the *shape* of the universe. We shall see that if the universe contained a lot of matter, then it would cause sufficient distortion for the whole of space to take on a "closed curvature". To imagine closed curvature in three-dimensional space is impossible, at least for us and, also, we suspect, for most other people. Instead, we shall return to the world of Two-land. This time, however, the surface on which our Two-landers live will no longer be a simple plane but curved.

Curved Two-land

When we talked about Two-land in Chapter 8, we thought of it as a flat plane populated by flat, two-dimensional beings and we noted that the word "flat" could be used in two different ways. First, the Two-landers themselves existed only in two dimensions, and could thus be called "flat", just as a sheet of paper is very thin and thus nearly flat. Secondly, the "sheet of space" on which the Two-landers lived was also flat in the sense that it contained no hills, valleys or "bends" in its surface. In what follows we are going to discuss what happens when we abandon the idea that the sheet is flat in the second sense: but it will still be a two-dimensional surface.

Let's first consider some of the properties curved Two-land must have in order to bear a useful resemblance to our real universe. Then we shall go on to discuss how it will appear from our three-dimensional perspective.

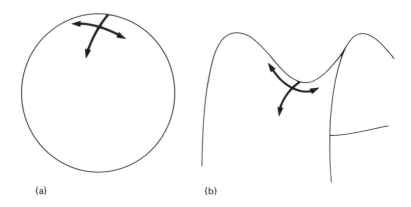

(a)   (b)

Fig. 9.2 — The sphere and the "saddle" exemplify small regions of space in a two-dimensional curved universe. Note that the sphere curves in the same way in two directions at right angles (a) while the "saddle" curves oppositely (b).

Because of our observations that our universe is isotropic and because of our assumption that it is also homogeneous (see Chapter 5), we require curved Two-land to look the same in all directions when viewed from any position. Furthermore, it must have no special points on its space.

Only two sorts of surface meet these requirements. The first is the surface of a sphere. Viewed from *on* the surface — and remembering that light can travel only *around* the surface in Two-land — it looks the same in all directions. The second sort of surface is called a right-hyperboloid, or a sort of "anti-sphere". Unfortunately, we can't imagine this second sort of flat-universe in its entirety, even with the advantage of our three-dimensional perspective. But we can approximate it very well in a fairly small region by a "saddle" shape that curves equally, but oppositely, in two directions at right angles rather like a point on the inner rim of a car's inner tube. Fig. 9.2 shows what we mean.

Flat Two-land, which we discussed earlier, is a special case of both spherical Two-land and hyperbolic Two-land when the curvature of the surface is very mild. In the case of the spherical Two-land, it is easy to see that this means: when the radius of the sphere becomes very large. The amount of curvature is harder to envisage in the case of hyperbolic Two-land, but the principle is the same.

The reader may be worried at this point. These spherical and hyperbolic universes are just mathematical curiosities, aren't they? Surely we know from common experience that the real universe is "flat". And hasn't the geometry of the ancient Greek mathematician, Euclid, been confirmed beyond doubt? Well, no: the whole of Euclidean geometry is a magnificent construction of closely-reasoned argument, extremely logical, but all based on some ideas called **postulates** which must be *assumed* before you start and which cannot be "proved" or deduced logically from other postulates.

Many mathematicians since the times of the Greeks have been very worried about one particular postulate concerning parallel lines. This postulate asserted that through every point it was possible to draw one *and only one* line parallel to any other line. The mathematicians were convinced that it should be possible to prove this result from other, simpler ideas. But no-one could. Nor can they today — because it simply isn't true! We now realize that on any surface it may be possible to draw infinitely many lines parallel to another line, just one parallel (as the Greeks believed), or none at all. It all depends on the **curvature** of the surface.

Consider two seemingly simple questions. First, "How many straight lines (i.e. geodesics) can be drawn through 2 points?". Of course, in everyday "ordinary" geometry, the answer is easy: there's just one. But, on the surface of a sphere, things are not quite so simple. Going back to our example of the two cities above: we found that the geodesic starts at Sydney, moves South to latitude 62 degrees, and then heads back North to Santiago. But of course there is another part to the great circle which leaves Sydney in exactly the opposite direction, travels through the northern hemisphere and arrives at Santiago the "long way round". These two parts of the same great circle are well known to amateur radio enthusiasts who can often alternately pick up distant signals arriving two ways by pointing their antennas in two exactly opposite directions. Furthermore, if two cities are exactly opposite on the surface of the Earth, then there are an *infinite* number of great circles joining them together — each one of exactly the same length!

Secondly, let's think about parallel lines. Can we draw a line parallel to another line on the surface of a sphere? We know that a "line" on the surface of a sphere is simply a great circle. But what do we mean by "parallel"? Presumably a line is parallel if it stays the same distance from the chosen line. Surprisingly, on a sphere, there aren't any parallel lines! To see why, let's consider another geographical example.

Think about a point on the Earth, perhaps the city of London. (Only an astronomer would call a whole city "a point"!) Consider a line drawn through London, say the zero longitude line or Greenwich meridian. Now, can we draw a line through another city, say Paris, which is also parallel to the Greenwich meridian? The answer is no! The line of longitude $2^1/_2$ degrees East passes through Paris and remains roughly 150 kilometres East of the Greenwich meridian for many degrees of latitude. But by the time we get to latitude 65 degrees the separation of the lines is reduced to 100 kilometres and by the time we reach the North Pole it has dropped to zero! Of course it *is* quite possible to remain the same distance from the Greenwich meridian as you travel North. But such a track is clearly not a line of longitude and mathematicians would not regard it as a "line" at all (i.e. it is not a geodesic), since its centre does not coincide with the centre of the Earth. On an "anti-spherical" surface similarly strange things happen. Without going into details, we shall just mention that infinitely many lines can be drawn through a point and parallel to another given line.

Strange though geometry may seem on the surface of a sphere or anti-sphere, it is just as logically impeccable as the Euclidean geometry of flat surfaces. Furthermore, the discovery of these other geometries and their three-dimensional counterparts raised the very interesting question as to what sort of geometry was needed to represent our real universe. Of course, the fact that we had been satisfied with Euclid's system for many years for building roads and bridges argued that the curvature of space could not be very great. But nor did it provide any evidence that the world was as simple as we had previously assumed.

These curved Two-lands obviously present us with some complex ideas. The only reason we were able to make these ideas comprehensible in an intuitive way was by viewing them from the privileged viewpoint of our three-dimensional space. Unfortunately, we can't hope to understand whether or not our real universe is curved in a comparable way, since we can't view it from space of a higher order. Does this then mean that we must abandon the fascinating question as to whether or not our universe really is "curved"? Fortunately, no. There are some very practical ways which the Two-landers could use to test the curvature of their space and which we can use to determine the shape of our space. Furthermore, following Einstein's formulation of the General Theory of Relativity and Hubble's discovery of the expanding universe, we could imagine *reasons* why our universe may have a more complex geometry than that described by Euclid.

Tests

(a) Mass and curvature
Einstein's work showed that the presence of matter in our universe tends to produce a closed, spherical curvature because it "pulls" space together, as we said earlier. On the other hand, the fact that the universe is expanding tends to produce a hyperbolic curvature. Depending on the amount of matter in our universe, therefore, it may have a hyperbolic, flat (Euclidean), or spherical geometry. This suggests that we should simply calculate how much mass the universe contains and use Einstein's equations to determine whether it is greater than or less than the critical amount needed to maintain a flat space.

Unfortunately, things are not quite so simple. As might be imagined, accurately estimating the total amount of matter in the universe is difficult. Certainly we can make estimates of the total number of galaxies we see and the numbers of stars they contain. But this is only the *luminous* matter and astronomers strongly suspect that large amounts of material are hidden from our view. There seem to be important problems in understanding the way in which galaxies (including our own) rotate in their far outer regions: the rotational velocities we measure are too large to be produced by the gravitational forces we deduce from the amount of matter we see.

This observation — which is reproduced in almost all other galaxies where we have good data — has led some astronomers to postulate that a large amount of the mass in galaxies is "hiding" in a form previously unsuspected. It is known as the problem of the **missing mass**. Yet again, other astronomers have concluded that there is something wrong with the basic laws of gravitational attraction. Perhaps Newton's law of gravitational attraction is not exactly an inverse square law at all: if the law should really be an inverse *linear* law on the largest distance scales in the universe, then the problem of the missing mass (and several other problems too) can be readily explained. But astronomers, like all other physicists, are very wary of introducing new laws until they have to: history has not been kind to those who did! Interestingly, the missing mass problem is reproduced even more starkly when we look at the large **clusters** of galaxies. And it screams out for solution when we try to estimate the mass of the universe as a whole.

(b) The standard yardstick

Now consider another property of space that could make its curvature detectable. It is well known that the apparent angular size of an object decreases in a particular way as it gets further away from us. For example, think about a ball 10 cm in diameter.When it is held at arm's length (say 70 cm from our eyes), it measures about 8 degrees across. At a distance of 2 metres, this angle has shrunk to just under 3 degrees. In general, the angular size A of the ball in "ordinary" space can be found from its diameter D and distance d by the formula;

$$\tan A = \frac{D}{2d}$$

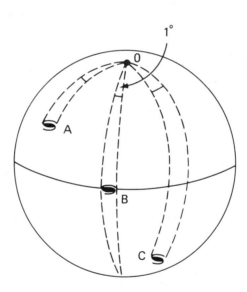

Fig. 9.3 — In a spherical two-land the angular size of an object of constant diameter at first decreases (from A to B) with increasing distance and then increases after passing the "equator" (C). Note also that two lines at a fixed angle at first increase their separation and then decrease as they approach the anti-pole.

Most objects in the universe that we are interested in have angular sizes much less than a degree and we can use the (very accurate) approximation

$$A = \frac{D}{2d}$$

where the angle A is measured in the mathematician's unit of radians. For these large distances and small angles, we notice the important result that the angular size decreases linearly with increasing distance. But this is only true for *flat* space. In our spherical Two-land, the angular size of an object first decreases with increasing distance and then increases up to infinity! Look at Fig. 9.3. Consider two geodesics which start out from us 1 degree apart. It is obvious that the separation of these lines at first increases and then decreases back to zero. Similarly, the angular size of an object of constant diameter will decrease until it is at the "equatorial" distance and then increase again until it reaches the "anti-pole".

In the hyperbolic sort of universe, the opposite happens. Here, the angular size of an object decreases with distance more quickly than expected using the simple, linear flat-space law. Furthermore, it continues to decrease as the object gets to great distances. If astronomers could measure the angular sizes of similar objects at different distances then they would have a method of testing for the curvature of space.

This test is, however, very difficult to make. Essentially, we are trying to use the diameter of a galaxy or perhaps a radio source as a standard candle or, rather, a standard "yardstick". Unfortunately we have little confidence that the objects we try to use are indeed of the same size: by the time they are at "cosmologically interesting" distance (redshifts around 1 or 2), they are also too small to recognize with any degree of confidence.

(c) Number counts

Consider a circle drawn on an ordinary flat sheet of paper. By a circle, we mean a curve that keeps the same distance from a central point and which joins up with itself. (Mathematicians would have a more accurate — and much longer! — way of describing a circle, but this will do for our purposes.) The circumference of a circle (the distance round the outside) can be calculated from the formula

$$C = \pi.D$$

where D is the circle's diameter and π is the constant number *3.1415* etc. Surprisingly, this relation is only true in flat space.

To see why, think about a circular cap of rubber cut out of an old beach ball (see Fig. 9.4(a)).

We can take this cap and press it down onto a flat table and measure its circumference and diameter. Sure enough, we find they are in the ratio π. But when we release the cap, we notice that the circumference decreases a little while the diameter stays much the same. Clearly the circumference of a cap cut from a spherical surface must be a little *less* than π times the diameter. Now imagine another circular piece of rubber but, this time, one cut from the inner rim of a large rubber inner tube,(see Fig. 9.4(b))

A little thought along the same lines as above will convince you that the circumference of this circular cap is slightly *more* than π times its diameter.

Curious though these results are, we are more interested in the *areas* of the caps. Imagine that someone had painted spots on our beachball and inner tube before we cut out the caps from them. The spots have been painted uniformly so that all parts of the surface are equally covered with an average of one spot per square centimetre. When we cut out the rubber caps, we are very careful to make the distance from the centre of each cap to its edge exactly the same in the two cases. Let's say this radius is 10 cm. Our question now is, "Which cap contains the most spots?".

After a little thought, the answer is obvious: the cap cut from the inner-tube has a greater circumference and thus a greater area. Hence it must also contain more spots on its surface. Furthermore, the larger the caps are, the bigger the excess of spots becomes. If we were Two-landers living on these beachball and inner-tube universes, we would, of course, observe that the number of spots increased as we looked farther away from us. But the *rate* at which our "spot-counts" increased would be different in the two cases. Sufficiently close to our position, the number would increase in proportion to the *square* of the distance from us. But, as we got farther away, the increase would be slower than the square power for the beachball (spherical) universe but faster than the square power for the inner-tube (hyperbolic) universe. If we can assume that the average density of spots is the same everywhere in our universe, then the way in which the count rises with increasing distance can be used to measure the curvature of the space we live in.

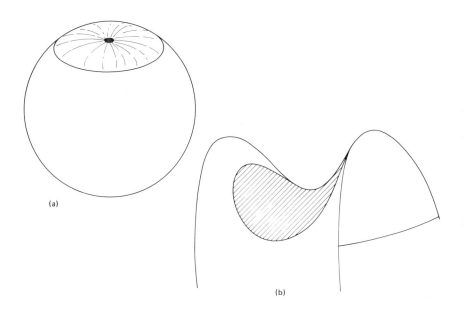

Fig. 9.4 — A circular cap cut from a rubber ball (a) is too small to be flattened unless stretched while a circular cap cut from a saddle-shape (b) is too large to stay flat.

This is the basis of the modern method of trying to determine the shape of space from galaxy and radio source counts. In our three-dimensional world we expect the total number of sources to increase as the cube power of the increasing distance[1] if the universe is truly flat. Alternatively, it will increase faster in a hyperbolic space and slower in a closed space. Once again, unfortunately, we encounter difficulties because we have no accurate way of measuring distances at cosmologically interesting distances. Galaxies and radio sources at redshifts of around 2 are exceedingly faint. And the bright quasars pose problems of their own which we shall discuss in detail later.

Despite these difficulties, radio source and galaxy counts have been extensively used for cosmological investigations. Instead of using distances, the numbers of objects brighter than a specific apparent brightness are plotted. If these galaxies all had much the same luminosity or radio power, then the apparent brightnesses should be related in a predictable way with distance. Thus, for any given hypothesized universal geometry, it is possible to predict how the counts should vary with apparent brightness. Fig. 9.5 shows some examples. Unfortunately, the "scatter" in the intrinsic luminosities of the objects plotted seems to confuse any obvious geometry effect. Even worse, there may be systematic effects at work in the data such that all the radio galaxies at large distances are brighter or fainter than those close by.

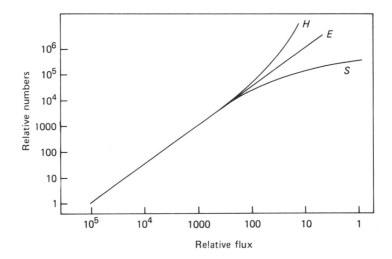

Fig. 9.5 — Examples of how the relative numbers of galaxies brighter than a certain relative flux (apparent brightness) change with decreasing flux in various cosmological models. Curve E is for flat Euclidian space while curves S and H are for curved spherical and hyperbolic space respectively.

Let us try to summarize what we have said so far: a model universe which is expanding and totally devoid of matter has a natural geometry which is

---

[1]Because the volume of an "ordinary sphere" is $\dfrac{4\pi R^3}{3}$.

hyperboloidal or "more open than flat". In this universe, it is possible to draw more than one "straight line" or space-geodesic through any point and parallel to another line and, if galaxies are evenly distributed throughout space, there will appear to be more at large distances than predicted in a flat (Euclidean) universe. If, on the other hand, our model universe is very full of matter, then its influence causes space to try to assume a closed spherical form. In the unlikely case that the amount of matter is exactly right, then the geometry of the universe is neither hyperbolic or spherical but flat.

The cosmos in motion

The presence of matter has another effect on the universe as well as defining its overall geometrical type: it decides the rate at which the universe slows down in its expansion. Let us say at once that we have no way of calculating why our universe is expanding at the *rate* it is. As far as we know, it *could* be expanding 1000 faster or 1000 times slower. If so, the Hubble parameter which we discussed in Chapter 8 would have a value 1000 times bigger or smaller. But we *do* know that the presence of matter acts as a "brake" on the rate of expansion.

So far in this chapter we have tried to avoid mathematics. The reason for this is that the equations of cosmology and general relativity are rather complicated. The ideas are fairly straightforward, but the translation of them into exact quantities requires an understanding of a branch of mathematics called **tensor calculus** and tends to get a bit messy. Tensor calculus makes geometrical and physical discussions possible without actually defining systems of coordinates or units. It makes statements that are accurate without requiring us to specify the exact reference frame to which they refer. We could continue to avoid mathematics, but we feel that the reader would miss a lot of the enjoyment of cosmology if we did. Fortunately, in the 1930s the English astronomers Milne and McCrea discovered a most important result. They showed that all the important cosmological results of general relativity could be described in Newtonian terms, provided we interpret several quantities in the "right" way. Note that this does *not* mean that Newtonian ideas accurately represent the universe: just that two different types of physics can be adequately described by the same type of mathematics. Bearing this important *caveat* in mind, we shall see what the approach of Milne and McCrea has to tell us about the rate of expansion of the universe.

First it was necessary to find some way of describing the size of the whole universe and how this size changed with time. In Chapter 8 we introduced the idea of the scale length of Two-land which we called R. We said that R could be the distance apart of any two reference marks in Two-land and we chose then to fix these as being two galaxies. All that mattered when we derived such quantities as the Hubble parameter, H_0, was the relative way in which R changed with time.

In what follows, we shall find it convenient to define R in a slightly different way and we shall take it to be the radius of spherical Two-land, (which is why we used the symbol R, for radius, earlier even though there was nothing "spherical" about flat Two-land.) If we wanted to talk about hyperbolic Two-land then it is more difficult to imagine what R is, but it is still related to the total amount of curvature.

There are now two ways of envisaging the Milne and McCrea results: one is to imagine that all the matter in the universe "grips" the fabric of space and causes the radius, R, to change. The other is to consider any small volume of space to be a miniature "replica" of the whole of the universe, which responds to the average amount of matter in its vicinity.

The basic idea used in the Milne and McCrea formulation is that the gravitational force of all the matter in the universe is related to its mass and size by the Newtonian equation

$$force = -\frac{GM^2}{R^2}$$

where M is the mass and R the scale size of the universe.

Newton's first law of motion tells us that the force per unit mass is the acceleration and so

$$acceleration\ of\ R = -\frac{G.M}{R^2}$$

which, since it is negative, is actually a *de* celeration. From this equation it follows that the rate, V, at which the universe is expanding is given[1] by

$$V^2 = \frac{2GM}{R} + a\ constant \qquad (Equation\ 9.1)$$

which implies that as the universe gets bigger (R gets larger) the speed of expansion will slow down.

The constant in the above equation is very important. Unfortunately our equations can not tell us its value. By assuming different values, we create different model universes which had different amounts of initial motion. Let's first find out what happens if we set the constant to zero. This will correspond to a particular universe — but not necessarily ours.

When this "zero" universe is very small (which means that R is also very small) then V is very big. It may be big in an "outward" direction (V positive) or an inward direction (V negative), since both are permitted when we take the square root of the right hand side of the equation. For the moment let's take the outward direction. Clearly our model universe will quickly expand. As it does so, it slows down according to Equation 9.1 but still continues to move outwards. Eventually, when it is very large indeed (R almost infinite), it will slow down nearly to a stop.

Let's skip over the (infinitely!) long time it spends at infinite radius and ask what would happen if it now were to get a very small *inward* velocity: not very much, but just enough to start it going again. In this case, it begins to fall inwards faster and faster until, by the time the radius is almost zero, it is falling inwards at an almost infinite rate!. Note carefully that we do *not* limit the infall velocity at the speed of light: once again, we are talking about the contraction of space itself, not motion through space.

Now what happens if we give our constant a small *positive* value? In this case everything starts much as before because the value of GM/R is much bigger than the constant when R is small. But, as R becomes large, the constant dominates the equation and the velocity takes up a near constant value which it will maintain for ever. There is no possibility of such a universe contacting again when R becomes infinite because it has an "excess" velocity at that time.

---

[1] The reader familiar with calculus will quickly be able to prove this result. Also note that what we call V here is exactly the same as the rate of change of R which we called R' in Chapter 8.

Finally let's see what we get when the constant is negative. This is the most interesting case, since it probably corresponds to our own universe. Again, our "negative" universe starts much as before, since the $2GM/R$ term is much bigger than our negative constant. As the universe expands, however, the $2GM/R$ term decreases and eventually becomes equal to the value of the constant except that, being positive, it counterbalances the negative constant. According to our equation this means that the expansion of the universe will stop since V is zero. And what happens next? The expansion will "turn around" and the whole universe start contracting, slowly at first and then faster, eventually to become infinitely small once more.

The important problem of cosmology can be simply thought of as drawing the correct graph of R as a function of time. If we knew what this curve looked like, we would know how the universe had expanded in the past and how it will behave in the future. We should know the value of the Hubble parameter at any time and how it changes. Perhaps it is not surprising that we are a very long way from being able to draw this curve with any real degree of confidence. In fact, the reader may be sceptical that a single curve can decide the whole history of the universe. Maybe different parts of the universe expand at different rates and thus require different "R"s? In principle this could be true: but it is forbidden by the arguments of Chapter 5, which showed it highly likely that the universe is both isotropic and homogeneous.

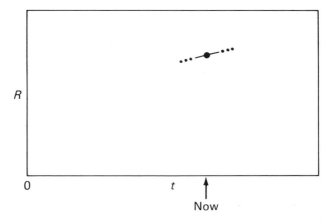

Fig. 9.6 — The sum total of our knowledge regarding the variation of the universal scale length R with time t. We believe the universe started at $R = 0$, that R is increasing at the present time (the curve slopes upwards) but that the rate of increase is negative (the curve is flattening-out).

Although we may not know precisely what $R(t)$ looks like, we do have some clues as to its shape. First, we know that the slope of the curve at the present time (which we call t_0) is as we determine from the present value of the Hubble parameter. Second, we think it likely that the universe began with a Big Bang about 20,000 million years ago. This allows us to define a point in time at which R was zero. Third, we know that the universe contains mass and energy and so the value of the Hubble parameter (and thus the slope of the curve) is likely to be decreasing with time. Only model universes with large "anti-gravity" cosmological constants (see earlier) can expand sufficiently quickly to counteract this effect.

Fig. 9.6 shows the sum total of our knowledge about cosmological models in which we have some confidence. Beyond this point, speculation begins. Those cosmologists who think that their observations suggest a particular cosmological model are attempting to draw the whole curve from the little we know. This is obviously a procedure fraught with danger.

At this point let us try and summarize what we have so far said in this chapter. We live in a universe which is expanding and which clearly contains matter. The rate at which this expansion is taking place is largely determined by the arbitrary initial violence of the moment of creation. On the other hand, the rate at which the universal expansion is slowing down is determined by the amount of mass the universe contains.

If our universe is of the flat or open type, then it is infinite in size and, presumably, contains an infinite number of galaxies. If, on the other hand, it has a spherical geometry then it is finite in size. Furthermore, it will not expand for ever but, instead, eventually collapse back on itself. In this latter case it is conceivable that by constructing a sufficiently powerful telescope we could gaze out into the depths of space right around the universe and see the Earth as it was many thousands of millions of years ago.

To determine what sort of universe we actually live in is a major problem for present and future observational cosmologists. Certainly if space had been *very* "closed" we should have been able to easily observe the effects of strong spherical curvature in the number counts and angular size distance relations. On the other hand, the amount of matter we see in the universe argues that space cannot be very "open". One of the great unexplained mysteries of cosmology is that our measurements suggest that the universe is very nearly "flat". On the other hand we cannot see sufficient matter in the universe to cause this degree of "closure". If the mass really *is* there, what form does it take. And why should it have almost exactly the right, unlikely, critical value to give space no net curvature?

To the edge of the universe

Early in this chapter we said that the idea of curved space could be used to explain the apparent paradox that the universe may be of finite size and yet not have an edge. We have now shown how spherical curvature can lead to a finite, but unbounded, space. Does this then mean that there can be no "edges" in the universe? Can we, at least in principle, see everything that exists? And what do astronomers mean when they talk about "edges" or "horizons" in the universe?

First, it is very unlikely that the universe has a limit in the sense of falling over the edge of a cliff at the seaside. We are confident that there is no place in the universe where we could fall off — nor is there a hard fence-like boundary beyond which it is possible to go. If the universe has an edge, then it takes the form of either a distance beyond which it is not possible to see because the universe is expanding too fast — or a distance beyond which we *can* see, but where we find no detectable matter (such as galaxies or quasars).

In one sense, an edge could simply mean the most distant object we can see. If we believe the redshifts of galaxies and quasars arise purely from the expansion of the universe (but see Chapter 16) then the most distant object will be the object of highest redshift. The difficulty with answering our basic question in the above terms is that it immediately suggests the questions,"Yes — but what lies beyond? Are there yet-more-distant objects?".

We believe the answer is almost certainly, "Yes". As we saw in Chapter 8, the cosmological redshift of a quasar is simply a measure of the scale length (or "radius") of the universe *now*,compared with the scale length the universe had when light left the quasar. In fact,

$$(1+z) = \frac{R_{now}}{R_{then}}$$

In principle, the radius of the universe at the time when light was emitted could be arbitrarily small compared to the radius now. Thus the redshift of an object could be arbitrarily large. But, in practice, it is likely that there was a time in the universe's history before which no quasars or galaxies had formed. If so, there will be a minimum radius — and thus maximum redshift — for detecting them. In any case, the apparent optical or radio strength of a quasar will decrease rapidly with increasing redshift, not only because of the increasing distance but because of the extra diminution of light caused by the expansion.

This means that it may not be possible to see objects beyond a certain maximum redshift. But is this *all* we are to understand by the "edge" of the universe? No: much more fundamental definitions of the edge can be stated by realizing the implications of the finite speed of light and the finite age of the universe.

Consider a simple universe which extends outwards for ever. It is *not* expanding and it has no strange geometry. A cosmologist would call it an **infinite, static, Euclidean universe**: we call it an infinite, static, flat Three-land. Let us suppose that all the galaxies in this universe were created 20,000 million years ago.

On an astronomical scale, the Large Magellanic Cloud is very close to us, a mere 180,000 lightyears away. We have no trouble seeing most of the stars in the LMC because they were born many millions of years ago and there has been plenty of time for their light to reach us. But what of a galaxy much more distant than the LMC? — perhaps one 19,000,000,000 lightyears away? The light which we are now receiving from this galaxy left it when it was only 5% of its present age. And what of galaxies 21,000,000,000 lightyears from us? (Remember, this universe is infinite in size.) Of course, we can't see them. There has simply not been enough time for their light to arrive yet.

In this infinite universe, therefore, there is a "boundary" beyond which we can't see things (at least at the present time). Because it is rather similar to the horizon one may see looking out of the window of an international jet plane, it, too, is referred to as an horizon. In this case, we call it a **particle horizon**[1].

Does this particle horizon always stay at the same distance from us, like a terrestrial horizon? The answer is no. Consider the view we would have had of this simple, imaginary universe if we had been living 10,000,000,000 years earlier. At

---

[1]The word "particle" may seem strange. After all, a whole galaxy is hardly a particle. The name is unfortunate and arose for historical reasons. What is meant here is something that exists for a long time, unlike the "events" that we shall discuss below.

that time we wouldn't have been able to observe objects (or "particles") farther away than 10,000,000,000 lightyears. The particle horizon is moving away from us as time goes on. In fact the imaginary boundary it defines is actually rushing away at the speed of light. In the very early history of the universe, it was very close to us. And, if our universe lasts forever, it will eventually be infinitely distant. The reason there is a particle horizon is because the universe is only of a finite age — that is, it had a beginning. This is also true in an expanding universe but the concept of a particle horizon then becomes considerably trickier. Before we look at this case though, let's consider another sort of horizon called an **event horizon**.

Imagine again that we are living in a simple, non-curved universe which is not expanding and is infinite in extent. But, this time, let our universe have existed for ever. Since it had no beginning, the particle horizon will lie infinitely far away from us and we might confidently expect to be able to observe all the galaxies in this universe. (Provided, of course, that we had sufficiently powerful telescopes!)

But imagine that our universe is destined to have an end. Perhaps 10,000 million years in the future. In this case we shall never see an event that is currently taking place in a galaxy 11,000 million lightyears away. Note carefully that we *shall* be aware that this galaxy exists: there has been ample time for its past light to reach us. It is simply that a present or fairly recent *event* (perhaps a supernova explosion) will never be observed because the whole universe, including ourselves, will have disappeared before the light gets here. The events that we shall be able to observe in the future remaining to us are those lying within a radius equal to the time before the universe will end. Thus, if this final apocalypse is 30,000 million years in the future, our boundary is presently at a distance of 30,000 million lightyears.

This new sort of boundary is called an **event horizon** and a moment's thought will show that it is contracting towards us at the speed of light. At first glance the idea of an event horizon may seem less realistic than a particle horizon. While we may concede that the universe probably had a beginning, it is less obvious that it will have an end, particularly in the flat geometry we referred to above. But the situation becomes more complicated in an expanding universe. While the light from distant galaxies and the events taking place in them is "trying" to reach us, the expansion of space may or may not allow us to receive this information, even if the universe is eternal.

Before discussing this tricky but fascinating point, let's recap an important result from Chapter 6. There we showed that the Special Theory of Relativity implies that the speed of any material body through space cannot exceed the speed of light (since then, for one thing, its total mass would become infinite). However, in the cosmological situation, we are not considering bodies moving through space, but expanding *with* space. In a fundamental sense, two galaxies at rest in the cosmic frame are not moving at all, even though their distance apart may be increasing at a velocity comparable with — or even greater than — the speed of light!

We shall try to make this last point clearer by returning to a spherical Two-land in which two "flat-ants" inhabit the surface of a large, expanding balloon (Fig. 9.7). Both of the ants agree that today they are feeling lazy. So they decide to sit down and close their eyes (whatever *that* means in flat-land!). They certainly don't feel as though they are doing any work and would definitely consider themselves "at rest". Unknown to the two ants, however, the balloon is being blown up as we said. Obviously the two ants get further apart as time goes on. But, providing that the ants are small compared with the size of the balloon, neither of them is aware of what's happening.

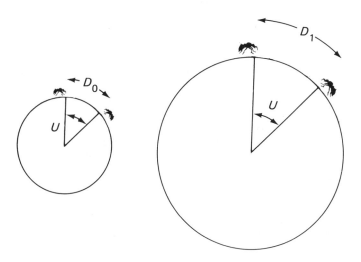

Fig. 9.7 — The increasing distance apart of two ants at rest in an expanding, spherically-curved universe.

The distance, D from one ant to the other at any time is given by,

$$D = R . U$$

where U is the angle (measured in radians) subtended by the ants at the centre of the balloon. Of course, the ants can't understand what U really means, because it is an angle lying "outside" their space. But U is important because it doesn't change as the balloon is blown up. This means that the velocity, v, with which the ants move apart and which is equal to the rate of change of the distance, D, is given by

$$v = (rate\ of\ change\ of\ R) . U$$

or, using our previous "dash" notation,

$$v = R'.U$$

and so,

$$v = \frac{R' D}{R}$$

which is, of course, the Hubble relation, $v = H.D$, since $H = R'/R$.

The distance at which v is equal to the speed of light, c, is

$$D_{critical} = cH$$

which is the speed of light divided by the Hubble constant. This equation is true for all times, which is why we have not put a subscript 0, meaning "now", on either the H or R.

From this relation, we can draw an important inference: for our two ants at rest, the critical distance will *increase* if the Hubble constant *decreases* with time. Conversely, if the Hubble constant increases, then $D_{critical}$ decreases.

Note that the Hubble parameter increasing with time is *not* the same thing as the universe expanding. For example, if we think of an "exponentially exploding" universe in which R is proportional to e^{time} then the Hubble parameter remains the same at all times. It is almost certain that our universe is not expanding anything like as violently as this and so most "real" universes will have decreasing Hubble parameters. Even if the speed of expansion were constant (i.e. R constant), then H would decrease inversely with time.

Now consider what the preceding arguments mean in terms of things we observe. If a galaxy (and the space in which it is located) is receding from us at the speed of light, and since light itself can only travel through space *at* the speed of light, then it is clear that the light of the galaxy can never reach us. This, however, is only true for light emitted *now*. If the Hubble constant is decreasing with time — that is, the universe is slowing down in its expansion — then a galaxy that is at the present particle horizon will eventually become visible. This follows since the particle horizon will be at a greater distance in the future than it is at present. In summary, a particle horizon divides the universe as seen from a particular point into two parts: the part that has been observed and the part that hasn't (yet).

(We have a problem with words here: we actually used the word "observed" rather than "observable" in the previous sentence. The trouble is that "not observable" has two meanings: it could mean "not yet observed because astronomers have not yet got around to doing it" or it could mean "not yet observed because not enough time has passed for the universe to be old enough". In using "observed" in the previous paragraph we took the liberty of assuming that our imaginary astronomers had been extremely industrious and observed everything in the sky that *could* be observed at a given time! This is obviously not realistic — but it should make the ideas clearer.)

Clearly the question of what can and cannot be seen and the concepts of particle and event horizons become complicated when the universe is expanding and we need not consider them further here. Suffice it to say that a particle horizon always exists in a universe which had a beginning after allowance is made for the nature of the expansion. Furthermore, an event horizon will exist for a universe that has an ending, again bearing in mind the nature of the expansion. The concepts of these horizons are well described in Harrison's book, *Cosmology* and the interested reader is referred there for a very readable and more extensive discussion.

10

The Dark Sky Problem

It is amazing that one of the most profound statements about the size and shape and age of the universe can be made simply by looking at it! In fact, it has been known for nearly 400 years that the darkness of the night sky tells us something about the remote regions of space. The seventeenth century astronomer Johannes Kepler is generally credited with having drawn attention to this fact first; since then it has been discussed by many people, including Halley (of comet fame). What we going to talk about in this chapter is, in fact, normally referred to as Olbers' Paradox after **Wilhelm Olbers** a nineteenth century German doctor and amateur astronomer. The name is unfortunate since it was neither first proposed by him, nor is it a paradox. Olbers submitted a short paper on the topic in 1823 ignoring the much earlier work. And everyone who has discussed the problem over the centuries had an answer that they thought resolved the problem. So the name is not really appropriate.

We'll start our discussion of what is better called "the Dark Sky Problem" by putting forward an argument which we must stress is *not* correct. But it will be instructive.

The problem

Consider a very simple universe — in fact the simplest universe possible. We shall suppose that space is "flat", which means that it obeys simple Euclidean geometry and stretches out away from the Earth, Sun and our galaxy for ever. Kepler argued that, if there were stars similar to our Sun distributed evenly throughout the whole of this infinite space, then the sky should be infinitely bright!

To see what he meant, consider the following analogy. Suppose that you are standing in the middle of a forest that is so big that you can consider it infinite in size. You yourself, are in a small clearing near the centre of this forest. But, no matter in which direction you look, you see the trunks of trees. Some of these trunks are fairly close and look relatively thick; some are farther away and look thinner. But you see wood in all directions. Furthermore, it doesn't matter how sparsely distributed the trees are, provided only that the forest is big enough. If a friendly axeman halves the number of trees in the forest by cutting down every other one at random, it simply reveals more trees to you at somewhat greater distances.

Returning now to Kepler's argument about the Dark Sky Problem, we can argue similarly as follows: if the stars stretched out into space for ever, then, *no matter how sparsely distributed they are*, we will see stars in *every* part of the sky.

To get a different view of this argument, let's look at it mathematically. Consider a series of "shells" each 1 million lightyears (Mly) thick stretching out from the Earth (see Fig. 10.1).

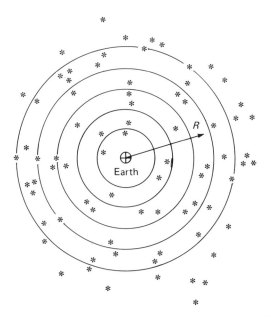

Fig. 10.1 — Spherical shells of constant thickness stretching away from the Earth have increasing volumes, which implies that they contain increasing numbers of stars. Each shell is 1 mega lightyear in thickness and so the first shell has an average distance of 0.5 Mly, the second 1.5 Mly, the third 2.5 Mly and so on.

The density of stars in each shell, which we shall call ρ , is the same. We'll ignore the first shell in which the Earth lies and just look at the others farther away. Note that the volume of each of these shells is *not* the same. The second shell lies at a distance of about $^3/_2$ Mly from us and has a volume of

$$V_2 = 4.\pi.(^3/_2)^2 \quad cubic \; megalightyears \; (Mly^3) \; [1]$$

---

[1] This follows because the volume of a thin spherical shell of radius R is just its surface area, $4\pi R^2$, multiplied by its thickness, which is 1 Mly in our example.

The third shell lies about $^5/_2$ Mly from us and has a volume

$$V_3 = 4.\pi.(^5/_2)^2 \quad Mly^3$$

and so on.

Now let's estimate the total light we expect to receive from just one, typical shell. To make the argument general, we'll consider the shell to be at a distance of R from us. Furthermore, although it won't matter, we'll assume that all the stars in the universe have the same intrinsic luminosity, L.

The amount of energy we get from just *one* star at a distance of R is given by the inverse square law as:

$$s = \frac{L}{4.\pi.R^2}$$

The shell that lies at a distance of R has (using the same equation as before) a volume of

$$V = 4.\pi.R^2 \quad Mly^3$$

and so it must contain a total of

$$N = V.\rho = 4.\pi.R^2 \, \rho \quad stars.$$

So we can calculate the total light energy we receive from just this *one* shell of stars as

$$S = N.s = \frac{4.\pi.R^2.\rho.L}{4.\pi.R^2} \qquad (Equation\ 10.1)$$

which is just $= \rho.L$

Note one very important thing about this equation. It states that the total light we receive from each shell is the same: it does *not* get smaller as we look at shells which are further and further away. Although each star in a distant shell appears dimmer than stars in more nearby shells, the greater numbers of stars in distant shells exactly compensates for this effect. Thus the summed light energy contribution from each shell, whether near or far, is the same.

The final step in this argument is to note that, according to our postulate, the size of the universe — and thus the total numbers of shells — is infinite. And hence the total brightness of the night sky should be infinite, providing that our assumptions are valid!

Let's set out a summary of the above argument. We assumed:

(a) **The universe is infinite.**

(b) **Space is everywhere simply Euclidean.**

(c) Stars are distributed roughly uniformly throughout space.

(d) Each star has about the same intrinsic luminosity.

Using these assumptions, we inferred:

The night sky should be infinitely bright.

Well, clearly something is wrong! The night sky is, in fact, very dark. Kepler used this fact to speculate that the universe was not infinite but had a definite size. If so, there were no stars beyond a certain distance and so the number of shells we must add up is *not* infinite. And, of course, if the numbers of shells is not infinite, then the total light energy isn't either. Unfortunately, the Dark Sky Problem cannot be disposed of anything like as easily today.

So, what's the answer?

Before we turn to a discussion of the possible explanations as to why young lovers on clear summer evenings are not embarrassed by being bathed in a sea of infinite light, we should note that the discussion we gave above is slightly incorrect.

If stars stretch out from the Earth for ever, then eventually some will get in the way of others and block out the more distant light. The mathematics describing this more accurate calculation is somewhat more messy than that given above. Nevertheless we can summarize the simple result: we find that the night sky is not infinitely bright (even keeping the rest of the assumptions set out above) but, instead, it should be as bright as the surface of an average star. This is almost as bad as being infinitely bright! And it is certainly not what we see in practice.

So, what is the resolution of the Dark Sky Problem? To answer this, we'll consider which of the various assumptions might be wrong. In so doing, we are retracing the paths followed by many scientists over the years since the time of Kepler.

First, let's consider assumption (c): we now know that stars are not distributed uniformly through space — they are clustered together into galaxies. However, this doesn't affect the argument in any important way. Everywhere that we mentioned the word "stars" above, we should now replace it with the word "galaxies" and replace the luminosity of an average star with the luminosity of an average galaxy. But if the galaxies are distributed approximately uniformly in space (as we think they are), then we arrive at a similar conclusion: the night sky should be as bright as the surface of an average galaxy — which is still very bright indeed. There is no escape from our problem here.

Second, let's look at assumption (d). Does it matter that the galaxies are not all of the same intrinsic luminosity? A moment's thought will convince you that the answer is no. Even if the galaxies have a range of brightness in each shell, their total light contribution from that shell alone is very definitely finite: the more luminous galaxies "make up" for the less-luminous galaxies and our sky would still be as bright as an *average* galaxy. Provided only that the galaxies in the other shells have the same sorts of *distributions* of luminosity, then they will also have the same integrated luminosity. And so, when we add the contributions from all the shells together, we still arrive at an infinite result. (Or, more properly, a night sky as bright as the surface of an average galaxy.) Coming back to our forest analogy for a moment, we would say that it doesn't matter that some of the trees are really thick-trunked and some narrow: we still see only wood in all directions.

Note, though, that it *would* solve the problem if we could find a reason why the distant galaxies *as a whole* were fainter than expected. Our main difficulty can be seen to be the exact cancellation of the two terms in R^2 in Equation 10.1. If we could find a way in which the apparent brightnesses of the galaxies dropped off at a rate faster than $1/R^2$ with increasing distance, then we would have found the answer.

There are at least two ways in which this could happen. With the discovery of the phenomenon of redshift (see Chapter 7) it looked as though an answer might be in sight. The redshift of a galaxy caused by the overall expansion of the universe has two effects: one is obvious from the name — the light is changed to redder, or longer, wavelengths; the second is more subtle — the light also becomes dimmer, because long wavelength photons have less energy (per photon) than short wavelength photons.

The amount by which the redshift affects the Dark Sky Problem has been calculated by the American astronomer Edward Harrison. For all reasonable models of the universe, the redshift does *not* sufficiently reduce the total light received from the galaxies in anything like the right amount. Harrison finds that the dimming caused by redshift would only reduce the sky's predicted brightness to about $1/2$ or $1/3$ of that of a typical galaxy, which is nowhere near enough to resolve the Dark Sky Problem. But there is another, and more subtle, way of avoiding the problem. Perhaps the volumes of our shells don't increase in the expected way with distance? This is tantamount to questioning assumption (b) above. If space is not simply "flat" or "Euclidean", then the volume of each shell will not increase as R^2.

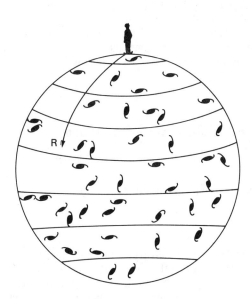

Fig. 10.2 — In a spherically closed universe the numbers of galaxies in each "shell" at first increases and then later decreases with increasing distance.

In Chapter 9 we looked at several two-dimensional universes that were much easier to imagine than our own real three-dimensional universe. Consider the spherical closed universe that we discussed there. Let us draw "shells" (which are actually annuli in the two-dimensional case) stretching away from the "flat-Earth" point in this universe (see Fig. 10.2). At first, their two-dimensional "volume" (i.e. area) increases with distance until the equator of the universe is reached. It then decreases back to zero by the time we reach the opposite "pole". In this sort of universe, the total number of galaxies is finite, not because they stop anywhere, but because the total "flat-volume" of space itself is finite.

If we really live in a closed universe, then there is no doubt that we would indeed see a night sky dimmer than the average surface brightness of a galaxy. Perhaps we could use this argument the other way round? Does the fact that the night sky *is* very dark, then, prove that we do, in fact, live in a finite closed universe? Well, no — unfortunately we can't make such a sweeping claim. Even if the universe *were* finite, the light from even a single (everlasting) star would eventually fill up space until the whole sky glowed as bright as the surface of the star.

The gravity problem

Before continuing our discussion let's look at another — but related — problem. If the universe really were infinite, what total gravitational force would it exert on the Earth? Kepler worried about this problem because he realized that an infinite universe, full of stars, should collapse on itself infinitely quickly! To answer the question, we must make some more calculations which will turn out to be very similar to those of the previous section.

Again, we shall divide the universe up into shells stretching out from the Earth. And we shall again also assume that the average number of galaxies in each shell is the same, independent of the distance of the shells from the Earth (that is, we shall assume our universe is homogeneous — see Chapter 5). The gravitational force per unit mass that a *single* galaxy of mass m exerts on the Earth is just

$$f = \frac{Gm}{R^2}$$

Just as before, we take the volume of a shell to be

$$V = 4.\pi.R^2$$

and the number of galaxies in this shell to be

$$N = \rho V$$

where ρ is the average density of galaxies in space.

Now, we might expect that the total force on the Earth from galaxies in this "R th" shell would be given by multiplying the force exerted by one of them by the number of galaxies in the shell. But this isn't correct: galaxies on opposite sides of the Earth (A and B in Fig. 10.3) pull in opposite directions. If two similar galaxies are exactly opposite to each other, are at the same distance as viewed from the Earth and have the same mass, then their attractions cancel out exactly.

To get around this problem, let's consider only galaxies lying in two cones directly opposite to each other as viewed from the Earth. If each cone represents a volume of only $^1/_{100}$ (say) of the total shell, then the number of galaxies in the "right-hand" shell is

$$N \ = \ 0.01.V.\rho \qquad\qquad (Equation\ 10.2)$$

and the total force they exert is

$$= \ 0.01.4.\pi.R^2.\frac{\rho.G.m}{R^2}$$

$$= \ 0.01.4.\pi.G.m.\rho$$

The important thing about this equation is that the force is again independent of the distance, R . In an infinite universe this means that the total of all the contributions from the separate shell-like parts of the cone will again sum up to infinity! On the other hand, it is true that this infinite force should be balanced by the cone on the other side. In addition, there should also be similar contributions, but acting in different directions, from galaxies lying in other directions.

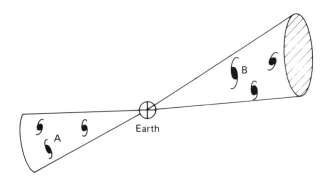

Fig. 10.3 — The total gravitational attractive force of galaxies in opposite directions as viewed from the Earth is infinitely large in an analogous way to the predicted brightness of the night sky.

What does all this mean? If our assumptions are valid, it means that the universe is in a state of extreme "tension" with a body like the Earth subject to infinite forces acting on it from all sides. The slightest amount of mis-cancellation in these forces and the Earth should start moving off in one direction with near-infinite acceleration! This doesn't sound very realistic. Clearly a "gravity" problem exists very similar to our dark sky problem.

Our two problems have come about primarily because we assumed that the universe was not only infinite in extent but that it also *appeared* infinite in extent. It is to this assumption that we shall now pay some attention. We shall return to the Dark Sky Problem and ask just how far back in time we *can* see.

Resolution

To the best of our knowledge, the universe began in a Big Bang some 10,000 million years ago (see Chapter 17). This implies that there isn't anything in the universe older than 10,000 million years. Furthermore, it means that the farthest objects that we can see have distances of less than 10,000 million lightyears: light from more distant objects wouldn't have had time to reach us. We shall now look at the effect of this finite distance on our previous arguments.

First we must put some numbers into our formulae. (When we came up with *infinite* answers it didn't matter what units the infinity was measured in — but when we get a *finite* answer (*123.4* , for example) it's very important what units we use!)

Astronomers have found that there is about 1 galaxy (on average) per 1000 cubic megalightyears[1]. Thus the number we have been calling ρ, the average space-density of galaxies, has a value of about 0.001 galaxies per cubic megalightyear. The total luminosity of each of these "average" galaxies is near 10^{43} ergs per square centimetre per second (ergs/cm^2/s), or about 10,000 million times more powerful than our Sun.

Equation 10.2, which gave the total number of galaxies in a shell at a distance of R Mly and of thickness 1 Mly, becomes:

$$N = 4.\pi.R^2 . \ 0.001$$

and the total energy received per second at the Earth from just this one shell is

$$S = 0.001 . \ 10^{43} \quad (ergs/cm^2/s)$$

But how many of these shells are there? Fortunately that's simple. We have supposed that each shell is 1 Mly in thickness. So, if we can see out into the universe "only" to a distance of 10,000 megalightyears, there can only be 10,000 shells contributing light. Therefore, finally, we can calculate the total light from *all* the universe as

$$Total \ Light \ = \ 10,000 \ . \ 0.001 \ . \ 10^{43} \ ergs/cm^2/s$$

or about 10^{44} ergs/cm^2/s, which is comparable to the energy produced by just one, large galaxy. So the total brightness of the night sky we expect is similar to that we would get if such a bright galaxy was "smeared out" over all the sky. Which is not very bright at all — and certainly a long way from being infinite!

At last, therefore, we have found a reason why the sky is not infinitely bright: put simply, it is because the universe is not very old. A "mere" 10,000 million years, in fact. Because the universe is not very old, light from the more distant parts has not had time to reach us. Thus, even if the universe *were* infinite, it would not

---

[1] Using values from C.W.Allen's book of data, *Astrophysical Quantities* (see Bibliography).

appear infinite simply because we couldn't see the farthest regions. A similar argument also explains the gravity problem. The gravitational forces on the Earth are small because gravity waves, too, can only travel at the speed of light.

Of course, the number we have used above for the age of the universe is uncertain by a factor of about 2: it depends on the accuracy of our observational material as well as the cosmological model we use to interpret the observations, as we discussed in Chapter 9. But none of this matters for our resolution of the Dark Sky Problem. What *is* important is that all reasonable values of the universe's age produce a finite — and small — number for the expected brightness of the night sky and the force on the Earth.

But there is another reason to expect a dark sky even if the universe *were* infinitely old. It is simply that the stars and galaxies don't live forever. The total life-expectancy of the brightest stars in our own, and other, galaxies is only about 10,000 years. A medium-sized star like our own Sun lives on its hydrogen fuel for about 10,000 million years and the dimmest stars last perhaps 100 times longer still. Furthermore, as we mentioned in Chapter 2, most of a galaxy's light comes from the bright, blue stars. On average, therefore, let's take a star's lifetime as something like that of our Sun — just 10,000 million years.

Using this average stellar "life-expectancy", any galaxy that is appreciably older than 10,000 million years old will have "burnt out" most of its stars. (Remember, we are now postulating that the universe is *infinitely* old). It will thus not shine, or, if it does, it will be very dim, with its light coming from just a few, low-mass, red stars. This means that, as we looked out into the universe, we could only see galaxies to a distance of around 10,000 million lightyears, *even if the universe were infinitely old and even if it were infinite in size.* Any galaxies that lie further away than this will not be visible — they will have faded away — and certainly will not contribute in our "adding up" of the shell's light.

Our resolution of the Kepler's Dark Sky Problem is now complete: when you gaze up at the night sky, ponder that it is dark either because stars die or because the universe had a beginning. Modern astronomy has shown that both of these statements are true. But either of them would be sufficient to resolve the Dark Sky Problem. It's as simple as that!

11

The First Quasars

It's often difficult in astronomy to say exactly when something was discovered. For example, the fuzzy clouds visible in the southern skies which we call the Magellanic Clouds had been well-known since the "Dreamtime" of the aboriginals. But their true nature as separate galaxies was not realized until the beginning of this present century. In the same way, the brightest quasars had been recorded on photographic plates for many years but only with the advent of radioastronomy in the late 1950s was their enormous importance recognized. Whether or not they would have been discovered without radioastronomy is an interesting — but quite hypothetical — question.

Radio surveys

The late 1950s saw the real start of radioastronomy as an alternative window on the universe. Cambridge was making its first surveys of the northern skies and the Sydney telescopes were mapping the southern skies. The strongest radio sources visible in the South, such as Taurus A, Virgo A and Centaurus A, were being identified with optical objects, most notably by John Bolton and his colleagues.

The state of radio technology at the time dictated that these early surveys had to be made at frequencies which are low by today's standards. Around 80 MHz was quite a typical frequency and 408 MHz was definitely "high". Thus, since the telescopes were making surveys at low frequencies, it isn't surprising that they tended to find radio sources that emitted preferentially at low frequencies. When their energy output, or **flux density**, was plotted on a graph against frequency, the line sloped steeply downwards from low to high frequencies. Such objects were called "steep-spectrum" objects. See Fig. 11.1.

It was natural to search for optical counterparts of these steep-spectrum sources. In some cases, faint, distorted galaxies were identified at or near the radio source positions. But such searches were by no means always successful. For example, in the early 1960s when the Third Cambridge (3C) Catalogue had been completed, less then one half of all the sources it contained had been identified with optically visible objects. Nevertheless, the prevailing opinion at the start of the 1960s was that the majority of radio sources were indeed some sort of colliding or exploding galaxy. Those that hadn't yet been identified were probably just too faint to be recorded on photographic plates.

But a few of the sources didn't have steep spectra. Instead their flux density was roughly the same at *all* frequencies and they were dubbed "flat-spectrum" sources (see Fig. 11.1). As more were found, it soon became apparent that they had another property unusual in the radio sources found up until then: they had very small angular sizes. In fact, to the telescopes available in the 1950's, they appeared just as point sources of radio emission, too small to show any "structure".

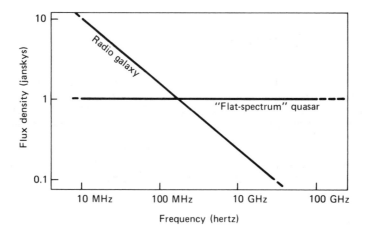

Fig. 11.1 — The radio spectra (radio flux density plotted against frequency) for a typical radio galaxy and a typical "flat spectrum" quasar. One jansky is equal to 10^{-26} Watts per square metre per Hertz of receiver bandwidth.

What were they? The most popular opinion was that they were stars in our own galaxy, somehow far more powerful at radio wavelengths than the Sun. At the time, the Sun was the only known true "radio star". Its closeness almost guaranteed its radio detection. But it was simple to calculate (from the inverse square law) that if other stars in our galaxy emitted roughly the same rates of energy as the Sun, they would be millions of times too weak to detect from the Earth. The flat-spectrum sources, if stars, had to be extremely powerful ones of a sort not previously suspected.

If they *were* stars, then perhaps they could be seen in optical telescopes? Unfortunately, the radio source positions available in the early 1960s were still relatively poor. When you look at 16th magnitude stars, for example, there are about 1000 objects per square degree. If your radio position is uncertain to $1/4$ of a degree , say, then you have a total of 40 objects that *might* be the correct identification. The identifications of Centaurus A and Virgo A had been made because these objects looked so very unusual. But unfortunately there are a lot of ordinary-looking stars in the sky! Clearly,better positions were needed. But how to get them?

Pin-pointing the quasars

The positional accuracy of a radio telescope is limited by the diameter of its mirror and by the frequency of the energy it collects. For reasonable frequencies, telescopes of several kilometres would be required to unambiguously pinpoint a flat spectrum source this approach was adopted with the building of the large arrays, . such as the Mill's Cross. Such telescopes are called **interferometers**.

The principle of their operation is as follows: if we have two radiotelescopes separated by a few hundred metres, radio waves will normally arrive at one telescope a fraction of a second before the other. Only if the radio source is directly overhead to both telescopes will the energy arrive at the same time. From all other directions, the waves arrive delayed at one dish relative to the other. See Fig. 11.2.

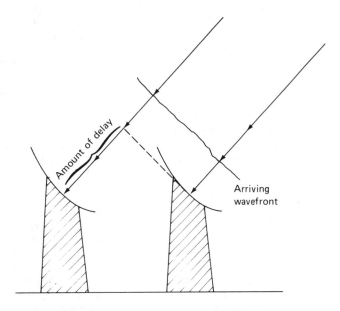

Fig. 11.2 — The two element radio interferometer. Waves from an astronomical radio source arrive at the left-hand telescope a little later than at the right hand telescope. The amount of the delay depends upon the direction of the radio source and the separation of the two telescopes.

The amount of this delay depends on two things: first, the separation of the dishes (which we assume we know) and, second, the angle of arrival of the waves, which depends on the position of the source in the sky. Thus, by accurately measuring the delay, we can determine the source's position. In practice, more than two dishes are often used to provide several interferometer "pairs", but the principle remains the same.

But there was another, better, way of measuring accurate positions for a few radio sources — by using the Moon! As the Moon orbits around the Earth, it passes in front of many much-more-distant celestial objects causing the radiation we receive from the distant object to disappear. In optical astronomy, the occasions when the Moon passes in front of stars are known as **occultations**. Accurate observations of the time a star disappears behind the Moon and the time it reappears provide very accurate determinations of the Moon's position.

The radio astronomers realized that similar sorts of measurements could be made with radio telescopes and radio sources. This time, though, the idea was not to measure the position of the Moon knowing the position of the stars but, rather, to measure the position of a radio source using the known position of the Moon! The radio telescope would track one of the new "radio star" sources and wait until the Moon moved across it. By accurately timing the disappearance of the source, its position could be found. Owing to a phenomenon known as diffraction, the disappearance and reappearance of the source would not be instantaneous events, but would be spread over a few seconds in each case. But the basic idea was simple.

A group of astronomers lead by Cyril Hazard together with colleagues Mackay and Shimmins decided to try to observe the occultation of the strong, flat-spectrum "radio star" **3C273** using the newly built Parkes radio telescope[1]. There were to be three such occultations in 1962: in April, August and October. On the first occasion, the team leader, Hazard, had been making a visit to Narrabri in northern NSW and was driving down to Parkes. Unfortunately he reckoned without the roughness of the country roads and was late for the experiment. Some data were taken, but they were not much good. One chance had gone: the second occulatation was the last *good* chance to observe this particularly strong source for over 19 years. There had better be no mistakes this time!

However, another problem now faced the team: the Parkes telescope could not point to directions near the horizon. Its angular motion from the zenith (known as **zenith angle**) was limited to angles of less than 60 degrees. This was a deliberate decision made in the design stage to reduce many of the engineering problems. The Parkes dish didn't need access to large zenith angles (and thus the northern radio sources) since there were plenty of northern telescopes to do the job. But it was unfortunate, in that the second occultation would take place when both 3C273 and the Moon were at a zenith angle of 61 degrees, just below the telescope's horizon! The calculations of position were checked but the answer was the same: the occultation would be just too low to observe. To John Bolton, who was then director at Parkes, the answer was simple: he arranged to dig a ditch around the telescope and remove some of the steelwork of the dish so that it would go lower! Furthermore, Bolton, who had a strong interest in these new quasars, took charge of operations.

The occultation started at 5.45 p.m. (local time) on 5 August and continued over teatime. By just after 7 p.m. it was known that the experiment had been a complete success, and the "occulters" looked forward to a delayed meal. Unfortunately the celebrating staff outside the telescope had scoffed the lot! More data were taken in

---

[1] This strange name indicates that it is the 273rd object in the Third Catalogue made at Cambridge, which we mentioned above.

October but the position of the Moon meant that a complete occulation couldn't be observed.

The successful occultations confirmed beyond all doubt that the radio source 3C273 was a bright 13th magnitude star-like object. But better optical pictures revealed that if it *was* a star, it was a most unusual one since it had a jet protruding from one side. The strangest feature, though, only became apparent when an optical spectrum was obtained. The Dutch-American astronomer Maarten Schmidt used the Mt Palomar telescope to get a spectrum of the new object which showed a blue continuum of energy, dominated by strong emission lines which corresponded to no known elements (see next chapter). It took many days and talks with several colleagues before Schmidt realized the answer. The lines were indeed of common elements, such as hydrogen: but they had been heavily redshifted by about 16%. This, of course, was not an astoundingly large redshift for a faint galaxy. But it was quite unprecedented for a bright star-like object.

3C273 was the first **quasar** to be discovered. At a redshift of 0.16, it seemed clear that this object must lie far outside our galaxy and must therefore be very luminous indeed. Actually, in retrospect, it is surprising that a spectrum had not been taken earlier. The accurate radio position obtained at Parkes was really not needed. The previously available position was perfectly good enough to suggest that the 13th magnitude "star" *might* be the correct identification. And to take a spectrum of an object this bright was quite easy, even with the insensitive spectrographs of the early 1960s. Perhaps it's an example of the astronomers *expecting* the correct identification to be much fainter and so not bothering with the obvious. Incidentally, the name "quasar" is derived from the words quasi-stellar-radio-source, since the earliest quasars were all radio sources and "looked like" stars. We now know that many quasars are not easily detectable radio sources at all and some people prefer the name "Quasi-Stellar Objects" (or QSO's). For the moment, however, we shall stick with the more popular appellation "quasars".

After the discovery of 3C273, several other flat-spectrum radio sources were identified with star-like objects and their optical spectra obtained. They, too, were recognized as objects of high redshift, following the vital clue provided by the 3C273 experience. Soon these redshifts exceeded 2, far greater than the highest known values for radio galaxies.

From the start, however, these high redshifts presented serious problems. Bright apparent magnitudes and very large distances implied extremely high luminosities. But how could such energy have originated in small, star-like objects? Were they some sort of compact exploding galaxy? And what was the importance of the jet-like structure seen in 3C273 and, as time went on, in a few other objects? These problems were compounded not long after when it was discovered that several of the new quasars were varying in the amounts of their optical and radio radiation over periods of time of a few weeks or so. Astronomers knew that this implied that the size of the emitting region must be very small. Let's see why.

Consider a large cluster of stars which is roughly spherical and has a radius, R, about 10 lightyears in size (see Fig. 11.3). This value would be typical of a globular cluster, although we will imagine that our cluster is a bit more smoothly spread out than the stars in a typical globular are. Furthermore, we will also assume that the cluster is very much farther away from us than its own size: in this way we can avoid some tricky, but not very interesting, mathematics. We will show that the *total* light from this cluster cannot change appreciably on a time scale of less than about 10 years.

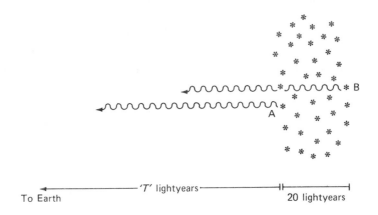

Fig. 11.3 — Light from an extended astronomical object is smeared out over a period of time corresponding to the time taken for light to travel across the object. In this example, light from variations in star B arrives 20 years after that from variations in star A even though both objects changed their brightness at the same time.

First imagine that all the stars in the cluster are all brightening and fading, not at random, but in synchronization. We don't have to worry *why* they are varying together, but we'll just ask what we see.

Consider the light leaving the parts of the cluster that are nearest to us. This light is radiated in all directions, but the only direction that concerns us is the one towards the Earth. The energy must travel for a time T, typically many thousands of years, before we see it. Only then do we notice that these "near-side" stars have brightened (or faded). On the other hand the light from the far side of the cluster has a longer journey to travel. It must travel not only for a time T but also the extra time needed to travel across the cluster, which is 20 years in our case. Thus, although all the stars may have brightened at the same time in reality, this brightening gets "smeared out" over about 20 years as observed by us. But what happens if we take the much more realistic case of stars brightening and fading at random? It is clear that the true, aggregate variation must be less than the variation in total light when the stars are in synchronization. Furthermore, we still have the effect of smearing caused by receiving information from the far side of the cluster later than the near side. Thus the light variations we observe will be even less than in the previous case and can still not occur faster than 20 years.

The above argument is very general. No information, including radio waves or light, can travel at a speed greater than the fundamental velocity ("speed of light"). This implies that no object can dramatically change its appearance on a time scale much less than the **crossing time**; i.e. the time taken for light to travel across it. The only reason we are not aware of this effect much more in everyday life, is that most objects are so small that light takes only thousandths of millionths of seconds to cross them.

The previous argument and the observed fast variations in the light from the quasars showed that the emitting regions were less than a few lightyears in diameter. This posed a serious problem: what energy process could equal the power of a whole galaxy but be contained in a region a thousand million times smaller in volume? We shall return to these problems in Chapters 14 and 15. For the moment, though, we shall look at how the first handful of quasars turned into hundreds.

The Radio Approach

By the mid-1960s, a few quasars had been discovered simply by looking for strangely coloured stars on photographic plates. But by far the most efficient method was still by using radio telescopes. Radio observatories around the world began the job of surveying the skies to look for more of these strange objects.

One of the most important of these new radio surveys was made at Parkes in central New South Wales using the 64-metre radiotelescope owned by the CSIRO. We shall look at this work in some detail, since it provided the prototype for many of the techniques which are still used at other observatories. The Parkes Survey began in 1967 and concluded around 1980. By then almost all the southern sky had been surveyed at the "search" frequency of 2700 MHz and complete information for all but the weakest sources had been obtained at the higher frequency of 5000 MHz. One of the many "spin-offs" from this massive project was the discovery and identification of over a 1000 quasars.

To start with, the telescope was scanned slowly backwards and forwards along adjoining lines over the area of the sky being surveyed, rather like a farmer ploughing a field. Any radio sources in this portion of the sky would cause a "blip" in the receiving electronics. By noting the position of the telescope at the time of the blip, an approximate location for each source was found. The painstaking work of cataloguing all the blips or potential sources was greatly assisted by computers.

Although a survey done in this way was good enough to show that there was probably a source *near* a particular position, it was not good enough to fix the position of the source accurately. It was therefore necessary to return to the approximate positions of all the potential sources and to scan through them in two directions at right angles in order to improve their positions to an accuracy of around 10 arcseconds. In this way, a large catalogue of many thousands of sources covering the whole sky was built up over the years.

When the sources had been accurately positioned, the next part of the task began. This required the vicinity of the position of the radio source to be examined on optical sky survey photographs. Unfortunately, one of the main problems facing southern astronomers for many years was the lack of a good, deep optical survey of the southern skies. While northern astronomers had the excellent Palomar Schmidt Sky Survey, southern astronomers were essentially "blind". Certainly surveys had been made with small telescopes, but these were relatively "shallow" and only showed objects brighter than the 12th magnitude — still far too faint to allow many radio sources to be identified.

Bolton initiated a new sky survey at Palomar to reach as far as possible into the southern skies. Unfortunately this would mean that the Schmidt telescope would spend most of its time pointing down in the south towards an horizon bespangled with man-made lights. It was clear that the new plates would not be as good as

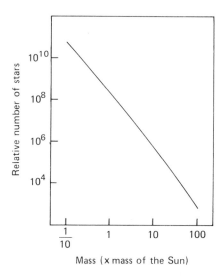

Fig. 11.4 — The relative numbers of stars in our galaxy (per unit mass range) as a function of their mass.

those for the more northern parts of the survey. But they would be a lot better than nothing and, together with the more northerly parts of the Palomar Sky Survey plates, they enabled Bolton and his colleagues to identify many of their newly discovered radio sources. This identification work accelerated greatly in the mid-1970s as the new United Kingdom Schmidt Telescope in New South Wales began its massive deep survey of the southern heavens.

The first step in making an optical identification of a radio source was to produce an "overlay". This is a small map of the known bright stars in the immediate vicinity of the radio source position; it also contains a marked position for the source. Producing these overlays on transparent plastic sheets to exactly the right scale was a tedious and exacting job, ideally suited to a computer. The overlay was then carefully placed on top of the optical photographs and the vicinity of the radio source examined for any evidence of a galaxy or quasar. About 50% of the radio sources investigated at Parkes led to an identification. Of these identifications about one-half were "fuzzy" radio galaxies and about one-half star-like objects which might be quasars.

But what was the probability that the star-like object was, in fact, just an ordinary star, coincidentally near the radio position? An optical spectrum would settle the question; but optical spectra require large amounts of time to obtain. Certainly it was impossible to get spectra for *all* the new suggested identifications. In answering the question, the colour of the star-like source turned out to be crucial. In order to see why, let's look at some of the properties of stars in our galaxy.

For reasons which are not totally clear, but which yet are indubitably true, it seems that the processes by which nature makes things always produce many more small things than large things. For example, when we shatter a fragile piece of pottery into many pieces by throwing it at the floor, there are almost always more small bits than large bits. So too in the universe. There are far more small stars in our galaxy than large ones and far more small galaxies in the universe than large ones. Fig. 11.4 shows the best available data for the total number of stars in our galaxy. Each group represents a different range of mass. There are several thousand times more stars in the range 1-10 times the mass of our Sun than in the range of 100 - 1000 solar masses. Interestingly, the *total* mass in each range is nowhere near as different — perhaps that result holds the clue to the distribution process.

Putting aside this interesting point, let us return to our main theme: the very different numbers of galactic stars in each mass range implies very different numbers of stars with a particular colour. Remember that the smallest stars are also the coolest and thus the reddest (see Chapter 12). On the other hand, the stars with the largest masses are the hottest and hence the bluest. We thus understand why there are many more red stars in the sky than blue stars.

The fact that there are many more red stars in our galaxy than blue stars does not, however, necessarily imply that red stars will be commoner on our photographic plates. An important complication has to be borne in mind: blue stars are intrinsically more luminous than red stars and can thus be seen to much greater distances. This is just the argument we met in talking about observational bias in Chapter 4. It means that as we look to greater distances we sample a greater volume of space and thus we include more stars. Of course this argument supposes that there always *will* be stars no matter how far away from the Sun we look. Clearly this cannot be true when the distances involved are larger than the size of our galaxy.

Allowing for this complication in calculating the expected numbers of stars on a plate is difficult, but it can be done. The result is that we do indeed expect many more faint red stars on deep photographic plates than blue stars. The importance of this result lies in that the chance of making a mistake in identifying a radio source with a faint, star-like object is greater if the object in question is red rather than if it is blue.

The average galaxy is rather red, as we remarked in Chapter 2, because it normally contains many more red stars than blue ones. On its own, this might suggest that galaxies would be easy to mis-identify with stars. On the other hand, all except the most distant galaxies are discernibly "fuzzy" and are generally quite easy to pinpoint if the radio position is good. (See Fig. 11.5.)

Potential quasar identifications were quite different. In general, they didn't show any nebulosity and were perfectly star-like. On the other hand, most of the quasars known in the mid-1960s were very blue indeed. This meant that there was little chance of confusing them with faint stars. Thus, even if a radio source position was quite poor, a quasar identification would often be claimed providing there was a strongly blue star near the position[1]. Before going further, though, let's ask why

---

[1] Perhaps the perspicacious reader can see a problem here? It was one that was to lead to serious problems a few years later. If there is a bias acting in favour of astronomers making identifications with very blue quasars, then perhaps it isn't surprising that most of the newly discovered quasars were blue. This, in turn, reinforced the existing dogma that all quasars were blue objects.

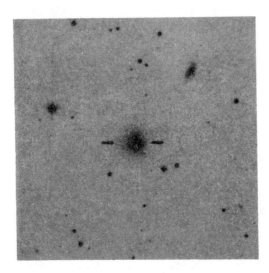

Fig. 11.5 — An example of a finding chart for a galaxy identified with a faint radio source. The galaxy's position is marked by the two horizontal lines. Note that the galaxy appears fuzzy, unlike the majority of the surrounding objects which are galactic stars.

the earliest discovered quasars were blue and also explain exactly what the astronomer means by this word.

In ordinary speech, a blue object is one that emits more blue light than any other colour. Similarly, to the optical astronomer, a blue star is one that emits more blue light than an ordinary white star[1]. The colours of stars can be determined quite quickly using photographic plates which have been exposed using special filters sensitive to two different colours.

Let's consider how these filters work. The purpose of an optical telescope is to collect and focus light. If we place a photographic plate at the telescope's focus, then this light exposes grains on the plate which can be later developed into permanent images. Now consider what happens if we place a red-coloured filter in the converging beam of light. By definition, a red filter is one which only allows red light to pass through it (or, at least, one which *preferentially* allows red light to pass through it). In this case, the red stars in the field will expose more grains than the blue stars in the field and their developed images will be brighter. On the other

---

[1] This approximate statement is sufficient for our purposes here. More precisely the colours of stars are defined by stating their **spectral type**. The letters **O,B,A,F,G,K,M** are used to describe a sequence of stars of decreasing "blueness" and increasing "redness" as measured by the distribution of continuum radiation and the presence or absence of certain spectral lines. Subdivisions of the basic scheme are obtained by using the digits **0** to **9**. Thus a star of spectral type **B5** is only slightly bluer than one of type **B7** but both are much bluer than a star of type **F5**, for example.

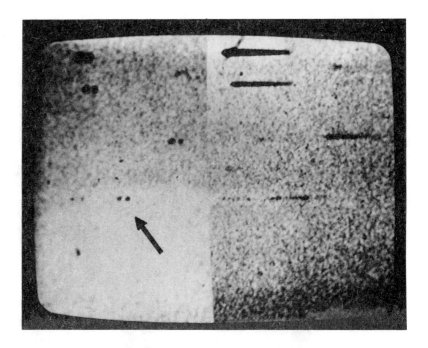

Fig. 11.6 — "Two colour" picture of stars.

hand, blue stars will have relatively faint images because little of their light will have been passed by the filter. See Fig. 11.6.

Now let's expose a second plate under identical conditions but using a blue filter. In this case, the blue star images will be brighter than the red star images. By carefully comparing images on both plates, the colours of the stars can be estimated.

Of course, checking these relative brightnesses can be a very time-consuming job. In the past, the most obvious way of lightening the burden was by using a **blink machine**, rather like a gigantic double microscope. The optics of these machines were so arranged that two photographic plates could be viewed at the same time but superimposed through the same eyepiece. After careful adjustment, the images of the two plates were brought into alignment and then a "flapper" was placed alternately in the light beams from the two individual plates so that the eyes looked first at one plate and then the other. A star that was equally bright on both plates would appear to stay steady while the flapping was going on. But a star that was either abnormally blue or red would appear to "blink".

Unfortunately this system suffered many disadvantages. First, the two plates were difficult to align properly: the plate scales (i.e. the distances between the same stars on the plate) would often be slightly different, resulting in slightly "blurred" images. Secondly, the plates had to have exactly the right exposure in order that stars that were neither red nor blue did *not* appear to blink. Finally — and perhaps most importantly — the astronomer (or his unfortunate assistant) had to spend many, many long hours hunched up over an eyepiece. A sure recipe for bad backs and strained eyes in old age!

It was clear that something much better was needed. The first radical improvement came with the building by John Bolton of his Automatic Measuring Machine (see Fig. 11.7).

Fig. 11.7 — The photographic plate measuring machine built by J. G. Bolton.

This machine used two TV cameras each looking at one of the two plates. The great advantage it possessed over the blink machine, however, was that the images could be combined electronically. This meant that if one of the images was electronically made *negative* then an subtraction of the two plates could be viewed on the TV screen. Neutral objects would then appear grey, while red or blue objects would stand out as white or black. Furthermore, the operator could sit back in a comfortable chair and view the images in comfort. If needed, the plate scales could also easily be adjusted electronically, the data images could be stored and recalled using video recorders and the data could even be "digitized" and stored in computers for later analysis. This last step has been developed extensively recently in the modern plate "engines", such as **COSMOS** at the Royal Observatory in Edinburgh and Kibblewhite's automatic plate measuring machine at the University of Cambridge.

By varying the relative amounts of brightness in the signals from the two TV cameras it is possible to adjust the final images on the TV screen so that they balance for almost any desired star colour. In practice, it was often found best to slightly displace the two images on the screen so that they could both be seen clearly. Fig. 11.8 shows a typical result with the blue image at the top and the red

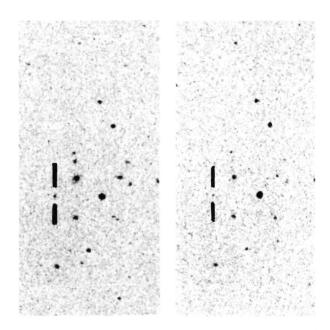

Fig. 11.8 — The appearance of the distant quasar PKS 2126-15 taken through a blue-sensitive filter (left hand) and red-sensitive filter (right hand). The position of the object is indicated by the vertical lines. Notice that the quasar appears considerably brighter on the blue plate than the red, showing that it is intrinsically a "blue" object.

image at the bottom. Note that the quasar in the picture (marked with an arrow) appears roughly equally bright on the print, while the ordinary stars (which are red) appear fainter on the top image.

If a quasar *is* blue though, might it not then be confused with a blue star? Yes indeed, it may. Fortunately, as we explained earlier, blue stars are comparatively rare. But the possibility of mis-identification is always present in looking for the faint optical counterparts of the radio quasars and the radio astronomer must take several things into account. First, he must decide if the measured radio position is sufficiently close to the stellar object (we'll stop calling it a star!). In doing so, he must bear in mind the flux density of the source, since a weak source will have larger positional errors than a strong source. Next, he must consider whether or not the source was extended — that is, had it a discernible angular size as measured by the radio telescope? If it *had* then, even though an accurate radio position is available for the source, that position may not be coincident with the optical position. Such a source may well be a radio galaxy with extended radio lobes. Lastly, the astronomer must take account of the colour of the possible identification, as we mentioned earlier: if the identification is with a *blue* star, then it is much more likely to be correct.

Bearing all of what we have said above in mind, a question may have suggested itself to the reader. Why is it necessary to do a radio survey at all? Why not just look for blue objects on photographic plates? Such surveys have indeed been made, as we shall mention below. However, they are a comparatively tedious way to find new quasars. Although we said earlier that the fraction of blue stars visible on photographic plates was small, unfortunately the total *number* is still enormous. Consider, for example, a survey which is perhaps trying to find about 100 quasars brighter than a limit of the 20th magnitude. To do this, we must survey about 25 square degrees of sky or about the size of 1 large Schmidt telescope survey plate. Such a plate will typically contain about 45,000 stars brighter than the 20th magnitude. True, only about 1500 of them will be *blue* stars; but to take spectra with a large optical telescope of over a thousand objects to test whether in fact these objects are quasars is a very large task indeed. To see why, consider the likely amount of time that a well-respected optical astronomer is likely to win on a large telescope.

First the time must be applied for by submitting an application to a selection committee. If the project is not thought worthwhile, then no time will be allocated at all. Even if the project gets the "nod of approval", the pressure of other applications to the committee will mean that the astronomer (and any colleagues) are unlikely to be allocated more than about four nights in any given quarter of the year. This is because only about ten nights of any month are suitable for taking spectra of faint objects: for the remainder of the month, the Moon is too bright. Furthermore, the time allocation committee is likely to be faced with over fifty applications for the "dark-time" in the three months in a typical round of applications. The observing team that wins four of these precious thirty nights a quarter is fortunate indeed! Certainly it would be most unusual to win four nights a quarter on a *regular* basis. And even if the group does, it is likely that the survey region they are studying is only available at night for about six months. During the rest of the year, the Sun is in the way.

But even if our group does get their four nights, their problems are only just beginning. Unlike his radioastronomical counterpart, the optical astronomer cannot observe 24 hours a day: the daytime is useless, except for checking out his equipment and catching up on badly needed sleep. On average, only about nine hours each night are suitable for faint-object work. Next, there is the ever-present worry of the weather. Some large telescopes around the world average about 80% usable observing hours while others fall to nearer 50%. In any case, the odds are in favour of losing a significant fraction of the precious scheduled time. Third, there is always the possibility of equipment breakdown — delicate electronic equipment does not take kindly to extremes of cold and heat ,and exposure to the atmosphere. In fact it's amazing that so little time is lost to this cause — it's a rare observatory that is out of action for more than 5% of all observing hours. Lastly, and often forgotten, it is impossible to arrange an observing night so that all the time is spent "sucking photons" on the desired programme objects. Calibration stars have to be measured and the telescope has to be driven from object to object. All this takes time, and it is rare for the actual total "exposure" times to exceed 50% of even a clear, eventless, observing night session. Taking all this into account, our astronomer is unlikely to have amassed more than a total of 25 hours' worth of exposures in any given year!

And how much time is needed to get a good spectrum of a faint quasar? Since most of the programme objects will be around 18th magnitude, the time required on a large 4 m telescope with the best modern spectrographic detectors will be about 60 to 90 minutes per object. This means that our astronomer is unlikely to have obtained good data on more than 20 or so quasars in any year. Furthermore, this number may well be less if a few objects had indeterminate spectra the first time around and required the observations to be repeated. Bearing all this in mind we can now understand that it is hardly feasible to get spectra for 1,000 blue stars!

Despite these formidable difficulties, several searches have been made using the shape of the continuum radiation to discover non-radio emitting quasars. Because many quasars are strongly blue in colour, photographic plates taken through blue and red filters can be used to pick them out. At the brighter magnitudes (say less than 16th) many of these objects in fact turn out to be stars, just as we feared above. But as we look at the fainter blue "stars", we are gaze out beyond the limits of our own galaxy and find a much greater fraction of true quasars. Even more successful results have been obtained by using three different colour filters, since then it becomes easier to discern quasars from confusing stars. Nevertheless, most astronomers remain sceptical of this method. In the end, there is no substitute for getting an optical spectrum to finally decide whether the potential "ident" is indeed a quasar or not. In the next chapter we shall look at how such spectra are produced, what they have to tell us and see how non-radio emitting quasars can be discovered by other optical methods.

12

Atoms, Spectra and Quasars

Over a cup of morning coffee at most astronomical observatories around the world, you can hear some amazing things: talk of galaxies exploding, each containing thousands of millions of stars and planets, talk of stars rushing through space at hundreds of kilometres each second. And talk of the formation of the whole universe in a Big Bang! Mind-boggling stuff if we stop and think about it! But, more astounding than any of these things is surely the fact that we puny human beings can actually comprehend even a small fraction of the universe!

At first glance it would seem quite out of the question that we could ever know about things far away from Earth. We are almost certain to be technologically incapable of making a voyage in person outside our solar system until the next century. Even with space probes, we will find gathering information difficult. And a journey to other stars, even those in our galaxy, is surely far in the future. How then can we know so much?

The answer lies in the versatile nature of light and our fairly thorough understanding of its nature and how it interacts with matter. Those are, of course, dangerous words. Words that I'm sure the physicists of the twenty-first century will smile about! Even so, from the careful analysis of the light a star emits we can tell its temperature, its velocity of motion towards or away from us, its speed of rotation, what elements its surface is made of and how much of each of them it contains, and much more. Furthermore, by using well-established laws of physics, we can go on to deduce the star's mass, size, and age. Light has been truly described as "the vibrating messenger"!

Atoms and molecules

Matter exists throughout most of the universe in the form of about 100 elements. But most of these elements are very rare, making up a negligible fraction of the total mass of the universe. Important elements, such as hydrogen and helium, number only about a dozen. Fig. 12.1 shows the relative importance, on a cosmic scale, of some of the commoner ones. Of course no-one has actually made accurate measurements of all the material bodies in the universe. But there are ways of accurately estimating the relative importance of each element and we believe the information is basically correct. (See Fig. 12.1.)

Here on Earth, most of the matter we know exists in the form of **molecules**. These are small groups of atoms — often of different elements — bound together by atomic forces. Even the oxygen and nitrogen in the air we breathe is not made up of atomic oxygen and nitrogen. At the relatively low temperatures and high gas

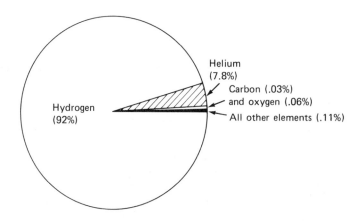

Fig. 12.1 — The relative abundance of elements in the universe.The numbers refer to the percentage of total numbers of atoms. The proportions of elements other than hydrogen, helium, oxygen and carbon are too small to show individually in this diagram.

densities which occur in our atmosphere, the atoms find "mates" and stick together as molecules.

But in space, things are different, because gas densities are typically much lower. For example, a molecule of oxygen may break up into two atoms, each likely to be travelling at several kilometres per second. Because of this speed and the low density, each "divorced" oxygen atom is unlikely to find another oxygen atom "mate" — at least for a long while. It therefore remains an atom. In regions of space where the gas density is higher and chance encounters occur more frequently — such as in the stars — another effect prevents the existence of molecules. The high temperatures occurring throughout the Sun, for example, are sufficient to break apart the weak bonding forces in molecules, again resulting in atoms.

More important than either of these effects, however, is the fact that molecules are easily destroyed by ultraviolet radiation. And space is permeated by ultraviolet radiation. When such a photon hits a molecule, it will split the molecule apart. One of the few safe refuges for molecules is on the surfaces of planets where cool, dense, shielded conditions prevail. Another is on the surfaces of dust grains which are to be found in the dense clouds of cool interstellar gas constituting the raw material from which the stars form. Certainly, here on Earth, we live in a very un-typical, un-atomic place!

The modern picture of an atom is very complex, resulting from intensive research by physicists over 50 years. However, we'll let you into a secret: most astronomers rarely need to envisage an atom as anything more complicated than a few minute balls whizzing around each other! More accurately, this picture is referred to as the **Bohr model** of an atom. With only slight modifications, it is the model proposed by the Danish physicist Niels Bohr in the 1920s. Let's look at it in more detail.

At the centre of every atom is a **nucleus** consisting of both **protons** and, in general, **neutrons**. For our purposes, the neutrons can be thought of as incredibly small indestructible balls with masses around 10^{-24} of a gram. The protons are essentially similar except that they have a positive electrical charge on them. The overall size of the nucleus is less than one million millionth of a centimetre, within which the protons are held together against their natural tendency to repel by a force known as the **strong nuclear interaction**. Orbiting around and far from the nucleus at a distance of about one hundred millionth of a centimetre are minute negatively charged particles called **electrons**. These electrons are only about $1/2000$ of the mass of the protons but have exactly the same amount of charge (except that it is negative).

Anybody who remembers their elementary physics and that opposite charges attract may be prompted to ask, "Yes — but why don't the electrons fall down into the nucleus?" The brief answer is that they don't because they are orbiting around the nucleus — just as the Moon moves around the Earth. The electrons *are* falling all the time — but their sideways motion keeps them moving in a circle. On a slightly deeper level, though, we *do* have a problem. Electrons "falling around" nuclei are being accelerated. One of the basic laws of physics says that accelerating electrons must radiate energy. In fact it is exactly this emission of light and radio waves from electrons accelerated in distant celestial bodies that makes observational astronomy possible.

Why then don't electrons lose energy and slowly fall into the nucleus of the atom? The simple (but uninformative) answer is that they don't because electrons and atoms are not like Moons and Earths. Their "physics" is different, and our simple Bohr picture of the atom breaks down. However, if we can just *accept* the difference as a fact of life (which is what atomic physicists do, although they use a mass of mathematics to disguise the fact!) then we can still use the Bohr model for everything we shall need to understand in this book.

Spectral lines

One question which occurs when talking about the make-up of atoms is, "What decides an electron's distance from the nucleus?" In the case of the Moon-Earth system or the Earth-Sun system, the orbiting body could, in principle, lie at any distance from the central object. But this is not true of an atom. As an electron moves away from the nucleus, it gains more energy, and the laws of atomic physics dictate that only certain well-specified distances and well-specified energies are possible. In order to move from one distance — or **energy level** — to the next, the atom must either gain or lose a precisely specified, **quantized** amount of energy. See Fig. 12.2. Small changes of distance from the nucleus, corresponding to slight changes of energy, are not permitted.

Hydrogen (in the atomic state) consists of a nucleus containing just one proton with one electron whizzing around it. In the cold depths of space, far from the stars, this electron will be in its most tightly bound, lowest-energy state. See Fig. 12.3. It cannot fall down into the nucleus because of the reasons mentioned above. This lowest energy state is referred to by astronomers as the **ground state**. Above the ground state are a very large number of levels having higher

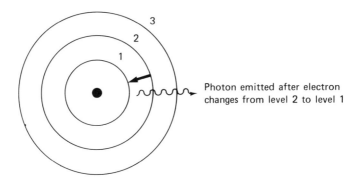

Photon emitted after electron
changes from level 2 to level 1

Fig. 12.2 — Energy levels in the Bohr atom.

energy. If the atom absorbs energy, the electron can move up to one of these levels until, finally, it gains so much energy that the electron leaves the atom altogether. Under these conditions, the atom is said to be *ionized*

Once in a while, though, our hydrogen atom may bump into another atom. Or it may get close enough to a star to absorb radiation and "warm-up" a bit. In either case the result is the same: the electron becomes **excited**[1]. This means that the electron moves up from the ground state and into the next more energetic state. Once there, one of two things might happen. First — and by far the most probable for an isolated atom — it may "sink back" into its ground state. To do this, it must lose energy by emitting a photon of wavelength equal to 1216 Ångstroms[2]. Before doing so, though, it will have spent about one hundred-millionth of a second in the higher level, a comparatively long period by atomic standards. During this time, the second possibility may occur: another photon might come along and "knock" the electron down again. This will occur when there are plenty of photons about. Thirdly, another atom might bang into our excited hydrogen atom and cause the electron to fall back to the ground state. This often happens when there are are plenty of atoms about but radiation is in short supply. For any of these three

---

[1] What a marvellous word! But it really is the one astrophysicists use.

[2] The position of a line in the spectrum of a star or galaxy is measured by its **wavelength**, properly expressed in **nanometres** (abbreviation **nm**) or one thousand-millionth of a metre. Much commoner in astronomy, however, is the older unit, the **Ångstrom**, which is ten times smaller. Thus the approximate wavelength of the maximum emission of light from the Sun can be written as 500 nanometres or 5000 Ångstroms.

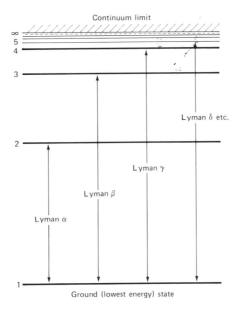

Fig. 12.3 — Energy levels for the hydrogen atom showing that the Lyman lines are produced by transitions between the ground, or lowest, energy state and an upper level. The continuum limit corresponds to a transition with enough energy to ionize the atom, that is to liberate the electron completely from the hydrogen atom.

possibilities, the net result is the same — an "extra" photon of wavelength equal to 1216 Ångstroms is emitted. This radiation produces one of the most important **spectral lines** in astronomy, the **Lyman** α (alpha) line.

Hydrogen can also produce other spectral lines: instead of our atom being excited into the next more energetic level, it may "skip" an energy state and go straight into the third level. If it now falls back all the way to the ground state, then radiation of around 1026 Ångstroms is emitted, called Lyman β (beta). In similar ways, spectral lines of Lyman γ, δ (gamma, delta) etc. are produced. See Fig. 12.3. Other elements can produce spectral lines in a manner very similar to hydrogen. The spectrum of the Sun, for example, contains thousands of lines of almost all the known elements. These lines appear as narrow dark "bands" in the solar spectrum, called **absorption lines,** and we now understand how they are produced.

Radiation from the solar interior is originally produced in the form of **X-rays,** as befits an interior temperature of around 10 million degrees Centigrade. By the time this radiation reaches the solar surface, it has been transformed into a near-"democratic" mix of colours. Yellow light is strongest, red light is somewhat less intense and blue light is considerably weaker. Because of its colour, our Sun is known as a yellow dwarf star. Some stars, whose interior processing is different, appear blue, while others are red. In the surface layers of the Sun, some of the emerging light is absorbed by gas with electrons in the atoms jumping from a lower to a higher energy level. The light thus removed may be re-emitted. More usually, however, it is used up in making the atom move a little faster. Eventually this energy is passed on to other atoms by collisions, thus maintaining the high temperatures of the star's surface layers.

Instead of absorbing radiation, some other stars radiate extra light at certain wavelengths, causing their spectra to contain bright **emission lines** rather than dark lines. The production of either emission or absorption lines is a natural result of electromagnetic radiation passing through hot gas. Essentially, if the intervening gas is *hotter* than the gas responsible for producing the original radiation, then the intervening gas will *add* bright emission lines to the spectrum. If, on the other hand, the gas is *cooler* than the radiation, it will *subtract* radiation from the spectrum at certain frequencies producing absorption lines.

In order to see emission or absorption lines in an astronomical object, we must use a spectrograph, as we discussed in Chapter 2. This instrument essentially produces a graph of the amounts of energy at different wavelengths. Most objects throughout the universe, including such distant bodies as galaxies and quasars, also show a **continuum** in their spectrum. That is, a general level of emitted light in regions of the spectrum where there are no emission or absorption lines. We shall look at the processes that cause these continua later in the chapter. First, though, we shall see what happens when emitting atoms move about.

Atoms on the move

So far we have argued that spectral lines — either emission or absorption — will be produced in atoms whose electrons are changing from one energy level to another. We also said that the energy of these levels couldn't differ by arbitrary amounts. But what decides exactly how much energy each level has?

To find the answer would take us deep into atomic physics. However, for our present purpose, we can think of atoms and the electrons they contain as **resonant oscillators**. One form of resonant oscillator is familiar to us all: think about a swing in a children's playground. If the swing is pushed at exactly the right frequency (about once every four seconds in our all-too-tedious experience), it is easy to get it swinging quite high. It is extracting energy from the pusher (as every parent knows!) and increasing the energy of the child and swing. But if the pushing is at even slightly the wrong frequency, then the swing stutters, stops and starts, and nothing much results.

It is much the same with atoms. An electron in an atom can be caused to resonate by absorbing energy from radiation of just the right frequency. In turn, the oscillating electron loses energy by radiating at this same frequency. Depending on the intensity of the radiation and the state of the atom, the electron may gain more energy from the radiation than it loses or vice versa. On the other hand, radiation at the wrong frequency has little effect on the electron's oscillation. (Although, of course, it may be at the right frequency for a different sort of atom.) There is thus a close and exact correspondence between the wavelength of a spectral line and the structure of atoms of the element producing it.

Bearing this in mind, we can understand the concern felt by the early astronomical spectroscopists when they found that some stars showed lines at the "wrong" wavelengths.

First we must clearly understand that the "wrong" wavelengths and frequencies *cannot* be caused by atoms emitting light at too low a frequency or too high a frequency: the laws of physics strongly forbid "quickly-emitting" atoms and "slowly-emitting" atoms. As we said above, an electron bound to an atom in a particular way can only respond to a precise frequency of radiation. Putting this another way, each element in a particular state of ionization has its "trade-mark wavelength" that no other element is allowed to "use". Furthermore, interaction of light with gas in interstellar space could not explain the observations. When a

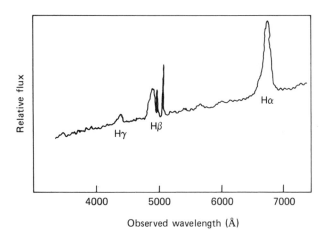

Fig. 12.4 — Schematic representation of the emission spectrum of the exploding galaxy M87.

photon is absorbed by a gas atom, it is lost altogether (in heating up the gas), it is re-emitted at the same wavelength, or it is emitted at a very different wavelength. The changes that are actually observed in stars and galaxies are small systematic changes of *all* the spectral lines in the same direction and by the same *fractional* amount.

To clarify this, let's look at an example. Consider the giant galaxy M87. Measurements in laboratories here on Earth show us that the main visible lines of hydrogen occur at wavelengths of 6562 Å, 4861 Å and 4340 Å. But in the spectrum of M87 we actually find lines which have strengths very similar to the laboratory hydrogen lines but at wavelengths of 6589 Å, 4881 Å and 4358 Å. (See Fig. 12.4.) This shift of the lines to the higher wavelength end of the spectrum can be described by saying that all the lines are shifted by 0.41%. Note that this is not the same number of Ångstroms for each line, but the same *proportional* amount.

To find an explanation for this effect, we must turn to the work of the German musician **Wolfgang Doppler** and a phenomenon discovered by him in connection with sound waves. Consider a car approaching you along a road at high speed, blowing its horn. As the car approaches, the pitch of the horn's note may be fairly high at first but then drops as it passes and recedes. This is known as the **Doppler effect** for sound waves. Fig. 12.5 shows what happens. As the car approaches, the sound waves are "squashed-up"; and, as it recedes, the sound is "stretched-out". Only at the precise moment when the car is passing, will we hear the tone which we would hear if the car were stationary.

To understand this important effect a little better, let's consider an analogy. Pretend that we are standing up in a small rowing boat, throwing apples to a friend

Fig. 12.5 — The Doppler effect for the sound of a car's horn approaching a stationary observer. The sound waves bunch up ahead of the car and are spread out behind it.

who is also standing in a similar rowing boat a few metres away. Furthermore, we have agreed that we will throw apples to our friend precisely at every second. Now, if the boats are stationary, our friend will also receive — we won't say catch! — our apples every second precisely. But if his boat is moving away from ours, the rate of arrival of apples will be slightly *slower* than once a second. Conversely, if he is moving towards us, then the apples will arrive slightly *faster* than every second.

The rate of arrival of the apples is analogous to the rate of arrival of the high pressure peaks of the sound waves in our car experiment and to the reception of photons of light (or radio waves) from astronomical bodies. If a star is approaching us, then we will receive photons at a higher frequency than that at which they were emitted. Conversely, if the star is receding, we shall receive photons at a lower frequency.

But, we hear the reader complain, didn't Einstein say that light is always received at the same speed, no matter how fast the emitting or receiving body is moving? Yes, that's true (see Chapter 6), which is why the apple experiment is only an analogy. A more correct explanation follows from the equations of Special Relativity, which describes how lengths and times change when viewed by moving bodies. The net result is the *same as if* the waves bunched up or stretched out. But in fact they do neither. For our purposes, however, it won't matter. What does matter is that we know how the Doppler effect works, both qualitatively and quantitatively.

For velocities, V, which are much smaller than the speed of light, c (about 300,000 km/s), the shifted frequency of a spectral line is given by

$$\nu_{shifted} = \nu_{emitted} \cdot (1 + V/c)$$

or, for wavelengths,

$$\lambda_{shifted} = \lambda_{emitted} \cdot (1 - V/c)$$

where the velocity is reckoned positive if away from us. When the velocities involved become comparable to the speed of light, then a more complex equation is needed. This, so-called, "relativistic equation" is of little use in astronomy and must certainly not be used in discussing redshifts on the cosmological scale (see Chapter 8).

A second result of the Doppler phenomenon is more subtle: the fact that the photons arrive less often when the emitting object is receding from us also implies that we will receive less energy in a given period of time (one second, say). The energy received per second is a measure of the apparent brightness of the radiation and so a receding body will look dimmer than it would if it were stationary.

The Doppler effect has been used extensively to determine how stars and the closest galaxies are moving through space. Furthermore, radio observations can be interpreted using Doppler shifted frequencies to show how our own galaxy is rotating

Radio, too

A hydrogen atom whose electron is in the ground state can not emit optical radiation. There is, however, one way in which the electron can change its energy by a small amount. Both electrons and the nucleus have a property know as **spin**. We can think of this as analogous to the daily spin of the Earth and the 26-day spin of the Sun. The electron can be spinning either in the same sense as the nucleus or oppositely. If it is spinning the *same* way it has just slightly *less* energy than if it were spinning the other way. This spin is of crucial importance to radio astronomers because the electron spin can change. When it does, our hydrogen atom either emits or absorbs some radio energy at 21cm[1]. Since most of the universe is in this cold state — and because cold neutral hydrogen emits no other sort of energy — radio observations of the spin-flip radiation are the only way we have of detecting most of the vast clouds of interstellar hydrogen. When we point our radiotelescopes towards the plane of our galaxy, we do indeed see large amounts of 21 cm radiation, but at frequencies slightly shifted by the Doppler effect.

These observations have shown us that we live in a large rotating galaxy. Near the centre of our galaxy, the rotation velocities are relatively small, only a few tens of kilometres per second. But, as we move out towards the position of the Sun, we find that the velocities increase up to several hundreds of kilometres per second in our neighbourhood.

---

[1] As an aside we should say that in calling the radiation just "21 cm radiation", we are doing it an injustice – the frequency of the hydrogen ground state, "spin-flip" radiation is one of the most precisely known quantities in the whole of physics. Its accurate value is 1420.40575168460 MHz !

Continuum processes

So far we have discussed atoms and the spectral line radiation they produce. But the majority of radiation emitted by astronomical bodies does not have its energy concentrated into a narrow band but spread out over a broad range of wavelengths. This energy is known as **continuum radiation** and it can be produced by a variety of processes.

All objects in the universe are constantly absorbing and radiating energy to some extent and over a range of frequencies. This occurs because all bodies at any temperature above absolute zero contain electrons which "jiggle" about. According to the laws of physics, jiggling electrons must radiate energy, which is how all radiation is produced in the universe. The amount and type of radiation emitted depends on the average way in which the electrons jiggle: fast-moving, violent jiggles produce intense, high-frequency radiation. Small, slow jiggles produce long-wavelength, weaker radiation.

Now, the "violence" with which electrons (and atoms) jiggle in a body is just a measure of its temperature. Thus, hot bodies should emit high-frequency, strong radiation and cooler bodies weaker, low-frequency radiation.

The quantitative version of this idea is known as Planck's Law after the German physicist Max Planck. The form of the law is shown in Fig. 12.6. We can see the amounts of energy emitted by a body at 300 kelvins (typical of you or me — unless you're sitting in a very cold or hot room!), a body at 1000 kelvins (typical of the melting point of many metals) and 5000 kelvins (typical of the outer layers of the Sun and many other stars) Note that the curves are plotted on a logarithmic scale and for bodies all of the same size. The actual amount of energy emitted will depend on the total surface area of the body as well. Note, too, that a star like the Sun radiates the great majority of its energy in the optical part of the electromagnetic spectrum whilst a body at normal room temperatures (say, 300 K) radiates in the infrared. And, as we'll see in Chapter 17, most of the energy of background radiation in the universe is in the form of microwave, radio energy corresponding to a temperature of about 3 K.

But an object doesn't only radiate. If it did, then it would soon lose all its energy. For example, you and I are radiating at a rate of about 100 watts. If nothing replenished this energy, then we would get so cold that we would die after a mere 1000 seconds! Why don't we? The answer is, of course, that as well as emitting radiation we are normally also receiving it. Here in the gentle environment of the planet Earth, we receive energy at almost exactly the same rate as we radiate. On the few occasions that we don't — such as immersion for a long time in a freezing cold sea — then death quickly follows. Of course, not all the energy losses and gains on Earth are by radiative means, conduction plays a part. But in the depths of space, radiative transfer is by far the most important. And a body will cool down until it receives insufficient radiation to balance its energy losses.

Mathematically, the total radiation emitted by any body summed over all wavelengths is given by

$$energy\ rate\ =\ const\ .\ T^4$$

a relation known as **Stefan's Law**. Because this energy rate depends on the temperature to the fourth power, it will rise very quickly with increasing temperature and fall very quickly with decreasing temperature.

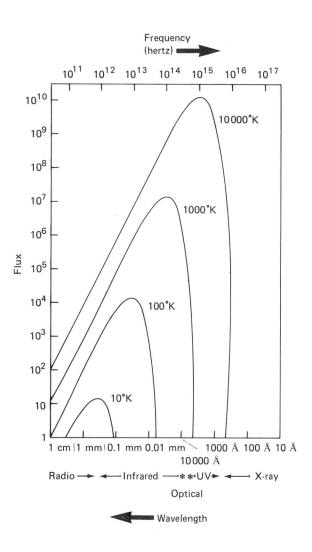

Fig. 12.6 — The Planck function for black bodies of different temperatures. Note that the curves are drawn logarithmically, that the peak of the curve moves to higher frequencies with increasing temperature and that the total energy (area under each curve) is far greater for higher temperatures than for lower temperatures.

To find the balance temperature that a body with a surface area A will attain when in a field of radiation of Q ergs per second per square cm, all we need to do is equate the incomings and the outgoings, as follows:

$$Q = E$$

or

$$Q . A = const . T^4 . A$$

In practice it is possible that the "A"s on the two sides of the previous equation may not be quite the same. For example, if we are talking about a planet — Earth, say — then it will be receiving radiation from only *one* side (the side nearest the Sun). On the other hand, because this energy becomes "well stirred up" owing to the Earth's atmosphere, it will be radiated equally from *all* parts of the surface. The difference is between an area of $2\pi R^2$ for the incoming radiation and an area of $4\pi R^2$ for the outgoing radiation — i.e. a factor of 2. Since, however, we will be taking a fourth root in calculating the balance temperature, this factor of 2 is not very important for a rough calculation.

The radiation has the form specified by Planck's law because the energy of the jiggling electrons in any body is governed by another law — the **Maxwell-Boltzman law**. Even in a body at a uniform temperature, not all the electrons will have the same amount of energy. The Maxwell-Boltzman law states the relative amounts of the total energy that the faster electrons in the body will have and the slower electrons will have.

Can objects have energy distributions different from Planck's law? Do all bodies at the same temperature have all their electrons jiggling in the same way? The answer to the second question is, "No". So far we have only discussed what is called thermal — or "random" — radiation. But there are other ways in which electrons can be accelerated and radiate.

The first of these is called **cyclotron radiation**, so named after a process that occurs in terrestrial "atom-smashing" machines. If a free electron (one *not* connected to an atom) encounters a magnetic field in space — perhaps one such as occurs naturally in sunspots on the surface of the Sun — then it will be made to move in a curve. Motion in a curve implies acceleration, and this acceleration causes the electron to radiate energy. The amount and frequency of the radiation depends only on the amount of the acceleration and this, in turn, depends only on the speed with which the electron is moving and the strength of the magnetic field. It does not depend on the temperature of the electron — in fact, it is very difficult to say what the temperature of a free electron *is* !

If the electron enters the magnetic field at a very high speed — in fact close to the speed of light — then we get a similar but even more important way of producing radiation. Here, the radiating energy produced by the acceleration is concentrated into a very narrow cone pointing in the direction of the electron's motion. This is one of the effects of time dilation and spatial contraction that follows from the restricted theory of general relativity. The radiation so-produced is called **synchrotron radiation**, again named after terrestrial machines. Synchrotron radiation is one of the most important energy production mechanisms in the universe (although not here on Earth) and is responsible for a large fraction of the energy emitted by supernovae remnants, exploding galaxies and the quasars.

There are two more ways in which electrons can be accelerated. The first of these occurs when a free electron passes close to an atomic nucleus with an electrical charge. In one of the most important cases this may just be the nucleus of a hydrogen atom, i.e. a single proton, that has been ionized (which is where the free electrons come from in the first place!). When the electron moves close enough to the proton its path curves because of the electrostatic attraction. The resultant acceleration produces radiation called **thermal bremsstrahlung**.

Finally an electron in free space can be accelerated simply by being hit by another particle. This could be either another electron or, possibly, an atom. This process is called **inverse Compton scattering**. "Inverse", because it is the opposite of a process by which photons passing through a gas can "hit" free electrons and become absorbed. Inverse Compton radiation is believed to occur in many of the violent extragalactic objects such as quasars.

All of the above energy generation processes have their inverse process, although so-far we have only mentioned inverse Compton scattering. It seems to be a fundamental law of physics that the great majority of physical events can take place just as easily — although not necessarily as *probably* — "backwards". This means that for every emission process there is a corresponding process which absorbs energy. What takes place predominantly depends on the physical conditions.

What is the frequency distribution of the radiation produced by these more exotic processes? Is it the Planck law, too? No, radiation distributed according to the Planck law is emitted from many astronomical bodies because the energies of the electrons are distributed according to the Maxwell-Boltzman law. But this law is irrelevant for free electrons: they can have almost *any* distribution of energies. Thus synchrotron emission, for example, has a frequency distribution very different from that of a black body law. Fig. 12.7 shows the flux emitted by the bright quasar 3C273 at different frequencies. It's easy to see that, relative to a black body law, the quasar has far too much energy at both high and low frequencies. For the sake of radio and X-ray astronomers, it is just as well it has. Otherwise it may never have been detected in the first place!

Light from the quasars

The optical spectrum of a quasar is the single most important piece of information we can have about it. It is our only point of contact with events which took place thousands of millions of years ago near the observable limits of the universe.

First we must define the limits of the radiation we are going to talk about. Normally by "optical" we mean what we can see with our naked eyes: that is, from about 4000 Ångstroms to about 7500 Ångstroms — violet to red. The full range of colours registrable on a photographic plate is a little more than this, stretching from about 3000 Ångstroms to about 8000 Ångstroms, or even further with suitably sensitive plates. However, in practice, the Earth's atmosphere cuts off the radiation with wavelengths shorter than about 3600 Ångstroms if we are near ground level. However, by going to higher altitudes, we can observe down to about 3100 Ångstroms, which is one reason why optical telescopes are almost always built on mountains.

Now the most useful information in the spectrum of a quasar is contained in the spectral region from about 912 Ångstroms (the **far-ultraviolet**) to about 7000 Ångstroms. The value of 912 Ångstroms is the maximum wavelength of the light emitted when an hydrogen atom recombines from being a proton and free electron to being a stable atom. As we said earlier, it is quite possible for more energetic (smaller wavelength) radiation to be produced in a recombination if the electron has surplus energy. On the other hand, the great majority of

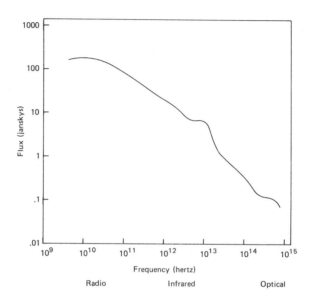

Fig. 12.7 — The energy emitted by the bright quasar 3C273 over a range of wavelengths from the radio to X-rays.

recombinations take place if the two particles have slight amounts of excess energy, since then it is easier for the electron to re-enter the atom. Thus most "recombination energy" is seen at wavelengths close to 912 Ångstroms which is termed the **Lyman Edge** or **Lyman Limit**.

The ultraviolet region of the spectrum between 912 Ångstroms and 3500 Ångstroms also contains many other important spectral lines. Lying between the Lyman limit and 1216 Ångstroms is the main Lyman series for hydrogen, corresponding to emission from captured electrons dropping to the ground state, or lowest-energy level, in the hydrogen atom. At longer wavelengths from 1216 Ångstroms and up into the visible regions of the spectrum are important lines of many other elements, such as carbon, oxygen and magnesium.

By comparison, the visible wavelength region of the spectrum from 3500 Å to 7000 Å is relatively devoid of important spectral lines. Certainly there are plenty of features to see, but these are generally not caused by resonance transitions to the ground state of the parent atoms. Unfortunately it is these resonance lines which are strongest and contain most of the important physical information. It is one of the great sorrows of most Earthbound optical astronomers that they can't look at the far-ultraviolet spectral region containing most of the "action". But the quasar astronomer is much more fortunate. Not because his equipment can see to shorter wavelengths, but because quasar redshifts cooperate nicely in bringing the ultraviolet regions of the spectrum into the visible part of the waveband.

Because of these large redshifts, it is no longer sufficient simply to refer to the "wavelength" of a particular spectral line. For quasars it becomes important to say

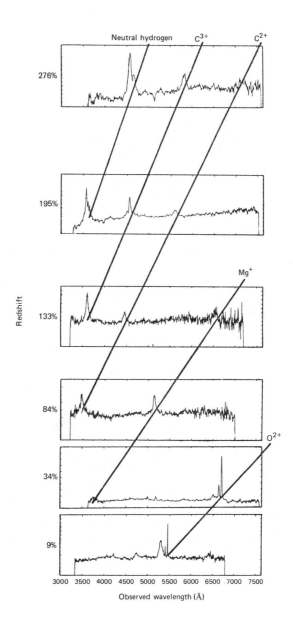

Fig. 12.8 — The appearance of the optical spectra of some quasars at different redshifts. The lines mark the same spectral lines but at different redshifts.

more precisely which of two wavelengths we are talking about: we'll use the term **emitted wavelength** to mean the wavelength of the radiation *as it was emitted* and the term **observed wavelength** to mean the wavelength *as received* by our telescope. The two wavelengths are related by;

$$\lambda_{observed} = (1+z).\ \lambda_{emitted}$$

Fig. 12.8 shows the spectra of several quasars of different redshifts. While the observed wavelength range is almost always from 3500-7500 Ångstroms, the emitted wavelengths stretch from under 900 Ångstroms to 7000 Ångstroms, giving us a fascinating glimpse into the invisible, far-ultraviolet region.

These spectra show three main features: first are the strong **emission lines** marked with the chemical symbols of the elements which produce them. These lines "sit" on top of the second important feature, the **continuum** radiation which contributes different amounts of energy over a very wide range of wavelengths. Lastly we see the narrow **absorption lines**, which are most noticeable to the "left" of the strong Lyman α emission line.

When visible at all, Lyman α is by far the strongest emission line in the spectrum of a typical quasar. This should come as no surprise when we consider how it is produced. Most captures of free electrons by the protons in an ionized gas are to the "upper" (excited) energy levels in the atom. The electron now "cascades" down through the levels, producing a variety of emission lines and finishes up by falling to the ground level from the level just above it, thus producing a Lyman α emission line. If the initial capture occurs to a lower level, then it will still probably pass through the two lowest levels on its way down. Only in the less likely event that the electron jumps straight from the third level (say) directly to the ground level will we get no Lyman α line. Instead, we'll get a Lyman β line, which is, indeed, another strong line found in many spectra. The other strong emission lines in Fig. 12.8 are produced by ionized magnesium (the so-called **Mg II line**), doubly and triply ionized carbon (**C III** and **C IV** lines), doubly ionized oxygen (**O III**), quadruply ionized nitrogen (**N V**) and triply ionized silicon (**Si IV**)[1].

Notice that all these emission lines are quite broad: the maximum width we would expect from Lyman α, for example, in a laboratory here on Earth would be only a small fraction of an Ångstrom. But the line we see in Fig. 12.9 has a width of over 100 Ångstroms. We believe that this width is caused by slightly different parts of the emitting gas travelling at slightly different speeds. By using our knowledge of the Doppler effect[2] , the range of speeds can be calculated from the width. It is convenient to define this width to mean the range that covers $^2/_3$ of the "area" of the line. In the example shown in Fig. 12.9, this wavelength width is around 120 Ångstroms.

---

[1] The naming of spectral lines is a source of great confusion to students of physics! It seems illogical that *tripley* ionized carbon should produce a carbon *four* line, for example. Unfortunately the early spectroscopists called the lines from *neutral* atoms the "one" lines which meant that *singly* ionized atoms produced the "two" lines.

[2] Notice that it *is* correct to use the Doppler formula here since we really are talking about the motion of something (in this case, the gas) *through* space.

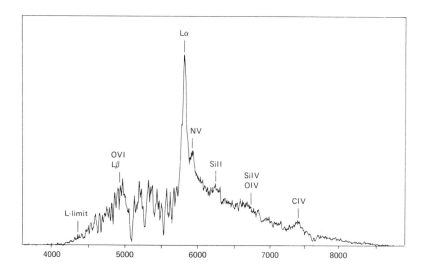

Fig. 12.9 — The spectrum of the high-redshift quasar PKS 2000-330. Some of the main emission lines are indicated.

We assume that this range is equally spaced about the "right" value for the emission redshift. If this is so, then we can calculate the range of velocities from the Doppler formula.

For the spread in velocity, we have:

$$\Delta v = c \cdot \frac{\Delta \lambda}{\lambda}$$

where $\Delta \lambda$ is the "wavelength width" of the observed line.

Unfortunately, this will not give us a correct value for the velocity of the gas near the quasar. Because the quasar is heavily redshifted, the width of the emission line is also increased and we have to reduce the range of velocities by dividing by $(1+z)$. In our example we find that the material emitting the Lyman α has a velocity spread of about 3000 km/s. So far no-one has convincingly explained why the emission lines are this wide. Astronomers believe that at the centre of a quasar is a very small **"central engine"** that produces essentially all the energy. Around the central engine is a much larger region composed of "blobs" of emitting gas.

The central source emits strong radiation which totally ionizes a large fraction of the surrounding gas and producing the emission lines. It may be that these blobs are moving outwards from the centre at high speeds, accelerated by the powerful flux of radiation from the nucleus. Alternatively, we may witnessing gas falling *into* the central engine to be swallowed up as a possible source of fuel for the quasar. We shall discuss some of these ideas later in Chapter 15.

Look again at Fig. 12.9. Less obvious than the emission lines but probably of more importance is the **continuum**, or general level of emission most clearly seen where neither emission nor absorption lines occur. The first thing to notice about the continuum is that it is "scruffy"; that is, it varies up and down from point to point across the spectrum. Some of this scruffiness or **noise** may be caused by real variations in the spectrum of the object. More often, though, it stems from the fact that quasars are so faint that there is simply not enough light to produce a "noiseless" spectrum.

Each point in the quasar's spectrum corresponds to a channel of the spectroscope used to obtain the spectrum. Let's say that each channel received roughly 100 photons during the whole time that the spectrum was being taken, which is the average level we would expect to see in each channel. In practice, however, we almost never get exactly 100 photons per channel because of random effects. Purely by chance, some of the channels may have received less than 100 photons while others will have received slightly more. Statistical theory tells us that the typical level of the noise is equal to the square root of the average number of photons in each channel. In our example this amounts to about 10 photons.

Look more closely at the continuum and you will see that the average level is not constant across the whole spectrum. The energy at short (blue) wavelengths is markedly brighter than at long (red) wavelengths, again confirming that the quasars are "blue", as we discussed in Chapter 11. In this respect they differ significantly from the "red" BL Lac objects which we shall talk about in Chapter 14.

What produces the continuum emission in quasars? It is certain that it cannot simply be thermal radiation from hot gas: to produce the amount of energy from the small volumes we infer, we would require the gas to have a temperature approaching 10^{12} degrees Centigrade. The spectral distribution of this energy would then be quite unlike that which we see. On the other hand, such brightness temperatures *are* quite easily produced by such non-thermal processes as **synchrotron emission** in which free electrons are accelerated in strong magnetic fields. We are not sure how these awesome amounts of energy are produced. The most plausible idea is that the central engine is fuelled by matter — perhaps whole stars — falling into an enormous black hole whose mass exceeds 100 million times that of the Sun. We shall return to discuss these fascinating ideas later, in Chapter 15.

Whatever the cause of the continuum emission, we believe that most of it comes directly from the central engine of the quasar with very little "processing" on its way to us. One reason for thinking this, is that we sometimes see the continuum level of a quasar vary considerably over a few weeks while the strength of the emission lines stays much the same. As we argued in Chapter 11, this implies that the continuum originates in a volume less than a few lightweeks in diameter. On the other hand, if the emission lines are formed in a much larger volume, they will vary only after a much longer period of time, roughly equal to the time needed for light to cross the emission zone.

As we mentioned in the previous chapter, the fact that quasars have spectra which show strong emission lines allows us to devise another method of discovering them in large numbers. We can install a thin prism across the front of a telescope that produces minute optical spectra of every star in the telescope's field of view onto a photographic plate. This method is called the **objective prism** technique. By carefully scanning the developed photographic plate it is possible to pick out those quasars with strong lines. The power of the method is that it applies to all quasar-like objects whether or not they are radio sources. Since the method was first used to find quasars in the mid-1970s, several thousand new "radio-quiet" sources have been discovered, many of which are not radio sources at all.

13

An Absorbing Problem

After the discovery of 3C273, the number of known quasars increased rapidly. By by the end of 1965, more than one hundred were known. Amongst these was **3C191**, an object which, like 3C273, had been found as a strong source during the third radio survey at Cambridge.

The problem

The redshift of 3C191, derived from its emission lines, was around 2. But the spectrum showed something unprecedented in the quasars known at that time: narrow *absorption* lines. These lines were identified with the same elements as the adjacent emission lines and had a redshift close to, but slightly smaller than, the emission redshift.

Astronomers knew that this absorption must be caused by material lying somewhere between us and the quasar. But where? The fact that the absorption redshift was very close to the emission redshift seemed to argue that the absorbing material had to be very close in space to the emitting material. Surely similar redshifts meant similar distances? Furthermore it was remembered that the photographs of 3C273 showed a faint jet-like feature, suggesting that something was being "blown out" of the central object. Was 3C191 similar? And, if so, was the absorption caused by this ejected material?

From the start, however, some astronomers favoured another explanation. The absorption might simply be caused by ordinary galaxies lying at random between the quasar and ourselves. Of course, at first glance, this looked rather unlikely since galaxies should presumably intersect our line of sight at *all* intermediate distances (and thus redshifts), not just at a redshift close to that of the quasar.

But there is trap here for the unwary: some elements — such as hydrogen in its Lyman α line — absorb very strongly, even when there are only very small amounts of gas. This follows simply from the quantum physics of hydrogen atoms — the atomic structure is such that they are very receptive to radiation. On the other hand, elements such as silicon absorb far more weakly for the same amount of material. This implies that a quasar whose redshift is such that the visible region of the spectrum contains the Lyman α line is much more likely to show strong absorption lines compared, for example, to those quasars where the visible region contains only weaker lines.

For wavelengths shorter than about 3300 Ångstroms, ultraviolet absorption by the Earth's atmosphere restricts observations from the ground. This means that it is impossible to see Lyman α absorption lines at redshifts smaller than about 1.8.

Furthermore, at the time of its discovery, 3C191 had one of the highest known redshifts (1.95) and was one of the few known quasars in which absorption *could* be seen. Perhaps the similarity of the emission and absorption redshifts in 3C191 was nothing more than a coincidence resulting from an observational selection effect?

The hypothesis that the absorbing material is associated with the quasar and possibly ejected from it has been called the **associated** explanation for the absorption lines. The other possibility — that the matter doing the absorbing lies all along the path between the quasar and ourselves — we will call the **intervening** hypothesis.

To distinguish between these two explanations looks, at first sight, to be one of the easier observing projects facing quasar spectroscopists. It would seem that all we need to do would be to calculate the expected number of lines and the strength of absorption that would be caused by galaxies lying along the line of sight to the quasar and compare it with the numbers and strengths of lines in actual observed spectra. We shall discuss what happened when these tests were made in the next section. When we do, we shall see that the programme of observations was not quite so easy to undertake as it at first appeared.

The main restriction in performing the test in the mid-1960s was that the observational data was simply not good enough. It is important to realize that these early quasar spectra were taken with telescopes and spectrographs that were quite insensitive by today's standards. For example, just after the quasars were discovered, a good spectrum of a 17th magnitude object required very considerable effort — perhaps a whole night at the telescope. Today, using electronic spectrographs, the same spectrum can be obtained in minutes and good spectra of 21st magnitude objects are commonplace.

This limited sensitivity had two consequences: first, very few quasars in the mid-1960s had optical spectra of sufficient quality to show the narrow absorption lines. Furthermore, the few spectra available were of the brighter objects, which tended to be *closer* objects of relatively low intrinsic luminosity. Such quasars will be relatively "non-violent" and thus maybe too weak to eject enough gas to form absorption lines. Alternatively, they may be close enough that very little intervening absorbing material lies between us and them.

In the mid-1960s, arguments were being propounded both for and against the intervening and associated hypotheses. But the number of quasars known to have absorption lines was too small to resolve the problem. What was clearly needed was a large sample of high-redshift quasar spectra, all of the highest quality so that faint absorption lines could be clearly seen and analysed.

Modern data

During the late 1960s and early 1970s, as more absorption line quasars were discovered, it was realized that 3C191 had been a very simple object to analyse. The new quasars showed many more absorption lines, most of which could not be interpreted as belonging to one — or even a few — absorption line systems. In fact it was often not even clear which elements most of the absorption lines were caused by.

However, one general feature of the multiplicity of absorption lines *was* clear. Look at Fig. 13.1. You will see that the number of absorption lines in a given wavelength range is far greater to the short-wavelength side of the weak Lyman α emission line (around 4700 Å) than in a similar range on the long-wavelength

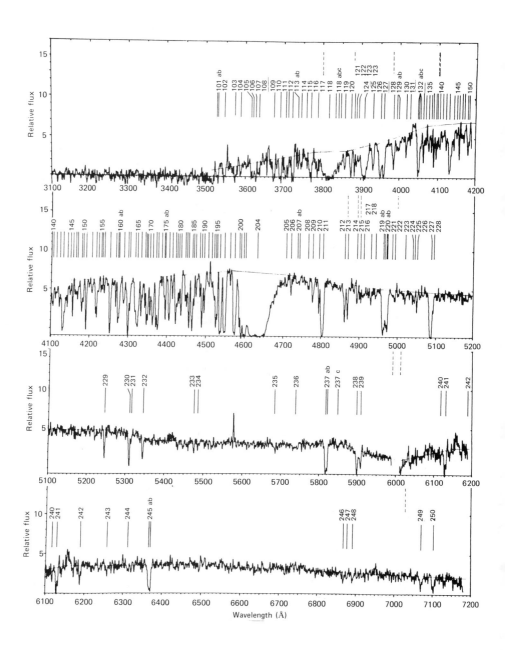

Fig. 13.1 — The spectrum of the quasar PKS 0528-250 showing many absorption lines (marked by numbers) particularly shortward of 4650 Å which is the expected position of the Lyman α emission line. Notice the continuum level drops to zero short-ward of about 3500 Å corresponding to strong absorption by the Lyman continuum "edge".

side[1]. This strongly suggests that these absorption lines are also Lyman α at redshifts less than the emission redshift. If so, then would we expect to see absorption lines of other elements at the same redshifts? Perhaps: but not necessarily.

Consider, for example, the line of triply-ionized carbon (the C IV line). This spectrum feature is, in fact, two lines lying very close together in wavelength at 1548 Å and 1550 Å. Atomic physics predicts that the 1548 line will be twice as strong as the 1550 line. When the C IV line occurs as an emission line, these two close lines are "smeared together" by the velocity of the line-producing material (see previous chapter). But when we look at Fig. 13.1 we see the sort of "doublet" we expect from C IV in absorption at 5900 Ångstroms. If this really *is* C IV then it has a redshift of 2.81 and we expect to see Lyman α absorption at a wavelength of 4630 Ångstroms. And we do. Furthermore we can also identify the elements of silicon, oxygen and nitrogen at the same redshift. Finding all these lines at the same redshift defines a **redshift system**, corresponding to a "lump" of material — either galaxy or ejectum from the quasar — moving at a similar speed. Most quasars with absorption lines contain not one, but several, identifiable absorption systems which together can often account for the great majority of the strong, longer-wavelength absorption lines seen in their spectra.

But the weaker lines *shortward* of the Lyman α emission seem, in most cases, to have no corresponding C IV absorption, nor, indeed, similarly redshifted lines of any other element. Why? One possibility is that most of the shortward lines are *not* , in fact, Lyman α at all. A more likely explanation, though, stems from the fact that Lyman α is such a strong line. As we said before, strong Lyman α can be produced even by very small amounts of hydrogen: amounts so small that other lines may not be seen. Let us consider a little more carefully how absorption lines are produced.

Think about a bright source of white light lying a long way from us. By "white" we mean that it contains equal strengths of light of all colours. This light source could be rather similar to some quasars, except that we will postulate that its intrinsic spectrum contains neither emission nor absorption lines but just a strong continuum. Now place a small amount of hydrogen gas somewhere along the line of sight, well away from both the quasar and ourselves. (See Fig. 13.2.) We shall also assume that the gas cloud is neither moving away nor towards us and that, at first, it contains only a very few atoms of hydrogen.

Photons leave the quasar in all directions. But the only ones that concern us are the ones which are heading straight for the Earth and which pass through the hydrogen gas cloud. Remember, though, that this cloud contains only a few hydrogen atoms and so the chance of any particular photon being absorbed by an atom is very small. Let's say this chance is just 1 in 1000. The majority of photons (999 out of 1000) pass right through the gas unaffected. In the diagram, we've shown the hydrogen atoms as hard round balls and we can imagine that these atoms simply "block" some of the light. The more light that gets blocked, the stronger the absorption line we see[2].

Of course, atoms are *not* really hard balls and we require quantum mechanics to give the exact answers. The funny thing is, though, that the hard-

---

[1]PKS 0528-250 is most unusual amongst quasars in having only very weak emission lines, including Ly α.

[2] For the reader interested in details, the calculation to find what fraction gets blocked is very similar to the one we shall make in section 13.3 to find the effective blocking power of whole galaxies.

ball approach gives an answer very close to the right one. We won't worry about that here — all we need to know is that the "blocking fraction" goes up with increasing number of atoms. In Fig. 13.2 the photons at wavelengths other than those of the Lyman α line pass straight through the gas (this is where our hard-ball approximation breaks down) while 1 in 1000 photons *at* 1216 Ångstroms are absorbed.

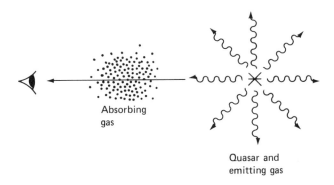

Fig. 13.2 — Absorption by a cloud of gas along the line of sight to a distant quasar.

If we were to double the number of atoms in the cloud then it might seem obvious that the amount of absorption would also double. And this is, indeed, what happens, providing that the overall number of atoms is very small. So, let us summarize: twice the density gives twice the amount of absorption (for the same path-length) and thus twice the strength of the absorption line, just as we might expect.

If the hydrogen absorbed photons having just a small range of wavelengths around 1216 Å, then we should expect to see a simple, rectangularly shaped absorption line. But real lines, even weak ones like some of those shown in Fig. 13.1, are never rectangular. Why not? One reason is that the atoms in a real gas are always moving. Hydrogen atoms at ordinary, everyday temperatures are moving at speeds of around a few kilometres per second. These motions cause the light absorbed and emitted by the gas to be slightly red-or blue-shifted by the Doppler effect. Thus a hydrogen atom absorbs Lyman α photons which it "sees" as being at at 1216 Å but which were actually emitted at a slightly different frequency.

Of course the majority of the atoms will not be moving directly towards or away from the quasar: there is a distribution of "front-back" velocities. This distribution of velocities looks like Fig. 13.3. Most atoms absorb close to a wavelength of 1216

Å because, on average, they are neither moving very fast towards us nor away from us. But, to a better approximation, our weak absorption is spread out over a range of velocities and has a smooth, **gaussian profile**. If we measure the width halfway up the absorption line, we get what astronomers call the **half-width velocity** of the absorbing gas. And when we talk about the strength of an absorption line, we mean the total amount of absorption "added-up" over all wavelengths (and thus all velocities) in the line — not just at the line centre.

So far we have only considered absorption by gas in a cloud which is stationary with respect to us. If the cloud is actually moving away, then the mechanism of absorption we have discussed remains just the same except that we shall see the Lyman α line redshifted by some amount. Furthermore, because redshifting multiplies the line wavelength by a factor *(1+z)* , the width of the lines will be increased by this same factor. We must remember to allow for this effect by dividing by *(1+z)* when measuring the strength or velocity width of an absorption line.

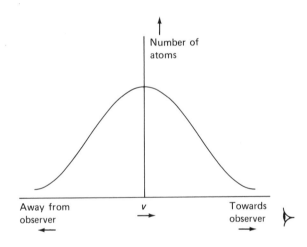

Fig. 13.3 — The velocity distribution of atoms in a hot gas. There are far more atoms with small velocities than with high velocities.

Now that we understand how the absorption is produced, we can make a most important calculation: simply by measuring the total strength of an absorption line, we can calculate *how much material there is doing the absorbing* . Or, to be more precise, we can calculate the number of atoms per unit cross-sectional area along a column in the line of sight.

Let's do this for a real object, the quasar PKS 0528-250[1]. The absorption line near 4020 Å is believed to be Lyman α at a redshift of about 2.3 . The hydrogen gas doing the absorbing removes a fraction of about 0.4 of the total light from the quasar at this wavelength. We estimate this value from the depth of the line and the level of the surrounding continuum. The absorption is spread out over a total wavelength range of about 1 Å and thus a velocity half-width of plus and minus 30 km/s. The final piece of information we need for our calculations is the "absorbing strength" of the Lyman α line derived from laboratory physics experiments which we can look up in such books as C.W.Allen's *Astrophysical Quantities*.

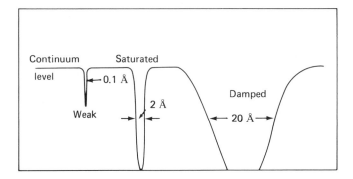

Fig. 13.4 — The profiles of an unsaturated (weak), saturated and damped absorption line, corresponding to increasing amounts of absorbing gas.

Using this data we deduce a column density of 10^{14} per square centimetre. To put this number in perspective, if the absorption is produced by a galaxy having a size similar to our own, then the density of the gas we infer is 10^{-32} times less dense than the gas in the Earth's atmosphere! This clearly demonstrates that the gas in extragalactic space must be very rarefied — and it also shows just how sensitive modern spectrographic techniques are!

Now what happens if we increase the number of atoms in our cloud of absorbing gas? As we might expect, the fraction of photons absorbed is larger and

[1]This is another of the strange naming systems that radioastronomers use for their objects! The "PKS" stands for the Parkes observatory while the "05 28" and "-250" parts are the **right ascension** and **declination** respectively – a sort of longitude and latitude system on the sky.

so the absorption line gets stronger. This continues until nearly all the photons at 1216 Å are being "stopped" by the hydrogen. The absorption line now stretches down to the bottom of the spectrum shown in Fig. 13.4, and has become totally black at the centre of the (redshifted) Lyman α line. Notice, though, that because the *edges* of the line are weaker than the centre, the outer parts of the line are not yet black. Under these circumstances, the absorption line is said to be **saturated** — although "surfeited" might be a better name! In our "hard-ball" model of the absorbing atoms, we can imagine that there are now so many balls that they are beginning to lie in each other's shadow, thus reducing their efficiency at absorbing.

And if we put still more gas into our cloud? To a first approximation, the centre of the line cannot get any "blacker" and its strength can only increase in the outer, velocity-broadened parts. In doing so, it changes its shape slightly and very slowly becomes "fatter". This goes on while the smaller amounts of fast-moving gas are also becoming saturated. Under these circumstances it is very hard to derive an accurate value for the density of the intervening gas because it may change by a large factor without appreciably affecting the total line strength.

Finally, if we have truly enormous amounts of gas, the line takes on a different shape again: it attains what is known as a **damping profile** as shown in Fig. 13.4 Here the line is extremely broad with wide "wings". The line area again begins to increase fairly rapidly with increasing density, not because it can get any "blacker", but because it is growing "fatter". (The strength actually rises as the square root of the density). The cause of the damping shape is tied up with quantum mechanics and we shan't discuss it here. Suffice it to say that a damped line implies enormous quantities of absorbing gas. A few quasars are known that have damped Lyman α lines: one of them is PKS 0528-250, as shown in greater detail in Fig. 13.5.

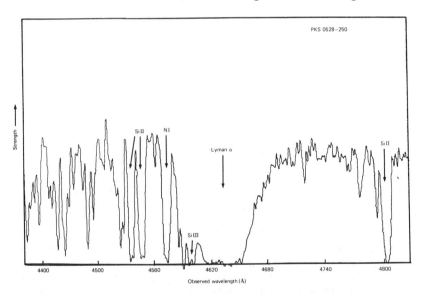

Fig. 13.5 — Detailed spectrum of the quasar PKS 0528-250 showing the strongly damped Lyman α absorption line.

All the preceding arguments can be summarized by Fig. 13.6. It shows how the strength of a Lyman α line changes as we increase the amount of absorbing gas. In books on astrophysics, this curve is known as a **curve of growth** because it describes how the line strength "grows" with column density. Of course, similar curves can be drawn for other elements. To get the column density of absorbing gas is easy — at least in principle. All the astronomer has to do is measure the total strength of an absorption line and then read off a value from his curve.

We can calculate what sort of hydrogen column density we would expect through a galaxy such as our own. When we do, we get a value of around 10^{20} atoms per square centimetre which is surprisingly close to the column densities we deduce from the strongest damped lines in quasars such as PKS 0528-250. It therefore seems reasonable to suppose that these damped quasar lines are also caused by galaxies similar to our own intruding onto the line of sight. On the other hand, most of the absorption lines we see in quasars are far weaker with deduced column densities of less than 10^{15} atoms per square centimetre. What are they?

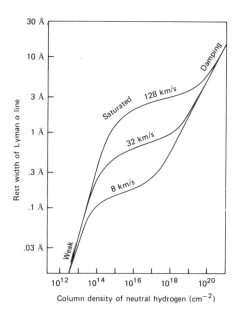

Fig. 13.6 — The "curve of growth" of the strength of the Lyman α absorption line with increasing amounts of absorbing gas (column density — expressed as a number of hydrogen atoms per square centimetre). On the saturated portion of this curve, the line strength depends on the velocity dispersion of the atoms.

As we mentioned above, we believe that they are caused by hydrogen. One reason is that they are so numerous that it is unlikely that any other element (or combination of elements) could produce so many lines. Furthermore the weak lines are only seen in very large numbers as we move "shortward" (i.e. to shorter wavelengths) of the Lyman α emission line. This is a strong indication that they are not only caused by hydrogen, but that they are also actually Lyman α lines.

If this conjecture is true then, as we move shortward of the Lyman β emission line at 1025 Å, we should expect to see lots of Lyman β absorption lines, too. Here we have a simple test: whatever the redshift of the intervening absorbing material, its Lyman α and Lyman β absorption lines should be seen at the *same* redshift. So, for every postulated Lyman α line, we should see a corresponding Lyman β line.

One point we have to bear in mind in making the test is that Lyman β is intrinsically a much weaker line (by a factor of about 5) than Lyman α. Furthermore it often lies in a region of a quasar's spectrum (around 3900 Å in Fig. 13.1) where the continuum level is weaker than where the Lyman α is found, further to the red in the spectrum. Both of these points mean that it comes as no surprise when we often don't see a Lyman β line corresponding to *every* Lyman α line.

One way of making the test mentioned above would be to take every line shortward of the Lyman α emission line, assume it really is a Lyman α absorption line, calculate the expected wavelength of the corresponding Lyman β line and see if it's there. Of course, we must give ourselves a little leeway to allow for errors in measuring the wavelengths of the Lyman α absorption lines.

In principle, the method is straightforward. But if the spectrum contains large numbers of lines, the task of matching Lyman α and β pairs "by hand" would be very tedious. The approach that astronomers normally use is to first measure the wavelength of *every* absorption line in the quasar's spectrum. These numbers are then fed into a computer, programmed to calculate the ratio of the wavelengths of every absorption line in the spectrum to every other absorption line. So, if a spectrum contains 100 absorption lines, we end up with a list of 10,000 (i.e. 100 x 100) ratios.

These numbers are useful because the wavelength ratio of two lines is the same *whether or not they are both redshifted* (provided, of course, it is by the same amount!). To demonstrate this more clearly remember that the measured wavelength of a spectral line is

$$\lambda_{measured} = \lambda_{at\ rest}.(1+z)$$

And so

$$\frac{\lambda_1\ measured}{\lambda_2\ measured} = \frac{\lambda_1\ at\ rest}{\lambda_2\ at\ rest}$$

since the redshift factor cancels out. For example, the ratio of 1216 (the Lyman α line) to 1025 Ångstroms (the Lyman β line) is 1.186. Thus we should be able to pick out Lyman α/Lyman β pairs at any redshift by seeing which pairs of lines have wavelengths in the ratio of 1.186.

Now imagine what would happen *if* all the lines in the spectrum of our quasar were indeed just Lyman α and Lyman β pairs. In this case, we would expect some values to occur much more frequently in our list of ratios than others. Fig. 13.7 shows this sort of number-ratios plot for the quasar PKS 1442+101

Actually we find the method is not quite so easy to use in practice as we might have hoped. For one thing, we will unfortunately, but unavoidably, end up taking the ratios of Lyman α lines at one redshift to Lyman α (or β) lines at a *different* redshift. Such ratios produce random values in our diagram and will show up as a source of "noise" on the plot, disguising some of the ratios we are looking for. Furthermore, not all of the absorption lines are caused by Lyman α and Lyman β. For one thing Lyman γ (which is even weaker than Lyman β) has a rest wavelength of 972 Ångstroms. Yet again, there are also lines of other elements, such as oxygen

VI and carbon **III** which occur at similar wavelengths. All of these will confuse the plot. Nevertheless, if the majority of the lines are caused by hydrogen, then we should still see a "peak" in the correlation plot at a value of about 1.186.

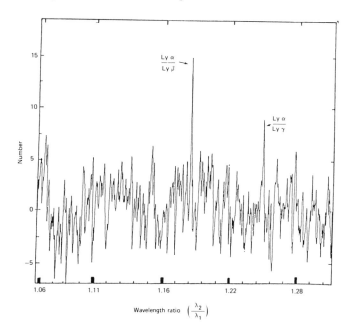

Fig. 13.7 — The number of occurrences of particular absorption line wavelength ratios in the quasar PKS 1442+101. Every line has been "ratio-ed" with every other line. Note that there are two significant peaks at ratios of about 1.19 and about 1.25, corresponding to the wavelength of Lyman β divided by Lyman α and Lyman γ divided by Lyman α.

What sort of results do we actually get? For the quasars where the data is good enough to perform the test, we almost always find a peak at the expected value, as in Fig. 13.7. Thus it looks certain that the majority of the absorption *is* caused by hydrogen. On the other hand, we have already shown that these lines are far too weak to be caused by the quantities of hydrogen typically found in galaxies such as our own. Astronomers are still not sure what these weak lines are caused by. We shall return to this question shortly. For the moment, though, since we seem to have reached an impasse, we shall pause and to turn our attention to another feature of the quasar absorption lines.

How often?

Let us now try to understand how often we might expect absorption to occur along the path to a typical quasar. To make the discussion concrete, let's consider a quasar at a (emission) redshift of 3.0 . We'll assume as a first guess that the universe is populated uniformly with galaxies rather like our own, all of diameter[1]

---

[1] This value is a little bigger than the size delineated by the visible stars in a typical spiral galaxy but will allow for the extended hydrogen gas discovered in our own and other galaxies by radio observations. Since we are talking about hydrogen absorption, this larger value is probably more relevant.

100,000 lightyears. We ask the question, "How many galaxies should we expect to 'get in the way' of our line of sight to the redshift 3 quasar?"

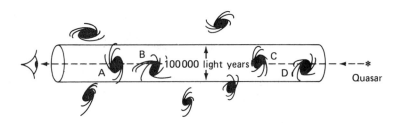

Fig. 13.8 — Calculation of the number of galaxies expected to intrude on the line of sight to a distant quasar. Since each galaxy is assumed to be 100,000 lightyears in diameter, only those objects whose centres lie in a cylinder of this size (marked A, B, C and D) intercept the line to the quasar and will thus produce absorption lines.

Fortunately, the calculation is quite easy. Look at Fig. 13.8. All we need to do is work out the number of galaxies whose *centres* will be contained in a hypothetical cylinder of diameter 100,000 lightyears, stretching out from us to the quasar. The length of the cylinder depends slightly on how we interpret the redshift in terms of the overall geometry of the universe (see Chapter 9). We'll adopt a fairly conventional approach and use a Hubble constant and cosmological model in which a redshift 3 quasar has a distance of around 10,000 million lightyears. The volume of our cylinder is then

$$volume = \pi.R^2.D$$

where D is the distance to the quasar and so we find

$$volume = 10^{20} \ cubic \ lightyears$$

The final step in our calculation is to determine how many galaxies we would expect to find in this volume. Looking in the tables of data given in C.W.Allen's book mentioned earlier, we see that there are about 0.02 galaxies per cubic megaparsec. Converting this number into the right units, we have

$$density\ of\ galaxies\ \approx\ 10^{-21}\ galaxies\ per\ cubic\ lightyear^{1}.$$

We now have what we want: the volume of our cylinder is 10^{20} cubic lightyears and we expect about 10^{-21} galaxies per cubic lightyear meaning that the predicted number of galaxies lying along the line of sight to a typical high-redshift quasar is only 0.1! Put another way, only 1 line of sight in 10 to a redshift 3 quasar should intersect a galaxy. If this were true, absorption in quasars should indeed be rare! Unfortunately the observational evidence shows that essentially *all* higher-redshift quasars have not just one absorption redshift but many. Why? Have we made a mistake in our calculations? Are the values we have used correct?

First remember that we had to interpret the redshifts to get a distance. Is our distance right? Certainly it is not likely to be wrong by more than a factor of 2 or 3 on the basis of any reasonable value for the Hubble constant and cosmological model *provided that the redshifts of the quasars are indeed cosmological* (but see Chapter 16). Bearing this important proviso in mind, we'll continue to assume that our distances are correct.

Next consider the value we used for the space density of the galaxies. This number is not known as well as we would like, but it is probably within a factor of 2 or 3 of being correct. On the other hand, it refers to galaxies of *all* sizes rather than those like our own, from which we assumed the 100,000 lightyear diameter. If we use a smaller value for the space density, we shall be more nearly correct. But this will only make our difficulty worse! We need *more* galaxies to produce the observed amount of absorption, not less.

We conclude that there simply aren't enough known galaxies to explain the ubiquity of quasar absorption lines. Again, we seem to be stuck: we have shown that both the uncommon strong absorption lines and the far more frequent weak lines are caused by hydrogen gas. But we have also shown that the weak lines are far *too* weak to be caused by galaxies similar to our own. This view is reinforced by considering the frequency with which they are seen: we see far too many for them to be caused by galaxies like ours.

Other sorts of galaxy?

Could the absorption be caused by galaxies of a different type? We require a galaxy which is more common than ordinary spirals but which is deficient in gas. Well, there *are* galaxies that contain little or no hydrogen: these are the elliptical galaxies, such as M87. But, at least in our part of the universe, they are rarer than the spiral galaxies.Thus, for every weak Lyman α line we see (caused by an elliptical galaxy), we should also see a very strong (saturated or damped) Lyman α line (caused by a spiral). Unfortunately we don't: — very strong Lyman α lines are very uncommon.

A first step towards resolving the problem came when astronomers studied how the Lyman α absorption lines occurred in different parts of a typical spectrum. Fig. 13.9 shows a graph of the number of lines as a function of redshift using data from several quasars. Note how these numbers rise as we move from lower to higher

---

[1] This number is, of course, very small since a cubic lightyear is a very small volume as far as a galaxy is concerned!

redshifts. Whatever is doing the absorbing seems to have been much more common in the universe at high redshifts — when the universe was young — than it is now. When we observe absorption in quasars at redshift 3, we are looking back to the first 10% of the lifespan of the universe. Perhaps "low-gas" galaxies were far commoner them? However we don't think this likely. It is true that the evolutionary sequence of galaxies is still far from being clear. Nevertheless, we believe that gas gets used up in forming stars as time goes on: we would expect the earliest galaxies to be *more* and not less "gassy".

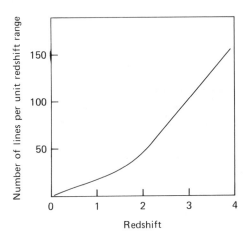

Fig. 13.9 — The number of absorption lines (per unit range of redshift) as a function of the redshift. The data are drawn from spectra of several different quasars. Notice how the numbers increase to higher redshifts, suggesting that absorption is much commoner at large distances.

The most exciting explanation for our problem suggested so far is that the weak quasar absorption lines are caused by galaxies in the process of actually forming. Unfortunately, the process of galaxy formation is by no means as clear to us as that of the formation of the stars. However, it seems likely that galaxies are born from large clouds of gas collapsing under their own gravity. If so, then such "all-gas" protogalaxies may be just what we need to explain the lines.

But even this explanation is not totally satisfactory: surely if protogalaxies are indeed responsible, we should expect to see very strong absorption systems instead of weak ones? Yes, that's true: but perhaps the collapsing protogalaxy was not a single cloud of gas but was instead composed of many smaller fragments? If so, there would be many more absorption lines but they would each be far weaker. Another effect we have not considered so far is that for every strong absorption system caused by the line of sight passing right through the centre of a galaxy, there should be many more where the line of sight just grazes the outer parts. In these outer areas we would expect the gas density to be much lower and thus produce weaker lines.

We could calculate the expected distribution of strengths and numbers of the absorption lines for both the above possibilities and compare it with the observations. The results of such tests are, unfortunately, ambiguous. Perhaps we are on the wrong track altogether: perhaps the weak absorption lines are not caused by intervening matter at all but in material ejected from the quasar?

Ejected?

Let us consider the possibility that a large fraction of all the weak quasar absorption lines are caused by "blobs" of ejected matter. Our first problem is to explain why the number of these blobs is far larger in high redshift quasars than in lower redshift objects. Fortunately, that's easy: for the same sort of reasons as we discussed in Chapter 4, when we look at a high redshift quasar we are almost certainly looking at a high luminosity quasar, too. If it had been a low luminosity object but still at high redshift, then it would almost certainly have been so faint that we shouldn't have discovered it. Since high luminosity quasars are such powerful objects, we need not be surprised to find that they eject more material than low luminosity quasars.

Our second problem is far more difficult: the weak Lyman α absorption lines are much narrower than the emission lines. As we mentioned earlier in this chapter, the width of a (weak) line is a measure of the velocity dispersion of the absorbing material.

Let's consider a typical case: we might have a quasar with (emission) redshift 3.00 whose spectrum contains a weak absorption line with a width of 5 Å at a wavelength of 4250 Å. Table 13.1 summarizes these values together with the implications we can draw from them.

Table 13.1

Observed wavelength of Ly α abs line	Determined abs redshift	Velocity of abs blob relative to quasar	Width of abs line	Determined velocity
4250	2.496	43,000 km/s	5 Å	350 kms/s

Look carefully at the velocity width of our typical line and compare it to the velocity at which the blob is travelling away from the quasar. Remember that this width is a measure of the velocity spread, or random motion, in the blob. Our problem is that the spread we observe is very small compared with the ejection velocity. It is extremely difficult to think of an ejection process that can accelerate blobs of gas up to velocities greater than 10% of the speed of light and yet not rip the blobs apart at the same time. It is as though you tried to throw a large handful of popcorn across a room without scattering it in all directions! This difficulty is so great that no convincing process has yet been put forward.

Despite this serious problem, most modern astronomers remain convinced that at least some of the absorption lines we see originate in matter ejected from the quasars. For one thing, atomic species such as triply ionized carbon and five-times ionized oxygen simply can't exist in cold intergalactic gas clouds: they need a hot radiation field, such as occurs near a quasar, to ionize them. Secondly, some quasars show the strong, very broad absorption lines which are the unmistakeable imprint of gas flowing outwards, but as a continuous stream of material rather than discrete blobs. Similar absorption is well-known in such stars as **P Cygni** where it is convincingly explained as being a result of gas blown out of the star by a strong radiation field.

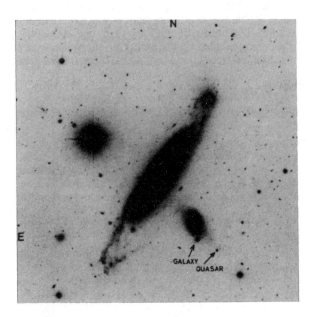

Fig 13.10 — A galaxy near a quasar

Summary

So where does the debate concerning the origin of the quasar absorption lines stand today? Despite the points discussed in the previous section there is also little doubt that *some* absorption lines are produced by intervening galaxies. Perhaps the strongest evidence for this idea is that, just occasionally, we see the galaxy! Fig. 13.10 shows one example. Although at first sight it may look as though our sight-line misses the galaxy, it must be remembered that radioastronomy has shown that gas in most spiral galaxies extends much farther from the centre than do the visible stars. The optical spectrum of PKS 0254-334 does indeed show absorption at exactly the determined emission redshift of the galaxy.

A second piece of evidence supporting the intervening hypothesis was discussed above: it is difficult to see how the strong, damped absorption lines we occasionally see could be produced by anything other than a large spiral galaxy, even if we can't see it directly.

But what of the great mass of absorption lines in high-redshift quasars that are neither strong nor of very high excitation? Certainly most of them seem to be the Lyman lines of hydrogen: but why so weak and why so numerous? Do they point to some previously suspected population of hydrogen fragments that existed only in the early history of the universe? Perhaps as some sort of precursor of the galaxies themselves? Or are they caused by blobs of material ejected by the exploding quasar itself? But, if so, how do they manage to survive while being accelerated up to velocities which are a significant fraction of the speed of light?

Such questions remain unanswered and pose a long-standing challenge to the best of today's and tomorrow's astronomers.

14

What are the Quasars?

In previous chapters we have related the history of the discovery of the quasars and discussed what their spectra have to tell us. But we have so far avoided discussion of what they actually *are*. We shall now tackle this question. Quasars are certainly very luminous objects lying outside our galaxy. Their redshifts suggest that they are very distant objects indeed. If so, then they shine as brightly as a whole galaxy of stars and yet their appearance is completely star-like[1] in the vast majority of cases.

Are they related to the galaxies? If so, which type? Ellipticals? Spirals? Perhaps a new, previously unrecognized class altogether? If they *are* related to galaxies, do they form an early part of the life history of the galaxy or a late part? Why are they only to be found at high redshifts? Or are there some close by which we don't recognize because they appear in a different guise?

These, and plenty more questions like them, are central to our problem of trying to understand these enigmatic objects on the fringe of our material universe. In this and the next few chapters we shall look at some of the arguments and possible answers. But we warn the reader in advance that this is currently one of the most controversial parts of the whole science of astronomy

The view from afar

The large redshifts and brightnesses of the quasars leads naturally to the suggestion that they are related to galaxies. On the other hand, the vast majority of quasars appear stellar, even when viewed with the world's largest optical telescopes. But, if the quasars really are related to galaxies, why don't they show an extended galaxy-type shape?

To answer this question, let's look at some numbers. First, the diameter of a fairly large galaxy, perhaps one rather like our own, is about 60,000 lightyears. A redshift of 0.1 corresponds to a distance of around 1,000 million lightyears. At this distance our typical galaxy will look rather small, a mere 10 arcseconds or so. By the time we get to a redshift of 0.5, which is typical of the lower-redshift quasars, we have an angular size of only 2 or 3 arcseconds, hardly bigger than the usual "seeing" size caused by the Earth's turbulent atmosphere. Thus, we won't have much chance of seeing a galaxy associated with a typical quasar unless the seeing is

---

[1] By "star-like" we don't, of course, mean that they have pretty points on them like a Christmas-tree star! Rather we mean point-like in that the only angular size they appear to have is that produced by the dispersion of light in the earth's atmosphere.

very good indeed or unless the associated galaxies are very much bigger than those we see locally. Of course, if there are closer examples of quasars in galaxies, the galaxy may indeed have a discernible size. But then we encounter another problem.

Let's consider how bright the quasar and galaxy will look. A galaxy similar to our own at a distance corresponding to a redshift of 0.5 would appear to have a magnitude of about 20. On the other hand, a typical quasar at this same redshift would have a magnitude of nearer 17. The 3 magnitudes difference corresponds to a brightness difference of about 16. This is the second problem we referred to: the galaxy is about 16 times weaker in its total light than the quasar. If the quasar lies in a galaxy at a distance such that both are smaller than the typical seeing size, then the quasar's light will swamp that of the galaxy. On the other hand, if they lie closer to us, the galaxy's light will be spread out over a larger area making the brightness ratio even worse than 1 to 16. In fact the amount of energy we receive from the galaxy *per unit area* stays the same irrespective of distance.

Of course, astronomers are rather inventive in making their observations. If the problem is simply that the compact central quasar is too bright, why not block it out and just observe the underlying galaxy? Specially prepared diaphragms have been used, shaped to remove most of the light from the quasar but which permit the fainter, outer areas of the galaxy to be seen. Furthermore, since we know that galaxies are usually reddish in colour while most quasars are blue or ultraviolet, we can observe through a red filter so as to decrease the relative importance of the light from the quasar relative to that of the galaxy.

Both these techniques have been tried, but with little real success. The principal difficulty is that the easy objects to try the tests on are those at very small redshifts because the expected size of the underlying galaxy is then large. Unfortunately, since we almost invariably work with samples selected according to their apparent brightness (see Chapter 4) the nearest quasars are also the least luminous. In fact many have luminosities which are hardly larger than those of the brightest galaxies. But, if we start with an object that is very likely just a bright galaxy anyway, then we really don't learn much about quasars if we show there really *is* a galaxy there all along! As we use our experimental techniques on quasars at higher and higher redshifts we become more and more confident of them actually *being* quasars. But we become less and less able to perform the experiment of detecting the underlying galaxy *at all!!*

What to do? At the heart of our problem is a curious coincidence. Why does the Earth's atmosphere limit our angular resolution by producing seeing discs with an angular size very similar to that shown by a typical galaxy at "cosmologically interesting" redshifts? If the physics of the Earth's atmosphere had been only a little different it might normally produce seeing discs of around 0.01 arcseconds. Perhaps all cosmological problems would then have been solved long ago. On the other hand, the seeing might normally be around 50 arcseconds, in which case it would be almost impossible to tell the difference between galaxies, stars and quasars. Perhaps the answer is to use the near-perfect seeing conditions of space in order to solve our cosmological problems, where even smallish telescopes will produce angular resolutions of less than $1/10$ of a second of arc. At present, astronomers strongly suspect that quasars are some sort of violent event in galaxies: but the observational evidence is not definite.

Quasars brought near

Our main problem in unravelling the mystery of the quasars is that they are just so far away. Even the lowest-redshift objects lie far beyond the well-studied galaxies.

What we would really like to do is to find a quasar much closer to us. But perhaps there *are* some closer to home and we simply do not recognize them?

To see if this is really the case, we will perform a thought experiment. On the basis of what we think we know about quasars, let us bring one in our imagination to the distance of a local galaxy and see if it resembles anything more familiar. First we must define our typical quasar: this should not be one of the brightest or most distant known objects, but should be truly typical. Here it is:

Redshift   2.0

Optical (blue or photographic magnitude)   18

and, if it's a radio source,

Radio flux density (at 2700 MHz)   0.25 Jy

Using the Hubble relationship with a constant of about 25 km/s per mega lightyear, the redshift we gave our typical quasar corresponds to a distance of about 10 thousand million lightyears. If we bring it to a distance of 30 million lightyears, comparable with one of the closest clusters of galaxies, it will be therefore about 300 times closer. By the inverse square law this implies a factor of about 10,000 in flux density and about 10 magnitudes in optical brightness. So, our quasar should now have the following appearance:

Redshift   =   0.007

Optical (blue) magnitude   =   8

Radio flux (2700 MHz)   =   2500 Jy

Actually this is not quite correct: as well as the reduction in brightness caused by increasing distance and the inverse square law, there is at least one extra effect that causes the brightness to decrease even faster. The diminution of light energy caused by the redshift itself and the "stretching effect" of the expanding universe, implies that a further factor of 3 (about one magnitude) should also be applied to these brightnesses. Thus we actually expect a 7th magnitude object with a radio flux density of 7500 Jy.

Unfortunately we don't know of any objects whose properties are as extreme as this. A 7th magnitude object could almost be seen with the naked eye and would be brilliant on photographic plates. Furthermore radio catalogues contain no compact source anywhere near as bright as 7500 Jy.

What does the lack of a close quasar mean? It *could* mean that quasars existed only in the earliest history of the universe and thus the only ones we now see will be at high redshifts. Nearby quasars, which we observe at a much later epoch, will be far weaker and we see only the faint ashes of their former glory. A second possibility is that the distances of quasars cannot be derived from their redshifts (see Chapter 16). If they are much closer, then the factor of 300 we applied in the distance should really be much smaller. The "local" quasars would then have much more mundane properties.

But there is a simpler explanation than either of these, which follows from our discussion of observational bias in Chapter 4. When we look out into the universe to redshifts near 2, we are encompassing objects in a volume of space around 300^3 larger than when we consider distances of only 30 million lightyears. Thus we would expect objects similar to our typical quasar to be around 300^3 rarer close to home. Since at present we have "only" found a few thousand quasars at redshift 2, the number of similar objects we would expect to find nearby is about 300^3 or about 3 million times smaller — much less than 1! And this is just what we get!

In other words, we should not expect to find any quasars, similar to those at high redshift, as close as the nearby clusters of galaxies: they are sufficiently rare in the universe that "nearby" space is too small to be likely to contain one. On the other hand we argued in Chapter 4 that for every highly luminous object we normally expect many more less luminous objects. If this is so for the quasars, perhaps we can gain some clues as to their nature by looking for weaker examples nearby?

The galaxy we mentioned earlier, M87 or Virgo A, is a possible example of a "weak quasar". Let's list its relevant properties and compare them to our typical quasar.

a) **It has an optical magnitude of around 9.**

b) **It lies at a distance of 30 million lightyears (which is why we chose this distance earlier).**

c) **Its 2700 MHz flux density is about 200 Jy.**

d) **The radio spectrum of M87 drops rapidly with increasing frequency, like many quasars but unlike the most luminous "flat spectrum" objects.**

e) **M87 is a strong source of X-rays, again like many quasars.**

f) **The diameter of M87 is such that at a distance corresponding to a redshift of z = 2, it would appear to have an angular size of only a second of arc or so and would appear essentially "star-like".**

g) **M87 has a "jet" which is visible on high-resolution photographic plates. This is similar to those found, or suspected, in several quasars such as 3C273.**

h) **High resolution *radio* photographs show that M87 has a compact radio core and a radio jet that is directed along the same line as the optical jet, again like many quasars.**

There are enough similarities here with the quasars to make it interesting to study the galaxy M87 a little closer.

At first glance, M87 is a typical — although bright — example of an elliptical galaxy. However, for many years it has been known that good optical photographs show a jet sticking out of the centre. See Fig. 14.1. When M87 was identified with the strong radio source Virgo A in the 1950s, it was soon realized that most of the radio emission came not from the centre of the galaxy but from this jet. In some way the jet was responsible for the unusual strength of the radio emission in this galaxy. The radio spectrum strongly suggests that the radio energy is synchrotron emission (see Chapter 12) and so is not produced by the normal emission processes from a hot gas but by high energy electrons orbiting in strong magnetic fields.

The jet is strange at optical wavelengths, too. Instead of the orangey-red light typical of the red stars in the bulk of the elliptical galaxy, the jet is much bluer. A blue colour would normally indicate the presence of hot ionized gas which we would expect to show up on optical spectra as strong emission lines. But the spectrum of the jet in M87 is completely featureless. This is unfortunate because it means that it is impossible to use the Doppler shift to measure the speed at which the jet is moving. So, although we may suspect that the jet is a mass of gas ejected from from the centre of M87, we can't prove it by direct measurement.

If the jet really *is* moving away from the centre of the galaxy, what causes it to do so? From both the optical and the radio observations we have reasons for suspecting that unusual events are going on in M87. But at first, when astronomers attempted to obtain highly detailed photos of the centre of this galaxy, they found nothing unusual. Only in the last few years was it realized that the stars near the centre of M87 were behaving strangely.

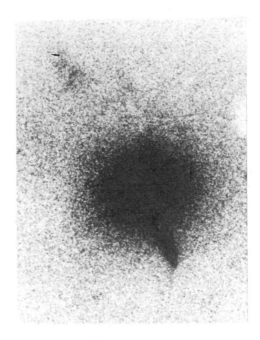

Fig. 14.1 — The exploding galaxy M87, showing the jet and possible "counter jet".

Stars moving in the gravitational field of any galaxy have different velocities.The spread in this velocity is termed the **velocity dispersion**. It is measured using the Doppler effect from the widths of the stellar spectral lines, in the same way as we discussed for the quasar absorption lines. The importance of the velocity dispersion is that it provides a means of measuring the mass of a galaxy.

To understand this, let's consider a related problem. Think about the Earth orbiting around the Sun. The mass of the Sun decides the speed at which the Earth must orbit in order to maintain its present orbit size. If the orbit were elliptical but still had the same maximum size, the Earth's speed would change at different positions in its orbit but its *average* speed would still be the same. Thus both the size of the orbit and the mass of the central body decide the average speed.

Imagine now that we change the mass of the Sun. Kepler's laws of orbital dynamics tell us what will happen. If the mass of the central body doubles and we insist that the size of the orbit stays the same, then the average speed must increase by the square root of 2.

The equation relating these values is,

$$V = 30 \sqrt{\frac{M}{A}} \quad km/s$$

where we are measuring M in terms of the Sun's mass and A in units of the Earth-Sun distance or **Astronomical Units (AUs)**. It is therefore simple to calculate the mass of the central body if the velocity dispersion is known.

But what if there *is* no central body — only a swarming mass of stars, such as we might expect in the centre of an elliptical galaxy? In this case, our equation still applies except that the mass we derive is no longer the mass of a single central object. Instead, the velocity dispersion at a particular distance D, from the centre is decided by the sum of all masses of all the stars lying within a sphere of radius D. This means that we have a direct method of estimating the mass of stars lying within different distances of the centre of the galaxy.

The observations of M87 showed that the calculated mass near the nucleus was far too big to be explained just by the visible stars. It was expected that the velocity dispersion would decrease as measurements were made closer and closer to the nucleus of M87 since we would expect less and less mass. Instead the astronomers found that the velocity dispersion measurements predicted an unseen, compact mass of around 10^8 solar masses lurking at the centre. Was this unseen mass responsible in some way for the unusual activity in the galaxy? We shall return to discuss what these objects might be in Chapter 15. For the moment, though, we shall turn our attention to the discovery of what appeared to be a different sort of object altogether.

The BL Lacs

In the mid-1960s an American radio telescope at the delightfully named Vermillion River Observatory was making a new survey. One of the radio sources found by the observers was designated VRO[1] 42.22.01. It was the first of a new class of object which was to prove crucial in understanding the quasars.

The great majority of radio sources emit smaller amounts of energy at high frequencies than at low frequencies, while many quasars have almost "flat" spectra and are roughly equally strong at both high and low frequencies. On the other hand, VRO 42.22.01 had a most unusual radio spectrum: it appeared to be much stronger at high than at low frequencies. This in itself suggested that it might be some sort of unusual powerful quasar. Astronomers made a search of the optical photographs covering the area of the sky around the source, but could make no identification. However, this was not surprising since VRO 42.22.01 lay close to the galactic plane where thousands of bright stars abound: the available radio position was simply not good enough to pinpoint one of them.

It required Canadian astronomers to determine a much better position for the source using the Algonquin Park telescope and find a 14th magnitude star-like object lying right on the radio position. Compared with an average quasar this was extremely bright and was strongly reminiscent of the discovery of 3C373 some

---

[1]The VRO of course stands for Vermillion River Observatory. The other numbers *do* have a meaning but they are of no importance to our story.

years earlier. But VRO 42.22.01 did not behave like a quasar: the star-like object which had been identified with it was violently variable, changing in brightness by a factor of 2 or more over just a few days.

Although a 14th magnitude quasar or radio galaxy would be very bright, this is very faint by the standards of ordinary catalogued stars. Even so, it occurred to the Canadians that such a spectacularly variable "star" might have been recorded on photographic plates taken years earlier. And so it turned out. The object was indeed well-known and catalogued under the variable star name of **BL Lacertae**. Since the "star" had been known by this name years before it appeared in the radio catalogues, it has since become the preferred designation.

In the years following BL Lacertae's discovery, many other similar objects have been found. Following the usual astronomical convention, astronomers have named this whole *class* of object as BL Lacertae objects, more usually spoken of as "**BL Lacs**". In some ways this is confusing and a pity, since it suggests that these extragalactic objects *are* variable stars which the BL Lacs most certainly are not. But the alternatives proposed over the years, such as **Blazars** and **Lacertae** just don't seem to have caught on.

As regards their variability, the BL Lacs appeared to be similar to, although much more extreme than the quasars. However in two other properties they were quite unlike the quasars. First was that at radio wavelengths they were very highly polarized. Let's consider what this means.

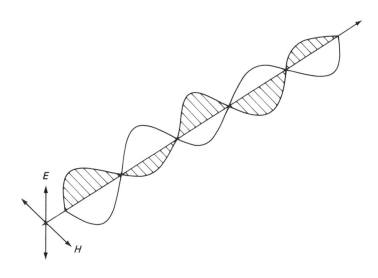

Fig. 14.2 — Schematic representation of a polarized electromagnetic wave showing the "*E* " and "*H* " components at right angles to each other and to the direction of the waves travel.

As we discussed in Chapter 3, electromagnetic radiation consists of an interaction of electrical and magnetic waves from vibrating electrons. The electrical part of the wave from each electron — called the *E* part — and the magnetic part of the wave — the H part — travel at right angles to each other. (See Fig 14.2.) Such a wave is called *polarized* and possesses special properties. For example, it may or may not pass through a block of plastic depending on whether the wave is aligned correctly with the atoms in the block. A familiar everyday example is the operation of "Polaroid" sun-glasses which prevent the glaring polarized light reflected off a roadway from entering a car driver's eyes. In general, however, we are often not aware of polarization effects because waves are generally emitted not from just one atom but from many. The random orientations of the vibrations of the electrons in these atoms causes the combined radiation to have very little polarization on average, even though the individual emissions do.

However, it is possible to find exceptions to this rule. In space, energetic charged particles, such as electrons may all be moving together in spirals in magnetic fields and *not* vibrating and radiating at random. The polarization of the individual contributions to the total radiation is determined by the shape of the magnetic field and how the particles are injected into it. If injection occurs at only a few places and the magnetic fields are sufficiently aligned then the emerging radiation can be highly polarized. We know that this occurs in some supernova remnants, such as the Crab Nebula for both optical and radio emission. It also seems to take place in the BL Lacs.

The high degree of polarization in the BL Lacs strongly suggested that the magnetic fields and particles responsible for the radio emission were very much more aligned than in either quasars or the radio galaxies. Furthermore it argued for an injection or explosion of highly energetic electrons from a relatively compact part of the object. In many ways BL Lac seemed somehow to be a "simpler" thing than a quasar. Furthermore its fast variability suggested it was *smaller*.

The second way in which the BL Lacs differed from quasars was that the optical spectrum of BL Lac showed neither strong emission or absorption lines. This was a severe shock. It was also rather disappointing since it implied that a redshift (and therefore a distance) to the object couldn't be determined. Another thing was apparent from the spectrum: the overall "shape" of the continuum radiation was very "red", suggesting that there was either a strong excess of red light from the object or a deficiency of blue light. Fig. 14.3 shows what we mean. In this regard BL Lac was quite unlike the blue colours of the majority of the quasars. What was the cause of this unusual spectrum?

Two things have to be present in order to produce emission lines, as we mentioned in Chapter 12. There must be gas available — and a sufficient source of high energy photons available to ionize it. The absence of emission lines in the spectrum of BL Lac suggested that at least one of these prerequisites was missing. But which one? The overall red continuum of BL Lac might suggest that it was the ultraviolet photons which were lacking. On the other hand, even a few such photons would be sufficient to produce at least weak emission lines. Furthermore, the strong radio emission argued that very energetic processes were taking place in the object. And recent observations have shown that BL Lac objects are very often strong X-ray sources. Both of these pieces of evidence suggest that there is indeed a plentiful supply of high energy radiation and that we should see emission lines in the BL Lacs if gas were present. Today, the reason for the lack of lines is still not completely resolved; however it seems clear that there must be relatively little gas around these objects, unlike the quasars.

There is one other well-known class of extragalactic object whose members are also both red and almost totally devoid of gas — the elliptical galaxies. Perhaps the BL Lacertae might be related to the giant elliptical galaxies? But there were several objections to this idea. First, if BL Lac were some sort of elliptical galaxy, why did it not show an extended diffuse appearance on a photograph: a typical giant elliptical of the 14th magnitude would have a size of many arcseconds and would be clearly visible on a plate. Second, elliptical galaxies cannot change their apparent brightness in periods of a week or so. This follows from the sort of argument we used in Chapter 11. The minimum time for variation corresponds to the light travel time across the galaxy's diameter. Third, and perhaps most convincingly, if BL Lac *was* an elliptical it should show the characteristic absorption lines of the aggregate of millions of small red stars in its optical spectrum. No, BL Lac clearly was not just a simple elliptical galaxy, even a very violent one.

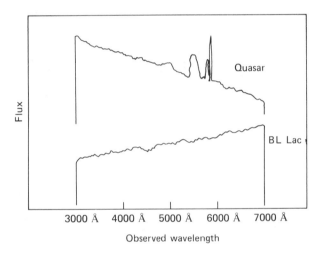

Fig. 14.3 — Representation of the typical spectra of a quasar (upper) and BL Lac (lower) showing that the BL Lac object is noticeably "redder" than the quasar.

So, what was it? A clue was provided when some very deep plates were taken of BL Lac. They showed that the object was indeed diffuse and showed a sort of "fuzzy" halo surrounding the bright central core. Astronomers slowly realized that BL Lac was actually some sort of bright explosive event occurring at the centre of a distant and much fainter galaxy. The key observations to confirm this were made by a group of Australian astronomers working on another object similar to BL Lac which showed many of the same properties.

This new object was called **AP Lib**. Once again, a recently identified radio source had been mistaken for a variable star. But AP Lib looked even more like a galaxy suffering a violent event than did BL Lac. (See Fig. 14.4.) The Australian astronomers obtained two optical spectra of AP Lib: one of the core region and one of the surrounding halo. The halo, when isolated from the far brighter central core object, indeed showed many of the spectral features suggestive of a galaxy. It certainly was beginning to look as though a quasar-like object had at last been found in an rather ordinary galaxy.

Fig. 14.4 — Photograph of the BL Lac object AP LIB showing that it is noticeably "fuzzy" and galaxy-like.

But there were still problems: the absorption spectrum of the halo "galaxy" — if indeed it *was* a galaxy — gave a redshift of only 0.05 . Although it was interesting to determine what was hoped to be the true distance to AP Lib, it also had the unfortunate implication that these objects were very close. If they were related to quasars then they were very close to us in universal terms and not very luminous. At best, they could only be described as "mini-quasars."

To the present

During the last twenty years, many more BL Lac objects have been discovered. Their redshifts now range up to nearly 3 and they can no longer be regarded as the "poor relations" of the quasar world. Their energy output is considerably greater than many objects which astronomers are quite happy to call quasars. The consensus of opinion is that the BL Lacs are some simple or "raw" form of a quasar which occurs when little gas is present in the parent galaxy. The lack of gas prevents the formation of emission lines. However, its absence also allows us to see right down to the core of the "central engine" which appears to be the prime site of the explosion. In a typical quasar, there is surrounding gas which re-processes the highly energetic radiation and particles coming from the central engine into a blue continuum of light and "smears out" fast variations in both light and radio waves. This gas becomes ionized by the radiation, thereby producing emission lines and often absorbing the radio emission from the central object. Because of this latter effect, quasars may or may not be detectable as radio sources. On the other hand, the BL Lacs, being nearly devoid of gas, should show no emission lines, while their radio emission should be strong since it is not attenuated by any gas.

And, indeed, modern observations show that all BL Lacs are radio sources, whereas relatively few of the known quasars show detectable levels of radio emission.

Whatever may be the true nature of the BL Lacs we are confident that they form an important link between the galaxies and the quasars. It is likely that they are providing us with our closest and clearest view yet of the explosive events which take place in the cores of the quasars.

15

The Central Engine

In the previous chapter we saw that both quasars and BL Lacs seem to be violently explosive events taking place in the centres of some galaxies. In fact some authors describe all such phenomena as **active galactic nuclei.** But where does the energy come from that powers these violent explosions? At first glance, the most luminous quasars and BL Lacs seem so far away that there appears to be little hope of ever answering the question. But one of the delights of astronomy is that even these seemingly "impossible" problems can be tackled by a judicious combination of observation and theoretical interpretation.

Energy processes

To start with, let's get some idea of the rough numbers involved. We know of many ways of liberating large amounts of energy here on Earth. Chemical explosions, electrical discharges and nuclear detonations all come to mind. Of these, nuclear fusion is undoubtedly the most powerful. It is the process which powers the Sun and stars and which, one day, may unfortunately destroy mankind.

The rate of energy output of the Sun is 10^{33} ergs per second. On the other hand, that of a bright, active quasar is in the vicinity of 10^{45} ergs per second, almost a million million times greater. Thus, if the energy production processes in the quasars were similar to those in the stars, then we would need around 10^{12} stars to do the job. Now we might think that this was reasonable: after all, there are around 10^{12} stars in some of the largest galaxies. But the size of the energy producing region in a typical quasar or BL Lac is very much less than that of a galaxy, as we saw in the previous chapter. If we consider only a region of a typical galaxy comparable in volume to the active region of a quasar, we would expect to find only 1 or 2 stars there at most; far too few to supply the required energy output. However, despite this problem, let us look at nuclear fusion in more detail.

Einstein's law of mass–energy equivalence, the famous $E = mc^2$, states that for every gram of mass totally converted into energy we liberate about 10^{21} ergs. In terrestrial terms, this is a staggering amount. For example, a teaspoonful of water, if totally annhililated, would produce enough energy to power a city the size of London for around a whole day! Yet again, the whole of the devastation of the Hiroshima bomb in 1944 was produced by the annihilation of only 1 gram of material. But even with this awesome efficiency, we would need to annihilate about 10^{24} grams of matter per second to produce energy at the same rate as a quasar.

Unfortunately *total* annihilation of matter is impossible in practice, even with the violent processes that occur in quasars. We would probably be nearer the mark in discussing efficiency rates of only 1% percent or so and thus talking about a necessary destruction rate of 10^{26} grams per second. Even so, 10^{26} grams is an enormous amount of mass, equal to about $1/60$ of the mass of the whole Earth. To power a quasar, therefore, we would need to destroy a mass the size of the Earth every minute. Or, to put it another way, each year the quasar would swallow up a mass equal to that of the Sun!

However, as we said above, the surprising thing about the energy output of the quasars is not that it is so large — after all, galaxies have comparable rates — but that it comes from such a small volume. We calculated in the previous chapter that the emitting region in a typical quasar or BL Lac could not be much bigger than the size of the solar system. We arrived at this figure by considering how fast the brightness of the quasars changed with time — we saw that it was very difficult to explain changes on a timescale as small as a few hours unless the size of the emitting region, too, was less than a few light-hours.

What can this enormously powerful and compact source of energy be? After all, nuclear fusion is the energy source that powers the stars. It is the most powerful energy source we know of and one we are still quite incapable of controlling here on Earth. To understand what powers the quasars, we need to find an energy source millions of times more efficient.

So far, there has only been one serious suggestion: gravity. A gravitational field is most unusual. It is the *only* force we know of which can lead to an almost unlimited release of energy. Before going on to discuss what we mean, though, let's think about a simple *non*-gravitational example.

Consider an ordinary, elastic band. When the band is stretched it has more energy than when it is loose. If the band is released, it looses energy until it regains its non-stretched shape. Thus the forces of elasticity act in such a way as to reduce the amount of energy in the band. Left to itself with no other forces acting on it, the band will quickly contract and reach a state of rest.

Now consider the case of a space probe out of control falling directly into the Sun. (We shan't be concerned about what happens when the space probe actually *hits* the Sun, just what goes on before that.) When the probe is far from the Sun, its kinetic energy (energy of motion) may be quite low. As it falls towards the Sun, its energy increases and at an ever increasing rate: there is no obvious "state of rest". Gravity is the only force in nature that we know of that behaves in this way: all other forces resemble the example of the elastic band and try to produce a state of rest. Physicists would say that the reason that gravity is different is because the "energy associated with a gravitational field is *negative* energy". But this is just a fancy way of restating what we said earlier — the energy of the body increases as it "gives in" to the force.

Of course, the probe falling into the Sun hits the surface and burns up: non-gravitational forces have come into play. But what would happen if the Sun were very small? In this case the probe would gather more and more kinetic energy as it fell. How much could it get if the Sun were infinitely compact? Well that's obviously just a theoretical question — but the theoretical answer is that it could get *infinite* energy. Clearly this is exactly the sort of energy source we are looking for to power the quasars!

However the reader may suspect that something is wrong with this argument. And he would be right. Real bodies in the universe can not become infinitely small — or rather, if they do, we cannot see them. Nor can in-falling objects attain infinite energy. As far as a serious discussion goes (meaning one in terms of physics we can believe in!) the most-compact object possible is a **black hole**. But to understand what these strange sounding objects are, we must look at gravity in more detail.

The nature of gravity

Consider two bodies: say, you and the Earth[1]. If you fall off a mountain, or even a chair, you feel the gravitational pull of the Earth. The Earth also feels exactly the same amount of pull because the forces are the same. On the other hand, the *results* of the two forces are *not* the same! The Earth hardly moves, while you certainly do. As viewed by an impartial, exterior observer, however, only one important thing has happened: you and the Earth have got closer together. In doing so, energy has been converted from the **potential energy** of the gravitational field into **kinetic energy** of your downfall and the Earth's "upfall".

Conversely, if we want to separate you from the Earth, we must supply energy to the gravitational field. The easiest way to do this is to reverse the process we described above. We supply you with a lot of kinetic energy, point you upwards and let you go. The kinetic energy is converted slowly into potential energy of the gravitational field as you slow down and, unfortunately for you, you probably convert the gravitational energy back into kinetic energy as you come clattering down. But you may not: if the amount of energy we give you is enough, then it is possible to escape from the Earth altogether. This is, of course, exactly what the Apollo astronauts did in the late 1960s and early 1970s as they began their epic journeys to the Moon. A sufficient amount of initial kinetic energy will allow you to escape from the Earth's gravitational field altogether. But how much is "sufficient"?

Fortunately the calculation is easy. We'll call the mass of the big body (perhaps the Earth) M. The mass of the little body (perhaps you) we'll call m. And we'll place the little body on the surface of the big body which we'll suppose has a radius R.

With these assumptions, Newtonian physics tells us that the gravitational potential energy of the *little* body in the field of the *big* body is equal to

$$-\frac{G.m.M}{R}$$

where the symbol G is a constant that has a value of about 6.7×10^{-8} if we use the "centimetre-gram-second" (**cgs**) system of units. If we wanted to measure the amount of the potential energy of the *big* body in the field of the *little* body, then the right expression would be

$$-\frac{G.M.m}{R}$$

which has exactly the same value This shows that the gravitational potential energy does *not* "belong" to one body or the other: rather it is a property of *both* bodies and their distance apart (which is also R in the present case, since we assuming that the size of the little body is trivial compared to R).

Notice, too, another thing about the above equation; it has a negative sign in front of it. This means that if the two bodies get closer together (R gets smaller) then the energy gets "bigger-in-a-negative-sense", meaning that it gets smaller.

---

[1] In this chapter we shall revert to talking about gravity in terms of the simple, old-fashioned Newtonian theory. This is not because the ideas of General Relativity we discussed in Chapter 6 are wrong, but because the Newtonian approach is much simpler to work with and quite adequate for our purposes. Everything we are about to say could be done using General Relativity – but this chapter would be three times as long!

Since we believe total energy can neither be created nor destroyed[1], only exchanged, this decreasing energy must be exactly counterbalanced by an increase of energy elsewhere: in this case, the kinetic energy of the infalling body. How negative can the gravitational energy get? Well that depends on how close we bring the two bodies: if they became extremely close (R very, small indeed) then, according to the above equation, the energy would become enormously negative, as we said earlier.

Of course, in the case of you and the Earth, there is no problem — you can't fall through the Earth's surface because it is solid (eventually). But we shall see that there are important exceptions elsewhere in the universe. How much energy would two bodies have that were very far apart? That's easy: we just put R = infinity into the above formula and we obtain an answer of zero, since any mass divided by an incredibly big number is essentially zero. This zero energy at infinity, then, is the *maximum* amount of energy that two gravitating bodies can have.

Now let's see where the gravitational energy goes when an object falls into a gravitational field. The expression for the kinetic energy of the little body, m , is

$$K = \frac{1}{2} m.V^2$$

We can now calculate how much kinetic energy we must supply to two bodies to completely free them from each other's gravitational influence by separating them to infinity. If they presently have a deficit (negative) energy of

$$-\frac{G.m.M}{R}$$

and we want to supply the amount of this deficit from kinetic energy, then the required amount must be

$$K = \frac{m.V^2}{2} = \frac{G.m.M}{R}$$

And so the speed that we need to give you so that you will never fall back to the Earth — or **escape velocity** — is

$$V_{escape} = \sqrt{\frac{2.G.M}{R}}$$

Notice an important thing here: the two "little m s" have cancelled, meaning that the escape velocity *does not* depend on the mass of the little body which is escaping. It is the same for all objects.

In the case of the Earth, this velocity is about 10 kilometres per second, equivalent to 7 miles per second or 40,000 km per hour. Fast indeed! And this is the speed you would have to attain to completely escape from the Earth's gravity. It is no wonder that the Atlas rockets used for the Apollo space missions used as much fuel in one second at blast-off as the average family car would consume in petrol in many years!

The idea of escape velocity was well understood even by Newton. He reasoned correctly that if a body were given enough speed it would escape from the Earth

---

[1] This is only true of physics experiments conducted over relatively small parts of the universe. For the universe as a whole, energy is *not* conserved, as we shall discuss in Chapter 17

forever. But how far? The calculation above suggests that if the rocket is given a velocity slightly greater than 10 km/s it will escape to infinity. But our derivation assumed that the Earth and rocket were the only two important gravitating bodies in the universe. The presence of other objects means that things aren't quite so simple.

The Earth is moving in a very nearly circular orbit around the Sun which has a dominating influence on the motions of the Earth and all other planets. So a rocket that escapes from the Earth will not necessarily escape from the solar system. But, just as we calculated the escape velocity from the Earth, so we can calculate the escape velocity from the solar system. At the average distance of the Earth from the Sun we find V_{escape} = 42 km/s, derived from our "escape velocity equation" using the Sun's mass (2×10^{23} g) for M and the Earth-Sun distance (1.5×10^{13} cm) for D. Even when free of the solar system our rocket cannot escape to infinity: it must also escape from the gravitational field of our galaxy. To do so, requires a further velocity of around 200 km/s

But before journeying too far into the depths of space, let's return to the solar system and think about what happens if our parent body is more massive than the Earth. We could, for example, imagine that we are living on Jupiter. Here the escape velocity is much higher, not just because the *mass* of Jupiter is larger than that of the earth, but because the important ratio M/R which occurs in the escape velocity equation is greater for Jupiter. Using the appropriate values for mass and radius we find that the escape velocity from Jupiter's surface is

$$V_{escape\,from\,Jupiter} \; = \; 61 \; km/s$$

In a like manner, we can also calculate the escape velocity from the Sun's surface (assuming you were brave enough to venture there!) as

$$V_{escape\,from\,Sun} \; = \; 620 \; km/s$$

But let us state the important point again. The escape velocity is not dictated by either the mass M or the radius R of the parent body: the escape velocity from our galaxy is smaller than from the Sun. Nor is it determined simply by the density ρ (which is proportional to M/R^3): the density of our galaxy is much smaller than that of the Earth, yet it has a higher escape velocity. Rather V_{escape} is decided by the ratio of M/R, a quantity which unfortunately has no name in physics. To help the discussion in the following sections we shall talk about this important ratio, M/R, as the "**compactness**".

From rockets to black holes

So far, we have talked about rockets flying away from the surface of other massive bodies. But what happens if we are talking about *light*? Any form of electromagnetic radiation consists of photons, or quanta, which can sometimes act like particles. In discussing rockets we said that the rocket lost its energy of motion as it climbed out of the gravitational field and thus slowed down. On the other hand, light always travels at the same speed c, as we discussed in Chapter 6. Does light behave like a rocket when climbing out of the gravitational field of a planet or star? If so, what does it mean to say that it loses energy?

Electromagnetic radiation leaving the surface of a star for a trip through space changes from high-energy blue quanta to lower-energy red quanta. Thus we expect light "climbing" out of a gravitational field to be redshifted. Unfortunately to rigorously determine the size of this redshift requires some rather involved physics. What follows is an argument that is not accurate — in fact it will probably have some physicists sadly shaking their heads. Nevertheless it will serve to show the reader the outline of an important result.

Think about a photon of light with a frequency v_0 at the surface of a large body of mass M and radius R [1]. The energy of this photon is related to its frequency by the equation

$$E_0 = hv_0$$

If the photon now climbs out of the gravitational field, it will be redshifted to a lower frequency v_1 and have an energy $E_1 = hv_1$. The loss of energy is

$$(E_0 - E_1) = h(v_0 - v_1)$$

which must have been gained by the gravitational field. If we think of a photon as having a mass m, then we can write

$$(E_0 - E_1) = h(v_0 - v_1) = \frac{GMm}{R}$$

But what *is* the mass of a photon? This is where our derivation becomes sloppy: we shall assume without justification that the energy of a photon, hv, is equal to the quantity mc^2 as suggested by Einstein's equation. Doing this we have

$$h(v_0 - v_1) = \frac{GM}{R} \cdot \frac{hv_1}{c^2}$$

or

$$\frac{(v_0 - v_1)}{v_1} = \frac{GM}{c^2R}$$

The quantity in brackets is, of course, just the redshift which we normally write as

$$z = \frac{(\lambda - \lambda_0)}{\lambda_0}$$

So we have calculated the redshift of light from a gravitating body as

$$z = \frac{GM}{Rc^2}$$

---

[1] We use frequency here rather than wavelength because it will make the equations a little simpler. Modern astronomers are quite used to talking about wavelengths and frequencies interchangeably. Just remember that wavelength multiplied by frequency is equal to the speed of light.

Notice an interesting thing: z is simply the ratio of the square of the escape velocity from the body to the square of the fundamental velocity. So we could write

$$z = \frac{V^2_{escape}}{c^2}$$

In the case of the Sun, we saw $V_{escape} = 42$ km/s and so z is only around 0.0001, which is very small indeed. On the other hand, some of the compact white dwarf stars have escape velocities of around several thousands of kilometres per second and hence correspondingly greater gravitational redshifts.

As the parent bodies become more and more compact, the escape velocity approaches the fundamental velocity c. Our equation would suggest that the redshift tends to 1. Actually things are much more spectacular: if we had used a full, rigorous derivation, we should have obtained the accurate relationship

$$1 + z = \frac{1}{1 - \frac{GM}{c^2R}}$$

which would show that the redshift becomes *infinite* when

$$\frac{GM}{R} = c^2$$

Objects for which the redshift becomes infinite and for which $GM/R = c^2$ have been called **black holes.** They are the most compact objects which our knowledge of physics allows us to discuss. Another way of defining a black hole is that it is an object which is sufficiently compact that the escape velocity from its surface is equal to the fundamental velocity. We must emphasize though that, so far, no convincing examples of these ultimately compact objects have been definitely observed by astronomers, although their presence is suspected in some binary X-ray emitting stars.

As we shall discuss in the next section, a massive black hole near the centre of a quasar could provide a very powerful source of energy. Massive black holes don't have to have a particularly high density: one with a mass equal to that of a typical galaxy would have a density lower than that of the air we breathe here on Earth! Nevertheless, their "compactness" is such that their total gravitational effect in redshifting light and liberating energy can be awesome

Energy from black holes

How good would a black hole be at producing the amounts of energy we need to power the quasars? In the previous section we saw that any black hole has a "compactness", M/R, so large that the escape velocity at its surface is approximately equal to the fundamental velocity, meaning that

$$c^2 \approx \frac{GM}{R}$$

Fig. 15.1 shows the radii and masses for several typical astronomical bodies.

Remember that GM/R in the above equation is the energy per unit mass that must be supplied to any object for it to escape to infinity from the surface of a body.

Equally it also gives the maximum amount of energy you can get by letting 1 gram of mass fall into a gravitating body[1].

This means is that if we have an amount of mass m falling into a black hole of mass M, then the maximum amount of energy we can get from it is equal to

$$E = m \cdot \frac{GM}{R}$$

or, since $GM/R = c^2$ for a black hole, we have $E = mc^2$.

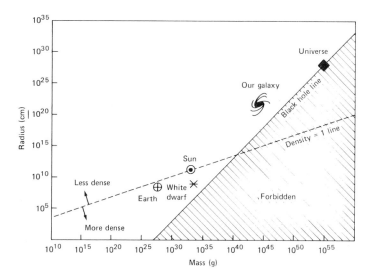

Fig. 15.1 — Several astronomical objects plotted on a (logarithmic) graph of radius versus mass. The "black hole line" shows the radius that an object of a particular mass must have in order to become a black hole. Objects more compact than this (smaller radii) are forbidden by the ordinary laws of physics. Also plotted is the line corresponding to unit density. Note that it is quite possible for an object much less dense than another to be in greater danger of becoming a black hole. The Earth and our galaxy form such a pair.

This expression should look very familiar to readers. It happens to be the same as Einstein's famous energy-mass equation. Put in other terms, the maximum amount of energy that we can obtain from a body falling into a black hole is, coincidentally, equal to the rest mass of the infalling body. This is encouraging in our search for the energy source of the quasars because we know we are looking

---

[1] To a very good approximation it doesn't matter where it falls from, because the overwhelming amount of energy is gained in the last few per cent of its infall: what went before hardly matters.

for a mechanism that can provide a power output equivalent to the complete destruction of one stellar mass every year.

Astronomers have speculated that the quasars may be galaxies which contain a massive black hole at their centre. Stars in the central regions of the galaxy fall into the black hole liberating large amounts of gravitational energy. But it is no use having a massive source of energy if this energy disappears into the black hole! We want it to be liberated as radiation, so that it can explain what we see coming from the bowels of the quasar.

To understand what might happen if a star were to fall into a black hole, we must first return to "ordinary" physics and understand something about **tidal effects.** Consider again the example of our space probe falling into the Sun. While still far from the Sun, the main force on the probe is just the simple "pull" of the Sun which causes it to move closer. But this force produces another although much weaker effect: if the probe is relatively large, the side nearer the Sun feels a slightly stronger force than the side of the probe which is farther from the Sun. This follows because the force of gravity is an inverse force — the farther away, the weaker the force becomes. The main effect is for the probe to fall towards the Sun in response to the average strength of these forces. But because the "near side" of the probe is attracted slightly more strongly than the "far side", the probe also feels a force that tries to "stretch" it out along a line pointing towards and away from the Sun. If the probe were not made of metal but of some very weak material, such as plastic, then it actually would deform.

The size of this stretching or "tidal" force can be easily computed. If a space probe has a radius r and is at a distance R from the Sun which has a mass of M, then the tidal force is

$$T = \frac{GM}{R^3} . 2r$$

Note that this tidal force equation has an R to the *cube* power on the "bottom", rather than the R squared we would expect for the actual gravity force itself. This cube power means that the stretching force increases more rapidly than the attracting force as a body gets closer to the central mass. However, in most of "ordinary" astronomy, the results of this stretching force are quite modest. For example, the water of the Earth's oceans rises and falls by only small amounts as a result of the combined tidal forces of the Sun and the Moon. But we shall see that, near to the very powerful gravitational fields of a black hole, things become far more spectacular.

Consider a star falling into a large black hole. To make things definite, we'll suppose that the star has a mass, m similar to the Sun's and that the black hole has a mass, M, considerably bigger than the Sun's[1]. This allows us to say that the Sun is falling into the black hole rather than the other way round! The force that holds the Sun together is, of course, also gravity and its value at the surface is equal to

$$f = \frac{G\,m}{r^2}$$

where r is the radius of the Sun. Now, if a stretching force of roughly this same amount, f, were to be applied to the Sun, it would clearly break apart. (Actually a

---

[1] The reader should not be confused by the fact that the mass of the Sun was called M in an earlier example but is m here. Just remember M is the bigger mass in both examples.

rather smaller force would do the job because the gas and radiation pressures in the Sun are trying to expand it anyway. But we are only after approximate answers here.) So, let's ask the question: "At what distance, D , from a black hole would the tidal force become equal to the bonding, gravity force of the Sun ?"

Clearly we must have

$$\frac{Gm}{r^2} = \frac{GM}{D^3} \cdot 2r$$

or, simplifying things a bit,

$$D^3 = 2 r^3 \frac{M}{m}$$

This equation gives the distance at which a typical star like the Sun would be ripped to bits by the black hole. Now let's put in some real numbers. For the Sun, we can use $r = 7 \times 10^{10}$ cm and $m = 2 \times 10^{33}$ g and we get

$$D = 0.7 . M^{1/3} \ cm$$

where M is measured in grams. As we might have expected, D gets bigger if M gets bigger. This relation is graphed in Fig. 15.2.

From before, we also know that the radius, R , of our black hole can be calculated from its mass by the relation

$$R = \frac{GM}{c^2}$$

and this relation, too, is shown in Fig. 15.2. This graph tells us a most important thing: if a star is falling into a *low*-mass black hole (line A in Fig. 15.2), then it will be ripped apart *before* it gets to the black hole's surface. On the other hand, a similar star approaching a *high* -mass black hole (line B) is "swallowed whole" by the black hole before it can be disrupted. This means that stars falling into high-mass black holes may produce lots of energy *but little or none of this energy escapes*. On the other hand, stars falling into low-mass black holes are ripped apart. Detailed calculations have shown that the fragments of the star will collide with each other in the strong gravitational field, becoming hot and radiating a broad spectrum of electromagnetic energy. In essence, the gravitational, "$E = mc^2$" energy of the black hole is made available to the outside world, just as we require to power our quasars.

Unfortunately we cannot go into the details of what takes place. Suffice it to say that theoretical astrophysicists have calculated that the best objects for producing the variety of radiation we see from the quasars are black holes whose masses are *just* less than the intersection mass in Fig. 15.2. This mass has a value somewhat bigger than 100 million times the mass of the Sun. Smaller black holes would not be as effective at capturing stars: larger black holes *would* be very effective but would "swallow the stars whole" without allowing the radiation to escape.

How to see them

If such violent events as we described in the previous section are going on at the centres of quasars, why can we not see them? The answer goes back to the calculation of the size of the emitting region which we made in Chapter 14. There

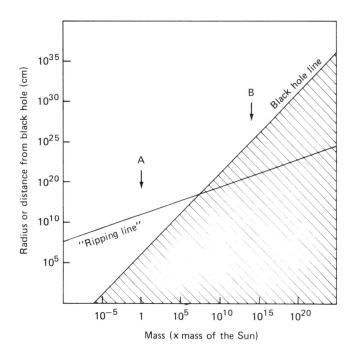

Fig. 15.2 — The distance at which a star of 1 solar mass is tidally ripped apart by a more massive object is plotted in the radius-mass diagram. Also shown is the "black hole line" as in Fig 15.1. A star approaching a black hole a few hundred solar masses in size (A) is ripped apart before being "swallowed" by the black hole. On the other hand, a high mass black hole (B) swallows the star before it can be ripped apart. The most efficient black holes for producing energy are probably those which have a high mass but also allow the energy to escape. They have a mass corresponding to the crossing point of the two lines in the figure.

we found a diameter of only a few lightyears or lightweeks, which implies an angular diameter of just a few thousandths of a second of arc at the distance of a typical quasar. Such a size is quite impossible to measure with an optical telescope because of the limitations imposed by the Earth's turbulent atmosphere.

The first chance of imaging the core regions of the quasars was provided by radio astronomy. In the earliest days of this new window on the universe, determined positions had been very poor, far worse than produced by optical telescopes. But radio interferometers changed all that. We discussed their operation in Chapter 11 in conjunction with the discovery of the first quasar, 3C273. However, "ordinary" interferometers are limited to positional accuracies of around $1/10$ of a second of arc because of the difficulties of electronically linking together widely separated telescopes.

In the late 1960s the technique of Very Long Baseline Interferometry (VLBI) was developed at the radio observatories in America and Canada[1]. This method did not link the telescopes electrically but, instead, recorded the signals arriving at both telescopes by means of video tape recorders. Tapes from these

---

[1] Actually the Canadians, with typical reserve, called it merely Long Baseline Interferometry. Only later did the Americans, with typical flamboyance, call it *Very* Long Baseline Interferometry!

recorders could later be brought together and played back in synchronization, thus "re-living" the observations.

The main difficulty with the technique is achieving the necessary very high levels of synchronization. This requires very accurate time signals to be recorded on a time track along with the sky signals. The "clocks" used are often hydrogen maser frequency standard and have an accuracy of better than a few seconds per century. Because there was no need to directly connect the telescopes there seemed to be no limitation as to how far apart the telescope antennas could be. In particular it was possible to use telescopes in different countries to achieve very long baselines.

The value of this technique in investigating the structure of radio sources at previously unprecedented resolutions was quickly realized around the world. By the late 1970s, many observatories, often on different continents, were collaborating to produce maps of sources showing structure on angular size scales as small as a thousandth of a second of arc — milliarcsecs).

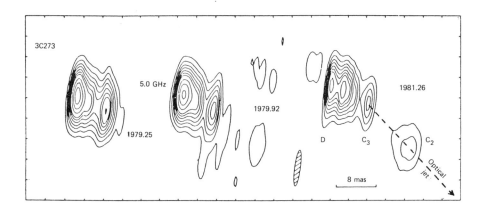

Fig. 15.3 — Radio contour plot of the central regions of the quasar 3C273 showing a component being ejected. (Courtesy *Astrophysical Journal*.)

These early results of observations of the flat-radio-spectrum quasars often showed a single point-like source right on the radio position and with a weaker, more extended structure around it. But, in some cases, the picture looked for all the world like a central source that had ejected another radio source component. (See Fig. 15.3.) Radio astronomers seemed to have found features very similar to the optical jets which optical astronomers had seen in 3C273 and M87 but on a much smaller and more detailed scale. Some observers argued that there was, as yet, no firm evidence that these "jets", as they were christened, actually *were* ejecta. However, the definitive test was obviously to see if these jets moved outwards with time.

At first the the radio data was too sparse to make proper maps: all that could be done was to *infer* movement. Computers were used to simulate what *would* be seen *if* the jets were moving in a particular way. These "computer fits" seemed to show that the jet sources did move and that the separations of the radio components increased appreciably over several months. But the greatest shock was that the rates of expansion of the jet appeared to be well in excess of the speed of light! If this really was an example of a large lump of matter thrown out from the core of some distant galaxy, it flatly contradicted the Special Theory of Relativity! To compound the problem, similar results were later also found for many of the BL Lac objects.

Because of the astonishing nature and importance of this discovery we shall look closely at the arguments used to determine these so-called **super-luminal** expansions in more detail. Consider a radio source which is made up of two compact components and lies at a distance D from us. If at a certain time its two components appear to have an *angular* separation, θ, then the actual or *linear* separation, S, of the two components is

$$S = D \cdot \theta$$

Furthermore, if at some later time we find that the separation has increased — say to an angular size $\theta+h$, where h is the "extra bit" — then the linear separation of the two components must also be bigger by an amount s given by

$$S+s = D \cdot (\theta+h)$$

or

$$s = D \cdot h$$

If this expansion has occurred during a time t, then the speed with which the expansion is taking place is given by the equation

$$\frac{s}{t} = D \cdot \frac{h}{t}$$

So far we have assumed that the jet is moving away from the central object along the plane of the sky: that is, in a direction making a right angle with our line of sight, which is rather unlikely. If, instead, the jet were coming almost straight at us, then the angular change we would measure would be far less than if it were moving "sideways". In fact, we can state a general rule: measuring the angular rate of expansion and using a known distance for a jet source gives us only a *lower limit* for the actual rate at which it is expanding. The problem posed by the VLBI observations of quasars was that many of them seemed to be expanding at speeds well in excess of the speed of light *even using this conservative estimate of the expansion rate* !

Let's see how astronomers came to this conclusion. In what follows, we shall ignore for the moment the complication of the direction of the expansion.

Using the equation we had above, the speed of expansion, V, is given by

$$V = D \cdot \frac{h}{t}$$

where V is the "real", linear expansion speed, measured in km per second. Remember that h is only the *change* in angular size and we can measure it from any convenient "zero" time. Rearranging this equation a bit, we get

$$h = \frac{V}{D} \cdot t$$

Now, if an object is expanding at constant speed, V, then all we have to do to measure the speed is plot a graph of h against t. The graph should be a straight line. And the *slope* of this line will tell us the important quantity (V/D).

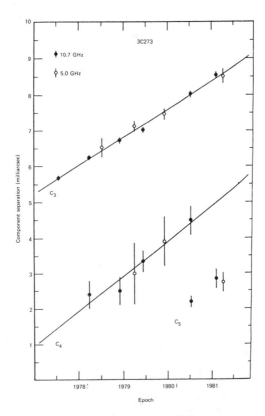

Fig. 15.4 — Some recent expansion data on the quasar 3C273 showing that components C3, C4 and C5 have separations that increase with time.

Fig. 15.4 shows some recent data for 3C273, and Table 15.1 shows the derived expansion velocities for this and some other quasars. We see at once that all the values of v are well in excess of the speed of light, c.

We shall return to discuss the significance of and a possible explanation for these superluminal expansions in the next chapter. For the moment we note that violent ejection events seem to be taking place in the centres of most quasars and BL Lac objects. The only plausible process so far put forward to explain these events is the attraction and destruction of material into a black hole. The details of the process by which this energy of tidal destruction gets turned into the outflowing jets is not at all clear. It is the subject of intensive work at observatories around the world.

Table 15.1 — The derived expansion velocities for a number of quasars.

Source	Redshift	Component	Expansion rate (milliarcsecs/yr)	Deduced V/c (if at redshift distance)
3C120	0.033	A	1.35	3.5
		B	2.57	6.8
		C	2.34	6.2
		D	1.65	4.3
BL Lac	0.070		0.6	3.3
3C273	0.158	C3	0.79	9.2
		C4	0.99	11.5
		C5	0.79	9.2
3C279	0.538		0.17	5.8
3C345	0.595	C2	0.42	15.8
		C3	0.17	6.5
			0.27	10.2
3C179	0.846		0.14	7.0
NRAO 140	1.258		0.13	9.0

(Based on data from Unwin & Biretta.)

Summary

Let us try to summarize what we have shown so far: the most powerful source of energy that we know of on Earth or in the solar system is nuclear fusion. But it is far too feeble to be the energy source of the quasars. By the time we have enough mass to power a quasar by fusion, we have an object far too big to show the rapid changes of brightness observed in the majority of objects.

A much more likely candidate for the energy source of the quasars appears to be gravity. However, we need objects with sizes very close to those of black holes to produce the large amounts of energy actually seen. To be really efficient, our black hole must have a mass close to 100 million solar masses: any bigger and the energy can't escape.

The final question we have to tackle is, "Why do we expect a black hole in a quasar, anyway?" Many astronomers suspect that the quasars are actually galaxies that developed a black hole near their centres. To start with they were perfectly ordinary galaxies full of young stars. As time went on, these stars became old and blew off their gaseous outer layers. This gas slowly fell into the centre of the galaxy and began to build up into a large, single mass. When it was small — perhaps just a few solar masses — this gas behaved much as a star itself. But eventually it became far too big to be a self-supporting star and collapsed into a black hole. Slowly at first, more stars fell into the black hole and a mini-quasar was born. As the black hole ate more and more stars, it became bigger and more effective at capturing even more objects.

When will this process end? Obviously when the supply of stars from the original galaxy runs out. The final years of the quasar when the mass of the black hole exceeds several hundred million solar masses will be relatively quiet. It can eat stars whole — but no energy will escape. Perhaps it may even be that our own galaxy is an example of a dead quasar with a massive black hole at its centre!

16

Long Ago and Far Away?

The idea that the redshifts of galaxies and quasars are directly and linearly related to their distances is at the very base of our understanding of the universe. If there should be anything wrong with this interpretation, then our only method of measuring distances to the overwhelming majority of objects in the universe would have broken down. Several times in previous chapters, however, we have encountered difficulties in believing quasars are indeed at the enormous distances their redshifts suggest. For example, in the previous chapter we saw that the apparently "superluminal" expansions in many radio quasars could be most easily explained by bringing them closer. With this in mind, in this chapter we ask "Can the redshift really be used to measure distance?"

The Hubble Law in question

Hubble first deduced his velocity–distance relation in 1929 from observations of galaxies out to a velocity of only 1000 km/s. In redshift terms this is a mere 0.003. By 1931, this relation had been extrapolated out to redshifts 20 times greater, corresponding to velocities of 20,000 km/s. Basic to Hubble's velocity — distance relation were, of course, accurate values for both distances and velocities.

The velocities were easy to measure. Originally Hubble believed they were simply Doppler shifts caused by the galaxies moving rapidly away from us. Later he seemed to be troubled by this interpretation and referred to them as "apparent velocity displacements". Of course, we now know that the redshifts of the galaxies are *not* caused by the Doppler effect (except perhaps for a small component resulting from local, gravitational motions) but are, instead, caused by the overall expansion of the universe (see Chapter 8). Whatever the cause, the recession velocities of most galaxies — even distant ones — are measured quite easily from the redshifts of their spectra.

Distances present much more of a problem. Such methods as parallax, that we discussed in Chapter 4, are hopelessly inadequate. One of the brightest and closest galaxies in the sky is M87, a giant exploding elliptical in the Virgo cluster, as we mentioned in Chapter 14. Its distance is estimated at a "mere" 30-odd million lightyears. But the angular parallax caused by the Earth's orbital motion around the Sun is a minuscule one ten-millionth of a second of arc. Such angles are quite unmeasurable with today's equipment and we confidently predict will remain so for many years to come.

However, the Earth has a much more important and faster motion that it shares with the Sun. This is its general orbital motion around our galaxy at a speed of about 250 km/s. How long must we wait in order to measure a detectable parallax change in M87 because of this motion? Even the modern methods of **Very Long Baseline Radio Interferometry (VLBI)** which we mentioned in the previous chapter have trouble measuring angles smaller than about one thousandth of a second of arc. Perhaps we might expect an improvement by a factor of 10 or even 100 in the near future with space-orbiting VLBI telescopes. But even so, the time we would have to wait between our measurements would be 100 years. Not perhaps an impossible period of time — but we should obviously start on this observing programme as soon as possible! Unfortunately M87 is one of the nearest galaxies that we are interested in and its distance can be reliably estimated by better means. In general, it looks as though we can dismiss the parallax method for the more distant objects.

To find the distances to objects in the greater part of the universe we have to use the concept of the standard candle that we discussed in Chapter 3. The reader will remember that the method relies on the fact that we somehow know the real, intrinsic brightness, or luminosity of an object. If so, then we can calculate its distance from the inverse square law by measuring how bright it *appears* to be in our telescopes.

There are two difficulties with this method: first, how sure are we of our estimates of the luminosity? And second, how do we know that the inverse square law really works — particularly at the large distances that we will be measuring in cosmology? These two problems are at the heart of our understanding of the universe and so it will pay us to look at them closely.

So far, mankind has travelled a negligible distance from the mother planet Earth. Negligible, that is, compared with the size even of the solar system, let alone the size of our galaxy or the universe. Similarly, most of our understanding of the true luminosity of objects in the universe must come from assuming that distant stars and galaxies are similar to those nearer home. In the case of the inverse square law, we have no direct proof that it is valid elsewhere in the universe and over distances much larger than the size of the solar system. We must put our faith in the idea of homogeneity; not only in the distribution of matter but also by assuming there is no reason for the laws of physics to differ in remote parts of the universe from those we derive locally. With the appropriate care and these assumptions it is possible to determine the luminosities of stars from their spectra and hence find their distances.

As we move farther afield in our galaxy, these spectroscopic distances become much more difficult to measure. Instead we must look for a new standard candle that is distributed regularly throughout the galaxy and one which we can recognize has having sufficiently constant properties. Another constraint on our choice is that there must also be sufficient examples of the new standard candle nearby so that it can be calibrated using the spectroscopic distance standard. This is the beginning of a long chain of calibration that links distances in the solar system to distances of the farthest known objects.

In the case of our galaxy, this "second type" of standard is the size of the ionized hydrogen regions, or **H II regions**[1]. Immediately we encounter a difficulty: while we are quite confident that the luminosities of stars of the same spectral class are sufficiently constant, the sizes of the H II regions are much more in doubt. Even worse, the images of two adjoining H II regions at large distances can become smeared on photographic plates into a single image, causing us to drastically underestimate their distances.

---

[1]The name **H II** ("aitch-two") region comes about because ionized hydrogen produces a sort of "second type" of spectral line: it would have been far more logical to to call them H *plus* regions.

Fortunately H II regions are not the only standards that we can use. In our galaxy there are several other methods that ensure that we have a good idea of the true size of things. Whenever several different methods agree, we can have confidence in all of them: where they disagree, we must inquire carefully as to the reasons.

Slipher's and Hubble's early work in the 1920s and 1930s relied to a large extent on recognizing and using the brightest stars in other galaxies (or "nebulae" as they were then called) as standard candles. They *assumed* that these brightest stars were essentially similar to the brightest stars in our own galaxy. This assumption was — and still is — very difficult to justify completely. Of course, if the brightest stars varied widely in luminosity from galaxy to galaxy, then we wouldn't get a linear redshift-distance relation at all. It would just be a random — or "scatter" — diagram. The fact that it isn't supports the assumption that our standard is a uniform one. But the standard could be *systematically* wrong. That is, while the brightest stars may, indeed, be all of roughly the same luminosity, that luminosity might be *different* from what we have assumed. This would occur if our calibration of the standard were wrong, possibly because we had exceeded the range of accuracy of our previous distance-determining method.

As we move beyond the galaxies in our immediate neighbourhood out into the universe, both H II regions and the brightest stars become increasingly difficult to recognize. Instead we must rely on other standards, such as the size and brightness of a whole galaxy. But how do we know that these remote galaxies are similar to those found locally? After all, they are seen at a much earlier epoch than the present. Again it is a matter of faith. Eventually, however, all such methods are bound to fail: for example, it is impossible to estimate the true luminosity of a galaxy if it is so distant that its shape and type can't be recognized. And it is at this point that astronomers are forced to make the enormous assumption that the redshift–distance relation is valid throughout all the universe. If so, we can measure a galaxy's redshift and immediately state its distance.

But how justifiable is this assumption? Let us pause to discuss an argument often put forward by the more conservative element of the astronomical community. It goes somewhat as follows:

> **Since we know from observations of lower redshift objects that the universe is expanding, then surely it is obvious that *all* redshifts must to be due to this expansion? If so, then distances in an expanding universe must also (by the arguments of Chapter 8) be proportional to the redshift.**

This is a seductive argument since it contains some statements which almost all astronomers would agree with: but it is flawed. Let's break it down into its main statements and assumptions:

a) **Galaxies (and quasars) have redshifts.**

b) **These redshifts are linearly related to distance for galaxies in our immediate vicinity (that is, for those galaxies for which the distances can be indubitably determined by other methods).**

c) **The linear redshift–distance relation is most readily explained by the idea that the whole universe is expanding.**

d) If the whole universe is expanding, galaxies everywhere should exhibit a linear redshift–distance relation.

Well, is the argument right or not? Everyone agrees with statement (a). It is also difficult to criticise (b), except that the Hubble constant defined by the slope of the line in the redshift–distance plot is open to some doubt for the reasons mentioned in the previous section. Statement (c) is also difficult to argue with, although other possibilities have been suggested from time to time. (Hoyle, for example, has argued that the observations can be equivalently explained by supposing that the universe is really static but that the mass of all particles is continually increasing with time.) Despite this, essentially all astronomers would accept (c).

It is with statement (d) that we must take issue. Of course, if the universe is expanding, then *some* part of the redshift of the galaxies will be caused by the expansion of the universe. But this doesn't prove that *all* of that redshift is caused by expansion. In a minor sense, we know that it isn't: galaxies typically have individual motions of around several hundreds of km/s relative to uniformly expanding space Thus at least part of the redshift (around 0.001) is due to other causes.

Furthermore, in the large clusters we see galaxies which are orbiting around each other. These show redshift discrepancies of up to 0.03 between galaxies which we are certain are in the same cluster. At this level, at least, the redshifts of galaxies are not caused by the universal expansion. Thus we are led to consider the possibility that a large fraction of the redshifts we measure for distant galaxies (and quasars) may be caused by something other than the universal expansion. If this *were* true, then clearly the distances we derive by extrapolating the nearby Hubble relation would be quite wrong.

Now if an object has an expansion redshift of $z_{expansion}$ and another redshift, z_x, due to something else[1], what is the *total* redshift we see? When both of the redshifts are very small, we have the simple approximation:

$$z_{total} = z_{expansion} + z_x$$

But, as soon as either of the redshifts become large, we must use the more accurate formula:

$$(1+z_{total}) = (1+z_{expansion}) \cdot (1+z_x)$$

(A little algebra will show that these relations are in fact consistent for small redshifts.)

But is it likely that a large part of the redshifts of galaxies and quasars could be caused by an effect other than the overall expansion of the universe? Why go looking for an alternative explanation where one is not needed?

This argument is essentially **Occam's** famous "Razor", which says that the most economical way to proceed in science is to stay with the smallest number of hypotheses and not to invent new ones needlessly. There is no doubt that this is excellent advice for dealing with most of the day-to-day problems that one meets as a working researcher: if we invented a new explanation for every effect we observed, there would be little coherence to our scientific understanding. But, from time to time, science has been forced to accept that new explanations are necessary. For example, in explaining the inner workings of the atom, Einstein,

---

[1]This could be due to a local, Doppler motion or perhaps some other, quite unknown, cause.

Heisenberg and others were led to postulate new laws of physics, laws which have since been amply confirmed and are much simpler than the convoluted — although "tried and trusted" — laws that they replaced. The new laws were necessary because the existing ones could not explain all the data. Of course, the new laws seemed "unnatural" at first, as does anything that is new. But this argument has no weight in science: all that matters is, " Does the new law explain more than the old ?"

In particular, while dealing with something as unfamiliar as the remote regions of the universe, we must be very careful. There are very few laws in physics that remain valid when extrapolated over as many orders of magnitude of physical size as that which spans from our Earthly experience to the edge of the universe. But that is exactly the extrapolation we are trying to make by using the locally-derived redshift–distance relation. Our expansion law has only been directly confirmed for distances out to a few million lightyears. In universal terms, this is merely our own backdoorstep. From there to the edge of the universe is a factor of a 1000 further in distance. Are we sure that the Hubble law will remain valid?

Let us accept, then, that the "obvious" argument in favour of Hubbelian redshifts is, at best, weak. A much stronger piece of evidence is provided by astronomers looking for absorption lines in the spectra of quasars caused by intervening galaxies. As we mentioned in Chapter 13, if a galaxy intrudes into our view of a distant quasar, then its gas will leave an "imprint" in the spectrum of the quasar *at a redshift corresponding to the redshift of the galaxy* . If we find such absorption lines, then we know that the galaxy must lie closer to us than the quasar and, providing we believe that the redshifts of the galaxies correctly indicate their distances, we can conclude that the quasar is further away than the galaxy. If we can find associations in which the quasar is at only a *slightly* higher redshift than a high-redshift galaxy, then we could hope to prove that the great majority of the quasar's redshift is cosmological (that is, caused by the expansion of the universe).

The main problem in carrying out this observing programme is to find enough pairs of quasars and galaxies which are (apparently) close enough together on the sky. The pair in Fig. 16.1 is one such set. A second problem is that the continuum radiation from the quasars is often weak, even if the emission lines are strong. Since it is the strength of the continuum that governs the detectability of an absorption line, this leads to an unfortunate tendency to select quasar–galaxy pairs containing some of the brightest quasars. I say "unfortunate" because the brightest quasars tend to be some of the nearest and so may not be suitable for testing the nature of the quasar redshifts at high redshifts.

Nevertheless the results of these observing programmes seem, at first sight, to be fairly convincing. Absorption lines are indeed often seen in the spectra of the adjacent quasars at a redshift corresponding to that of the nearby galaxy. On the other hand, the galaxies in these samples are often at extremely low redshift, thus proving only that the quasars are beyond a certain, rather small, distance. Even the most radical of astronomers believes that a large part of the redshifts comes from the universal expansion, and so the situation remains unclear. There is, in addition, and perhaps more insidiously, the rather "immoral" practice of only publishing spectra for the pairs of quasars and galaxies for which absorption lines *have* been found. Presumably there are many examples of objects that *don't* show absorption whose spectra are *not* published because they don't bolster up the preconceived notions of the astronomers.

The breach in the wall

Despite these problems, there is no doubt that the majority of astronomers are prepared to believe that the quasars lie beyond the nearer galaxies. On the other hand, from the time of the discovery of the first quasars, some astronomers have not been happy that these enigmatic objects lay at the huge distances their redshifts suggested.

The earliest arguments pointed to the enormous and quite unprecedented luminosities that the distances implied. There were no known processes that could produce these large amounts of energy from the small volumes implied by the quasars' light variations (see Chapter 14). Today, this argument is less convincing: comparable processes seem to be taking place in some nearby galaxies and theoretical calculations have pointed to massive black holes as a possible energy source.

A strong piece of evidence against the cosmological interpretation of the quasar redshifts came in the late 1960s with the discovery of several **quasar pairs.** At that time, John Bolton and his colleagues found that several of the radio sources in the recently begun Parkes Radio Survey seemed to be identifiable not just with one optical quasar but with two. The two star-like objects lay side by side on the sky separated by typically just a few seconds of arc. When optical spectra were obtained both objects were shown, without doubt, to be quasars.

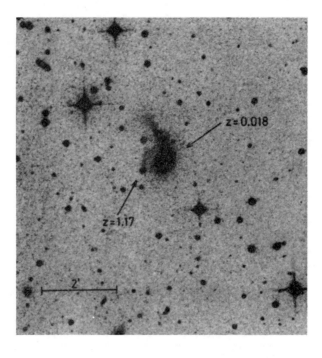

Fig. 16.1 — The quasar-galaxy pair PKS 1327-206

Of course, pairs of *galaxies* are not unusual. They are binary systems in which the galaxies orbit around each other and have almost identical redshifts: because they are very close together in space they thus lie at almost identical distances from us.

But the pairs of *quasars* were a complete surprise. For one thing, quasars are far rarer than galaxies. Thus the probability of two of them lying very close together on the sky simply by chance was very small. The bigger shock, though, was that the quasars had very different redshifts! If they really were physically related and not just chance juxtapositions on the sky, then at least one of the two quasar redshifts could not be caused by the expansion of the universe. After all, two objects very close together in space can not also be at two widely different distances from us!

But were these quasar pairs physically related? After all, there are many examples of pairs of stars in the sky, called **asterisms**, which look as though they are binary systems but which are, in fact, just line-of-sight coincidences. The trouble with this explanation, as we said above, was that while there are many, many stars in the sky, there are relatively few quasars. A quick statistical calculation suggested to Bolton and his colleagues that the quasar pairs were *not* line-of-sight coincidences.

Let's consider the argument they used: assume that over the sky we have performed a detailed survey and have found a total of N quasars. If the area of the sky surveyed is A square degrees, then the average number of stars per square degree is N/A. Since we have no reason to expect that the number of quasars per square degree will be different in different parts of the sky (see Chapter 5), we can use this average as the expected surface density of quasars in *any* part of the sky.

Say that our survey found two quasars which we think might form a physically connected pair. Clearly, our attention has only been directed to this part of the sky because there was at least *one* object there! We ask the following question: "Given that it is no coincidence that one quasar is where it is, what is the probability that a second object would lie close by?"

Actually we must provide a little more information before we can answer the question: we must know how close the second object is. Let's keep the discussion general and assume that the angular separation is x degrees. The *random* chance of this occurring is,

$$p = \frac{\pi.x^2.N}{A}$$

If we adopt the best available observed values for the average surface density of quasars (N/A) then we find that it is rather unlikely that we would discover a quasar within a few arcseconds of another purely by chance.

But wait a moment: although there may only be a 1 in 100 chance of finding a quasar within a few arcseconds of another by chance, if we consider more than 100 or so objects, then surely it is odds-on that we'll find a close pair? Yes, that's right! And it's here that the interpretive waters become very muddy. In practice it is very difficult to know how many quasars astronomers have looked at to find the few pairs we know of. Clearly it must be fewer than the number of *all* discovered quasars — some of them will have only got a cursory glance — but what fraction?

Perhaps even more invidious is the fact that astronomers who believe that quasar pairs are important will pay correspondingly greater attention to their photographic plates in the hopes of finding still more! At the present time many close quasar pairs are known. Unfortunately the statistics don't give a clear answer whether this is as expected purely by chance or whether it points to a non-cosmological origin of the quasar redshifts. On balance, the latter possibility seems suggested by the available evidence.

During the last few years, several apparent pairs of quasar images have been discovered which *do* have almost identical redshifts. They are believed to be produced by a *single* quasar but one whose light travels to us by two different paths through space. It is thought likely that the gravitational field of an unseen galaxy lying somewhere between ourselves produces a **"gravitational lens"** and causes light from the quasar to be both bent and focussed. (See Fig. 16.2.) producing the two images.

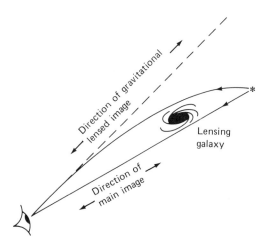

Fig. 16.2 — Production of a gravitational lensed image of a distant quasar by a (possibly invisible) galaxy near the line-of-sight.

This explanation has been supported by observations that flux variations seen in one image are followed a little time later by variations in the other image. This delay is thought to correspond to the different time taken for light to arrive at the Earth via the two slightly different paths. It seems likely that this lens explanation is correct for most of the quasar image pairs which have near-identical redshifts. If so, it strongly suggests that at least these quasars are at great distances. On the other hand it does *not* provide conclusive evidence that the distances derived using the Hubble relation from the redshifts are correct.

In summary, quasar pairs seem to provide evidence both for and against the cosmological nature of the redshifts. The gravitational lens images with very similar redshifts argue strongly that the quasars are indeed far away. On the other hand, the close pairs with discordant redshifts pose an irritating problem for astronomers favouring a conservative view of the nature of the quasar redshifts.

The Cosmological Connection

Another piece of evidence against the idea that the quasar redshifts were "cosmological" came from associations between quasars and galaxies. If a galaxy at a relatively *low* redshift and a quasar at a much higher redshift could be shown to be physically connected, and thus at much the same distance, then the whole redshift debate would be over.

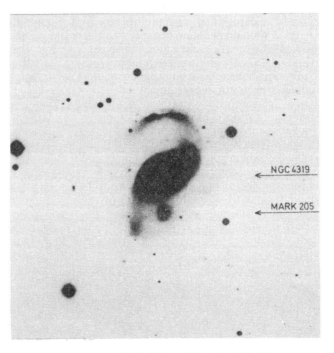

Fig. 16.3 — The quasar–galaxy pair NGC 4319 and Markarian 205. (Photo courtesy Dr H. Arp).

In 1971, Halton Arp proposed that the galaxy known as **NGC 4319** and the quasar-like **Markarian 205** were indeed such a pair. The redshift of NGC 4319 had been previously measured and corresponded to 1700 km/s. The redshift of Markarian 205 was similarly known to be 21,000 km/s. Although these two objects appeared to be very close together on the sky, most researchers had previously dismissed the pair as merely an interesting coincidence. The thing that Arp brought to the world's attention was that his excellent photographs showed that there appeared to be a faint connecting bridge between the two objects. (See Fig. 16.3.) One explanation that sprang to mind was that the galaxy had suffered a violent outburst of energy at its centre and had ejected the quasar at high speed. This would give the quasar a large Doppler velocity (in addition to its cosmological expansion velocity) and would confirm beyond doubt that substantial non-cosmological redshifts were possible. And, if this were true, then probably other quasars which were even further from their "parent" galaxy would also have substantial non-cosmological components to their redshifts, too.

But was the bridge real? Since the whole controversy hung on this question, it was investigated very closely.

The first thing to do was obviously to take more photographic plates of the same pair of objects to see if the bridge was just an artifact, perhaps of the photographic development process. Optical photographic astronomers are very familiar with these "plate flaws". Perhaps a hair gets into the developer or maybe the dish was not agitated sufficiently. One difficulty in repeating the observations of Markarian 205 was that Arp was an excellent observational astronomer and had used one of the world's best telescopes: it wouldn't be easy to duplicate his work. But finally, equally good photographs were obtained. And they showed the same bridge.

The attack by his critics now took a different direction. They began to talk about **non-linearity** effects in the photographic process. The idea here is that the total effect of two photons of light on a photographic plate can be greater than the sum of the individual effects. Let's see how.

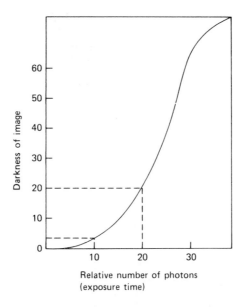

Fig. 16.4 — The strength of an image on a photographic plate does not increase linearly with increasing exposure time (number of incident photons) for low (and high) light levels.

Look at the curve in Fig. 16.4. It shows the "darkness" of a photographic plate when it is exposed to light of different intensities. When the light is very weak, the grains show almost no response at all. As the light becomes stronger, the photons begin to have an effect and, as the light gets stronger still, the relative response becomes even greater. (Although it doesn't concern us here, we should mention that at very strong light levels the response "tails-off" and saturates.)

Now we can see what happens if, first, we expose our plate to light of 10 units of intensity. The response is 5 units of darkness. (This is, of course, not the usual way we measure these things, but it will keep the arithmetic easy — after all, the *idea* is the thing we are trying to understand.) Next, if we expose our plate to another source of light of strength 10 units, we again, of course, get a darkness of 5. But what if we expose the plate to both sources of light *at the same time* ? This is the same as 20 units of light and we see from Fig. 16.4 that the response is *not* the 10 units of darkness we may expect, but rather 20 units! There is no magic in this, it's just that the presence of light on the undeveloped grains of a photographic plate make that same grain more responsive to still more light.

The idea put forward by Arp's critics was as follows. The image of both the galaxy and the quasar in Fig. 16.3 extended out to large distances from their centres. At large distances from the parent object, this light was very weak. So weak that it could not *on its own* activate a photographic grain. But what if this "far-out" light coincided in position with other weak light from the companion object? It would then combine in the way we've described above and could cause activation of the grains out of proportion to that expected just from linear arguments. The region of the photograph that would be expected to show this non-linear effect most strongly would, of course, be that lying between the galaxy and the quasar where the far-out light combined most effectively. And this was just where the apparent bridge was found.

Was this the correct explanation? It seemed to Arp that the connection was not of the expected "hour-glass" shape to be caused by this effect. But obviously further observations were needed to either prove or disprove the reality of the apparent connection.

A possible test was to re-observe Markarian 205 and its companion quasar with an instrument that would respond *linearly* to light. There is such a device: it is called a charge coupled device (CCD) array. Instead of on a photographic plate, the light is collected in an array of electronic sensors that produce minute electrical charges that can be read out by other electronic equipment. If the bridge was a non-linear artifact, it should disappear when imaged by the CCD array. But it didn't. After combining results from several exposures of excellent quality, the bridge was again clearly visible. Even more exciting, a filament seemed to extend backwards into the centre of NGC 4319, exactly as expected if an ejection from the nucleus had taken place.

Today, many other examples of galaxy–galaxy bridges and galaxy–quasar bridges are known. One of the best examples is the Parkes radio source PKS 1327-206 at a redshift of 1.17 and a companion galaxy 20 arcseconds away which has a redshift of only 0.018. Despite this evidence, many astronomers remain critical, dismissing these bridges as coincidence or superposition of images from background objects.

Faster than a speeding photon

Now let us turn to what many people regard as the strongest evidence against the redshifts of the quasars being "cosmological": the **superluminal expansions**. As we discussed in the previous chapter, VLBI observations have clearly shown that radio sources at the cores of some quasars are expanding so fast that they appear to be travelling faster than light. By far the simplest way of removing these difficulties would be to bring the parent quasars closer to us by a factor of around 5 or so. This would reduce the ejection velocities we determine by a similar factor to less then c. However it would also imply that the redshifts did not obey the local Hubble relation.

This idea is so abhorrent to many astronomers that strenuous attempts have been made to find an alternative and less radical explanation for the apparently superluminal expansions. Of these, the most promising has been the "aligned beam" model.

If a lump of material is blasted out from the centre of a quasar almost exactly in our direction and if it is also travelling at a large fraction of the speed of light, then it will appear to have several unusual properties.

The first is that it will be heavily *blue*-shifted relative to the central object. Second, it will appear to be much brighter than it really is. This is a secondary effect of the blueshift and is caused by the shift of the emitted photons to higher energies (bluer) and by their increased arrival rate (see Chapter 12). The third effect is more subtle: the blob of material will seem to be moving sideways faster than it really is. Of course if the blob were moving *exactly* towards us, then we should see no sideways motion at all. But a particularly strange relativistic effect takes place if the blob is ejected in a direction just *slightly* different from our line-of-sight. Consider Fig. 16.5.

At time t_1 light leaves the blob at A in our direction. At a later time t_3, light leaves the blob at C again in our direction. At an intermediate time t_2 the light from the blob at A has just drawn level with where the blob *will be* at C. By the time the blob reaches C, the light from A is at D. The distance AC is

$$V.(t_3 - t_1)$$

and so

$$AB = AC.cos\ \theta = V.(t_3 - t_1)\ cos\ \theta$$

Also the distance

$$AD = (t_3 - t_1).c$$

and so the distance

$$BD = AD - AB = (t_3 - t_1).(c - V\ cos\ \theta)$$

The time light takes to travel from B to D is therefore

$$(t_3 - t_2) = \frac{BD}{c} = \frac{(t_3 - t_1)\ (c - V\ cos\ \theta)}{c}$$

But this is the same time as the blob takes to *apparently* move sideways by a distance

$$BC = AC.sin\ \theta = (t_3 - t_1).V.sin\ \theta$$

Thus the *apparent* sideways velocity of blob

$$= \frac{AC.sin\ \theta}{(t_3 - t_2)}$$

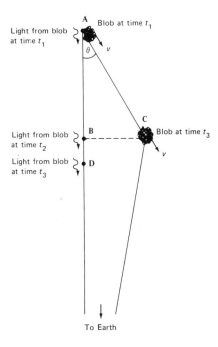

Fig. 16.5 — Diagram showing the geometry of a radio emitting "blob" ejected from a quasar at an angle almost along the line-of-sight. The points B and D mark the position of light from the blob when it was at A but at times t_2 and t_3 respectively. At time t_3 the blob has moved to C.

$$= \frac{V.sin\ \theta}{1 - \dfrac{V.cos\ \theta}{c}}$$

For small angles, $cos\ \theta$ is nearly equal to 1 and the function

$$\frac{sin\ \theta}{1 - \dfrac{V}{c}}$$

becomes very big as V approaches c

The net result is that a blob of material ejected almost towards us could appear to move *sideways* at a velocity exceeding the speed of light. This is a strange result, indeed, and two objections have been levelled at it as an explanation for the observed superluminal expansions.

First, it would seem unlikely that a large fraction of all quasars and BL Lacs objects would be ejecting material in *our* direction. To get a good superluminal effect we need the ejection to take place within about 20 degrees of our line of sight. On the other hand, random chance stipulates that only about 1 in 50 jets should be so-aligned. Thus the discovery that more than half of all well-observed objects show superluminal velocities would appear to rule out the relativistic explanation.

But a very cunning argument has been suggested: perhaps there *are* a large number of quasars (and BL Lacs) which eject material away from us but we don't discover them in our radio surveys. Remember that a blob of radio-emitting material ejected towards us suffers a very strong Doppler enhancement of its luminosity. Such objects would have much larger radio fluxes than similar, but non-aligned, objects and thus would, for the reasons we discussed in Chapter 4, dominate the sources found in our radio surveys.

This model has been called the **"beaming model"** of quasars because the radio emission is beamed at us. It has several consequences and poses several problems.

First, what happens to the ejected radio emitting material? If the jet does *not* point at us, the radio emission will be weak and we probably shan't detect the quasar as a radio source at all. This probably accounts for the dominant number of "radio-quiet" quasars. If we *do* detect it in our radio surveys, it will probably appear as one of the steep-spectrum objects with extended double radio lobes. This is made more likely if we assume that our "central object" actually ejects *two* jets in opposite directions. Because neither is coming (nearly) directly towards or away from us, they will appear roughly equally bright.

On the other hand, if the radio jets *are* aligned along our line of sight, one will appear very luminous and the other undetectably weak. Because of their apparent strength, such objects will be "unfairly" over-represented in our surveys and radio catalogues. More importantly they are exactly the sorts of object which we expect will show superluminal expansions!

Attractive though this beaming model is, it may well not explain all superluminal expansions. A few quasars show both double radio lobes *and* also superluminal expansion. It is as though the jets are pointed both away from us and towards us. How can this be? Perhaps the central source is rotating so that the jets were directed sideways in the past but are now pointed towards us.

Unfortunately we do not have space to discuss more details of this fascinating model. Suffice it to say that the apparent superluminal expansions strain the cosmological interpretation of the quasar redshifts to its limit and may well be its downfall.

The state of play

The controversy about the quasar redshifts started shortly after their discovery and is still not settled today. It is one of the longest-lasting arguments in the history of astronomy. While perhaps, four out of five astronomers would today favour the hypothesis that the redshifts of the quasars are, indeed, essentially all due to Hubbelian expansion of the universe, it is noteworthy that some of the best-known and most-respected names in extragalactic astronomy have seriously questioned this interpretation.

Why the continuing uncertainty? Is it just a problem of not having enough data? I think not: a satisfactory resolution of the controversy can only come by *independently measuring an accurate distance for an object of high redshift*. But we presently do not have such an independent method. And so the opinions held by the researchers are governed more by belief than by evidence.

Unfortunately these beliefs vary widely. It is in the nature of scientific research that if one person puts forward a particular hypothesis, then it is certain that a second person will put forward an alternative hypothesis. Such confrontation should occasion no surprise: there is little glory in publishing a straight confirmation of someone else's work. How much more fun to shoot it down in flames!

Furthermore, it is seen as a duty by many scientists to hold the opposite view; rather like the opposing sides of government in the Westminster system. And who's to say this is wrong? The physical sciences have such a high moral integrity today only because of observation of this duty coupled with the search for fame and glory.

Perhaps most important of all in understanding the redshift debate, though, is the fear that, if the "cosmological hypothesis" were thrown out of the window, then the vast edifice of modern extragalactic astronomy would come toppling down. Without redshift as the means of determining extragalactic distances, essentially all the last 75 years' work would be wasted. Most other discoveries in astronomy rely heavily on distances for their interpretation. In particular, we would probably have to abandon any hope of determining the shape and size of the universe. Obviously we can't look at the fine details when the broad picture is still in doubt. We feel that the fear of "non-cosmological" redshifts has been an important factor in arguments about whether or not the redshifts really are caused by the expansion of the universe There is certainly a strong "vested interest" in them being so!

This admission that vested interest and hope play a part in modern science should not horrify the reader. It has always been so. The white-coated dedicated scientist beloved of the popular press is a myth. If anything, it has been our experience that the modern astronomer is a more volatile and passionate creature (as regards his science!) than most of his academic colleagues in other fields. In the end, however, scientists have a supreme arbiter of all their arguments: they can go and observe the way the universe really is. This is a privilege denied to their colleagues studying in other academic fields — those studying the works of Shakespeare, for example, may argue for ever about the way Lear should *really* be played. Unfortunately, having carefully *observed* the universe, the astronomer must interpret his results. It is in this very human field of endeavour that the problems arise.

Perhaps, then, we should try to summarize the present state of this crucial, redshift debate. We shall make no attempt to be impartial, since few astronomers are — at least of the ones we know — who have worked in the field and are qualified to express an opinion.We freely confess that we have grave doubts that the redshifts are solely cosmological or "Hubbelian". Our main reason for holding this opinion is that a conservative approach may lead to the state of mind in which one sits back and does not further question the nature of the redshifts. But, if many people are attempting to prove that the redshifts are not wholly caused by the expansion of the universe *and fail*, then we will have learned something. Of course, if they succeed...!

The *direct* evidence in favour of the quasar redshifts being cosmological is almost non-existent: on the other hand, the *indirect* evidence is strong. Let us explain what we mean. As we said above, direct evidence for the Hubbelian nature of the redshifts would be a straight, independent distance measurement, say by parallax, standard candle or some other technique. Such a measurement has never been made for either galaxies or quasars at the high redshifts which are cosmologically interesting. In contrast, the direct evidence against the redshifts being solely cosmological is strong. One thinks particularly of the bridge in PKS 1327-206 and its associated galaxy and the problems in convincingly explaining the superluminal velocities seen in the flat-spectrum radio sources.

On the other hand, there is no doubt that many of the observations put forward in the past to disprove the cosmological nature of the quasars have failed. One thinks of the difficulties in explaining the power outputs of the quasars if their redshifts were cosmological. While it is true that we are far from understanding exactly how a quasar produces its energy, it seems clear that stellar annihilation in a large black hole offers a possible explanation.

Whatever the outcome of the redshift controversy, it is of the greatest importance for the whole of extragalactic astronomy and is fundamental to our understanding of the size of the universe. Ultimately it will only be resolved by new and more sensitive astronomical observations interpreted by intelligent and unbiased minds.

17

The Glow from the Edge

If anybody could be said to have discovered the edge of the universe, it is probably the two American radioastronomers **Arno Penzias** and **Bob Wilson**. In 1964 they were working at the Bell telephone laboratories near Princetown trying to measure exactly how much energy was arriving at the Earth from certain radio sources. Instead they discovered a source of radio "noise" older and more distant than anything previously found in the history of the universe. Their finding caused a major upheaval in the science of cosmology by resolving a long-standing controversy concerning the origin of the universe. However, to realize the significance of this noise and to see why it had not been discovered before, we must understand what Penzias and Wilson were trying to do.

How strong?

Most of the time astronomers don't directly measure apparent brightnesses or strengths for the heavenly bodies they study. With an optical telescope, for example, it is usually sufficient to show that the object of interest — a quasar, perhaps — is exactly 12.3 times weaker than a certain standard star which, in turn, is known to have a brightness of 9.87 magnitudes. In this way the strength of the quasar is measured *relative* to the strength of the star. Similarly in radio astronomy, a particular radio galaxy may be found to be 521 times weaker than another "calibrator" source whose strength has been previously measured as 21.1 janskys.

But the obvious question is, "How do we know that the calibrator sources are really as strong as we assume them to be?" This question is as important as it is difficult to answer. It involves measuring the **absolute strengths** of astronomical objects. (In what follows, for once, we shall be using the word "absolute" not in contradistinction to "apparent" but to distinguish it from relative measurements. For this reason we shall try to avoid the word "apparent" altogether in this chapter and talk about "strength" or "flux".) To simplify matters we'll just talk about the problem in radioastronomy where the units of measurement are somewhat simpler to calculate with than the logarithmic magnitudes beloved of optical astronomers. But what we have to say will be equally applicable to optical astronomy as well as all the other branches of the science.

Let's first consider what an astronomer means by an *absolute* measurement. In essence, the main function of any telescope is to receive radiation from objects in the universe and turn these photons into an understandable form. We would very much like to determine how many photons of a particular frequency are received from an astronomical object per second and per square centimetre of a perfect telescope's mirror located above the Earth's atmosphere. This is the object's absolute flux or strength. If we know this strength and also the object's distance, we can quickly calculate its luminosity from the inverse square law.

The first step in trying to estimate an absolute flux is to measure the electrical signals produced by the received radiation in our instrument's electronics. Unfortunately these measurements are affected by many sources of error. For one thing, photons are absorbed in the atmosphere on the way down to the Earth's surface. For another, not all the photons entering the telescope will arrive at the receiving electronics: some will be absorbed by the telescope optics. Furthermore, we have to estimate how much of the electrical signals in our receiver are really made by photons arriving from astronomical objects and how much is produced by internal "noise".

The usual solution is to dismiss the whole problem as being unnecessary and also too hard. By making only *relative* measurements and comparing one radio source to another, we can avoid the great majority of these problems, since they will affect both sources equally. Ultimately, however, someone has to tackle the problem of "pinning down" the absolute strengths of a few sources which will be used as absolute calibrators. This was the work that occupied Penzias and Wilson and it required the greatest care and skill.

Their programme required a careful estimate of the exact collecting area of a specially built telescope. Unfortunately the area which is effective in collecting energy in a radiotelescope is not quite the same as the "physical" area because of wave diffraction effects. To make this problem a little less difficult, their instrument had been constructed as a "horn", rather like a square-cross-sectioned, giant version of those old gramophone horns which always seemed to have a dog listening to them! One difficulty is that these horns have to be built very accurately, which restricts them to being quite small and implies that they can only accurately measure the strongest sources. When Penzias and Wilson pointed their horn in the direction of strong radio sources, they found the expected sort of response. But they also measured signals when pointing at supposedly *blank* parts of the sky.

At first glance, this result didn't surprise them: part of the noise measured by any radiotelescope does not come from space at all. It is produced by the random motions of electrons in the receiving electronics. As we mentioned in Chapter 3, radio telescope receivers turn the radio radiation received from space into minute electric currents. But these are not the only electrical currents flowing in the receiver. In order to amplify the faint signals, power must be applied to the receiver electronics. Unfortunately this power also produces unwanted electrical noise. Receiver designers try to make this noise as small as possible but, even so, it is almost always much larger than the energy arriving from a typical astronomical radio source. Almost invariably, radio astronomers seem to be looking for the proverbial needle, not in a haystack, but in an enormous field of high electrical "grass"!

Let's try to quantify the problem. Most of the time, radio astronomers find it confusing to think in terms of voltages and currents. Instead they compare the strength of the signals coming from the sky and the currents in the receiving electronics with a temperature. This temperature is the temperature that a resistor would need to have in order to produce the same amount of electrical noise. Typically the summed contributions from the receiver noise and the local sky noise in the best receivers is around 50 kelvins. By way of comparison, a bright radio source will have an equivalent temperature of around only a degree or so!

Despite the difficult problem which radio astronomers face in picking out the needle from the grass, it can be done relatively easily if the radio source has a small angular size. The usual trick employed is to point the telescope first at the radio source of interest and then to move it off to one side. By subtracting the amount of energy received "off-source" from the amount "on-source", the extra contribution from just the astronomical object can be determined.

But this method fails for radio sources which extend over a large area of the sky. In this case there is no adjacent part of the sky to move off-source to! In order to determine the absolute brightness of extended sources, very careful and painstaking methods are necessary. In particular it is difficult to estimate exactly how much energy is received from the Earth's atmosphere.

We are now in a position to understand the unexpected result that faced Penzias and Wilson. Even when due allowance had been made for the expected levels of receiver noise and the contribution of the Earth's atmosphere, there was still a substantial amount of signal remaining. Did this originate out in space? Or was it produced by some unknown source of electrical noise in the receiver or the telescope? An important clue was that the excess signal appeared to come equally from all directions wherever the telescope was pointed. This seemed to suggest that the problem lay very close to home, in the atmosphere, telescope or receiver.

Penzias and Wilson spent several months searching for an answer. The telescope was cleaned out several times and the receivers carefully checked. Slowly it began to look as though the signals *must* come from out in space. But what were they? If the radio energy originated within our galaxy surely it should follow the shape of our galaxy's disc? But it didn't. If it was produced by other galaxies, it should be strongest in the directions where the other galaxies congregate. But it wasn't. It seemed to permeate the universe equally in all directions.

Penzias and Wilson were puzzled by their result and discussed it with colleagues. The breakthrough came when they learned that a group of astronomers at Princeton University had been trying to understand how the elements could have been produced if the universe had begun in a Big Bang. In order to explain the amount of helium we see in space today the Princeton astronomers needed the early universe to have once been permeated with strong, hot radiation. As the universe expanded, this radiation would cool down until, at the present time, it was predicted to be visible mainly at radio wavelengths. It looked like the mystery of the cosmic radio noise was solved. More importantly, it also seemed as though definite evidence had at last been obtained that the universe had indeed begun with a Bang.

In the beginning

The first million years of the universe's existence accounts for less than one thousandth of its total age. During this previous time there were no stars and no galaxies. Matter existed only as protons and electrons, the raw constituents of hydrogen atoms. While the universe was still very young, it was also very hot. At these very high temperatures, hydrogen is rapidly converted into helium (and other heavier elements) by the process of nuclear fusion, whereby simple atoms join to form more complex ones. On the other hand, we find that only a small fraction of the matter in the universe presently exists in the form of helium. Why? Astronomers believe that in order to prevent the conversion of too much hydrogen to helium there must have been a very intense field of very hot radiation present in the early universe at the same time as the protons and electrons and interacting with them. During the first three minutes after the universe was created, this strong radiation would "blast apart" any helium that tried to form.

But the universe was expanding and, as it expanded, the radiation cooled. Part of this cooling was caused by the redshifting effect of the expansion of space: red photons have less energy than blue photons. But there was another process at work also caused by the expansion: every time a photon encountered a proton or electron, it found that it was, on average, moving away from the photon. This sort of collision meant that, again on average, the photons lost energy. Funnily enough, the protons and electrons lost energy too. Where did this energy go? The answer is "nowhere", which may come as a shock to people brought up on laboratory physics. One of the great surprises of cosmological astrophysics is that, *in the universe as a whole energy is not conserved.*[1]

The decreasing energy of the radiation and the matter (protons and electrons) can each be measured by temperatures. When the universe was very new, matter and radiation interacted both strongly and frequently. This meant that the temperature of the radiation and the temperature of the matter were much the same.

Perhaps we should pause and consider how these temperatures are defined. The radiation from a black body (see Chapter 12) takes place over a range of frequencies. The total amount of radiation is given by Stefan's law and its strength at any particular frequency is described by Planck's law. There is little very-low-frequency radiation and even less very-high-frequency radiation. At some intermediate frequency, the radiation has a maximum. As we saw in Chapter 12, the higher the temperature of the emitting body, the higher this frequency of maximum emission. The important thing for us to note here is that a black body at any temperature emits energy with a specific and predictable distribution over a range of frequencies.

If radiation has a frequency distribution exactly corresponding with that of a black body, then it is convenient to define the "temperature" of the radiation as that of the equivalent black body. If the distribution is somewhat different from that of a black body, then we do a "best-fit" to the distribution pattern and find a "best-fit" temperature. In either case, this temperature is merely a convenient "shorthand" way of describing the total strength and the frequency distribution of the radiation.

The temperature of matter is easier to understand. By the word "temperature", physicists simply describe the violence of the random motions of particles. As we know, the molecules of any gas are bumping around into each other. The hotter the gas, the faster they bump around. Of course, it doesn't matter at all what the *overall* motion of the gas is: it may be being ejected from the back of a rocket or orbiting around the centre of our galaxy. But the random internal, or *thermal*, motions give the gas its temperature.

Now let us resume our summary of the early days of the universe. Initially each photon of radiation travelled only a very short distance before encountering either protons or electrons. This meant that the frequency distribution of the radiation maintained a very close correspondence with the physical temperature of the matter from which it had been emitted. But, as we said above, the expanding universe caused the photons to lose energy. If the radiation tried to cool too fast (i.e. lose too much high-frequency energy relative to the lower-frequency energy) then the next few encounters with the protons and electrons would quickly "warm it up". On the other hand, if the matter tried to cool too fast, then it would, itself, be warmed up by the high-frequency radiation.

To start with, both the matter and the radiation cooled down together at exactly the same rate as the universe expanded. But eventually the close interaction stopped: the universe had expanded so much that collisions between photons and matter particles no longer took place often enough to maintain the temperature balance.

The temperatures had now reduced to about 3000 K, permitting the protons and the electrons to combine and form stable hydrogen atoms. This epoch in the universe's history is known as the **decoupling time**. After this period the

---

[1] For an excellent discussion of this fascinating point see Harrison's book, *Cosmology*.

photons could no longer interact with the bulk of the matter in the universe —
except in a few unusual places called stars! Furthermore the fact that most particles
never again encountered another particle or photon meant that we were provided
with a "snapshot" of the universe which is still available for us now to observe.

Unfortunately the decoupling period occurred so long ago that we have to look
back in time to a redshift of about 1000 to see it. At this early time in the universe's
history no galaxies or quasars existed. And, even if they had, their light would be
so dimmed by redshift and distance that we could not see them.

However the remnant noise of the Big Bang is a different matter. At a redshift of
1000, radiation which initially had a temperature of 3000 K will now look as
though it has a temperature of

$$T_{now} = \frac{3000}{(1+z)}$$

or approximately 3 K. Planck's law predicts that radiation at this temperature has
the maximum of its emission in the microwave radio region of the spectrum at
around 1 millimetre or 300 GHz. This was the cosmic glow discovered by Penzias
and Wilson in 1964.

Problems

After the discovery of the cosmic microwave background radiation, some
astronomers concentrated on trying to measure an exact value for its temperature.
Other groups realized the importance of proving that the radiation did, indeed, have
a black-body character as predicted by the Big Bang theory. If it didn't, another
explanation would have to be found. Unfortunately, as we mentioned above, the
peak radiation from a black body at a temperature of 3 K lies at a wavelength of
around 1 millimetre. This is a region of the electromagnetic spectrum which is
notoriously difficult to study because of absorption by our atmosphere and because
of difficult receiver technology. But only by finding the peak would it be possible
to say for sure whether the spectrum was indeed that of a black body or not.

Over the next few years, however, these problems were overcome and the
cosmic radiation was indeed shown to be that of a 3 K black body, thus firmly
establishing it as coming from the Big Bang. Only one prediction remained
untested: if the universe really *were* homogeneous and isotropic (see Chapter 5), the
strength and the wavelength distribution of the radiation should be identical in all
directions. This required a detailed survey of the cosmic radiation over the whole
sky.

The results of the survey showed that the microwave background was *not* the
same in all directions. It was slightly "cooler" and less intense than average in one
direction and slightly "warmer" and more intense in a diametrically opposite
direction. Astronomers realized that this anisotropy implied that the Earth and Sun
were moving at a speed of around 600 km/s approximately in the direction of the
constellation of Hydra: the Doppler effect of this motion caused the radiation to be
stronger in the direction towards which the Earth was moving.

At this point we should perhaps discuss a problem that may have occurred to the
reader. If Einstein's Special Theory of Relativity says that all motion is relative (see
Chapter 6), why can we detect motion of ourselves relative to the background of
microwave radiation? Is this background playing the part of an absolute reference
frame which the Michelson–Morely experiment discounted?

The answer is rather surprising. In the universe at large, it turns out that neither
space nor time is relative. Instead there exists an absolute cosmic time and an

absolute spatial reference frame relative to which it *does* make sense to talk about absolute motion. What the anisotropy of the background radiation shows is that the Earth and Sun are moving *absolutely* at a speed of around 600 km/s in a direction towards the constellation of Hydra.

The sensitive radio observations showed that the microwave background temperatures differed in opposite parts of the sky by about 0.006 degrees. Small though this was, it amounted to 0.2% of the measured average temperature of 3 K, meaning that the Earth's total velocity relative to the fundamental frame of the universe was only 0.2% of the speed of light. In ordinary terms, this is around 600 km/s, as we mentioned earlier.

Now, many optical measurements of stars in our galaxy and radio measurements using the 21 cm neutral hydrogen spectral line have previously established that the Earth and Sun move around the galactic centre at about 250 km/s. But this on its own could not explain the observed anisotropy in the background radiation. Fortunately there are other methods of estimating our velocity with respect to the closer galaxies.

One of the most precise modern methods of measuring distances for nearby galaxies is provided by the collaboration of infrared astronomers and radio astronomers in what is known as the "Fisher–Tully" relation. It is named after Ric Fisher and Brent Tully who determined[1] that there is a very good correlation between the width of the neutral hydrogen 21cm line and the *absolute* amount of infrared emission emitted by a spiral galaxy. By restricting the galaxies chosen for this experiment to those of a precise type, such as the open-armed spirals, the correlation becomes very good indeed.

The importance of this relation is that by measuring the radio line width it is possible to accurately predict the absolute infrared luminosity of a galaxy which is an excellent "standard candle". A simple measurement of the *apparent* infrared flux then gives us the distance by using the inverse square law. Once the distances are accurately known, the overall effects of the universal expansion can be allowed for and any "peculiar" (i.e. Doppler) motions determined.

The Fisher–Tully relation has been vital in providing accurate distances to the galaxies for which the radio line width can be accurately measured. At the moment this is only out to a redshift of 0.03. Small though this volume of space is, it contains many of the nearest and best-observed galaxies. In particular, it also includes the important Virgo Supercluster.

As we said in Chapter 2 our galaxy is just one of many galaxies comprising the Local Group. On the larger scale, the Local Group is one of several other groups clustered together in space. The centre of this large concentration lies roughly in the direction of the constellation of Virgo and is known as the **Local** or **Virgo Supercluster**. The Fisher–Tully radio observations have shown that our galaxy is falling into the centre of this supercluster. And we can explain this motion by the combined gravitational attraction of all the galaxies in the supercluster.

Furthermore similar observations have shown that not only is our galaxy falling into the Local Supercluster, but also that this supercluster *itself* is moving through space. In fact it seems to be falling towards another nearby supercluster, in the Hydra–Centaurus region of the sky. All of these motions can be reconciled with the observed anisotropy in the cosmic microwave background, as we show in Fig. 17.1.

---

[1] Actually Fisher and Tully originally used *optical* data in establishing their relation. However the infrared data is somewhat superior and the principle is the same.

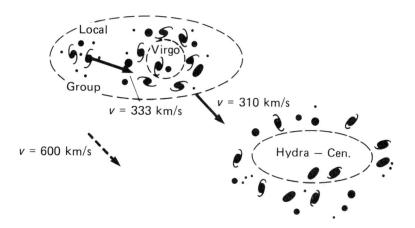

Fig. 17.1 — Schematic representation of the positions and velocities of some objects in the Local Group, the Virgo supercluster and the nearby Hydra-Centaurus supercluster. The velocity of the Local group is about 333 km/s relative to the centre of the Virgo Supercluster while the velocity of the Virgo Supercluster is about 310 km/s towards the Hydra-Centaurus supercluster. The combination of these two velocities adds up to give the motion of our galaxy relative to the frame of reference defined by the distant cosmic microwave background radiation (about 600 km/s).

One problem currently troubling astronomers is that there seems to be no reason for this motion: the number of galaxies in the Hydra–Centaurus Supercluster appears far too small to cause the infall. Does this mean that we have a clear-cut example of the missing mass problem, with the Hydra–Centaurus Supercluster containing much more mass than it seems to? Or does it perhaps suggest that the simple inverse square law of gravitational dynamics is wrong on the intergalactic distance scale? As yet we have no answers to these crucially important questions.

Perhaps much more surprising, though, than the slight anisotropy of the microwave background, is the fact that it is generally so uniform. After all, there are no other observations in astronomy that are the same in all parts of the sky to an accuracy of 0.2%. On the other hand, of course, the microwave background is unique: we have never measured any other information that comes to us from a redshift of 1000 !

But careful thought reveals another problem: when we look out with our radiotelescopes to this edge of the universe at redshift 1000, we are looking at distant regions which have probably never been in communication with each other. They are simply so far apart, and the universe has been expanding so fast, that information travelling even at the speed of light could not have passed from one extremity to another. And since the speed of light is the maximum velocity at which *any* information can travel, these distant parts of the universe can never have been in contact. But, if they haven't been in contact, how did they get to be so similar?

To put this problem another way, consider an analogy. Imagine that we decided to give a fancy-dress party for all our friends. These guests live all over the country, far apart. In the invitations we send out, we tell them only when and where the party will take place. We make no stipulations about what costumes they should wear beyond the fact that they won't be admitted unless they *do* turn up in fancy dress. Imagine our great surprise when the night of the party arrives and we find that all the guests have come as the *same character* and are wearing similar dresses. Of course, this *could* be just coincidence. On the other hand we would strongly suspect that they had somehow communicated with each other and decided to come similarly dressed as a joke. But if were told definitely that they had *not* been in contact with each other, we should be astonished.

The extreme isotropy of the universe (after allowance has been made for the small, local Doppler motions) comes as just as great a surprise to astronomers. To the best of our knowledge, the different parts of the universe that we now see as being so similar can *never* have been in contact. So how then do they "know" to be so uniform?

We don't know for certain. This remains one of the exciting problems that observational cosmologists are currently desperately trying to answer. Let's recap on our previous argument: the similarity of widely separated parts of the universe comes as a shock simply because we do not believe they have ever been in contact or communicated with each other. The reason they have never been in contact is that the universe expanded so quickly in the past that information travelling from one part even at the speed of light could not have caught up with the other. And we know that the universe must have expanded quickly, on average, in order to be as big as we see it at the present time.

So where is the loophole in this argument? One suggested solution invokes a scenario known as the **inflationary universe**. We may not have paid enough attention to the phrase "on average" in the previous paragraph. If the universe expanded very quickly at *some* stage of its history, it could afford to expand much less quickly at other times, while still maintaining the same *average* rate. This is the "escape clause" used by proponents of the Inflationary Universe Theory. They suggest that there was a period of very rapid expansion early in the universe's history . Later the universe slowed down, allowing photons and other information to pass freely between its different parts and establishing the surprising uniformity we find today.

Whatever the answer, the cosmic microwave background radiation is the second most important cosmological discovery of the twentieth Century. (The first, of course, was Hubble's discovery of the universal expansion). It has confirmed beyond reasonable doubt that the universe began in a Big Bang and has provided evidence that the universe is remarkably homogeneous and isotropic on the large scale. Furthermore this "glow from the edge" is by far the most distant and oldest thing we have ever observed with our telescopes. At a redshift of 1000, we are looking back to the first 0.1% of the age of the universe when it was a mere $1/1000$ of its present size. It is highly unlikely that any bodies such as galaxies or quasars could have formed before the decoupling time. And even if they did, we

could not observe them through the opaque blanket of the microwave glow. No —
if we are searching for the edge of the universe and demand to *see* it, then here it is:
the faint hiss of radio noise first recorded by Penzias and Wilson in 1964 is as far
and as early as we are ever likely to observe.

Of course, such statements are dangerous in any science and particularly so in
astronomy. We may be quite wrong. The one idea of which we are certain is that, at
the forefront of modern astronomical research, the only thing to be expected is the
unexpected.

Epilogue

The observers finished their meal and hurried back to the AAT dome. The inside of
the lift was now bathed in a dim red light, making the journey up to the control
room far more eerie than earlier. This light was turned on by the night assistant
when he came to work each night in order to preserve the dark-adaption of the
observers. Strong white light would spoil the ability to see faint objects through the
telescope. Most of the time this red light was no longer necessary, since the
astronomers would be working in a well-lit control room all night. But for an
observer taking photos and riding the telescope all night, it was essential in order to
see the faint star images.

When the lift stopped, no voices could be heard from the kitchen. Obviously
work was in hand. Turning to the left down the corridor, they opened a smartly
grained wooden door and passed through into the control room. This was the heart
of the telescope, where almost all observing was done. Using its control desk, the
telescope could be pointed to any position on the sky. To its computers came all the
data collected by the telescope's instruments.

The control room was long and thin, forming a sort of semi-circular "band"
around the upper half of the telescope dome. A walk down the length of this room
past banks of blue-coloured computer equipment brought the observers to the main
desk. Sitting at the desk was the scheduled night assistant, who would be keeping
the astronomers company through the night. His speciality was the engineering
well-being of the telescope. But his main function tonight would be to assist the
observers to make the best possible use of every minute they were scheduled on the
telescope. In addition, he had the delicate job of safeguarding the telescope, bearing
in mind the often over-enthusiastic nature of many astronomers. If all went well, he
would be working at the control desk alongside the astronomers for the next 12
hours.

The night assistant, Fred, was an old friend of the astronomers, noted for his
good humour and jokes and yet extremely efficient at managing the telescope. Only
18 months earlier he had assisted at the discovery of a high-redshift quasar which
had made it the most distant discovered object in the known universe. Its discovery
had broken a ten year record for farthest object, previously held by a group of
astronomers from California. The underlying but unspoken hope about tonight's
work was that a yet-more-distant object would be discovered, pushing back the
edge of the known universe a bit further. Fred was particularly keen to do
everything he could to help. The astronomers had presented him with a nice bottle
of malt whisky after their previous discovery — and he certainly wouldn't mind
another!

After a couple of pleasantries were exchanged, Fred mentioned that "the rest of
them are out in the cage". John and Peter left the control desk and went through a
nearby door out into the dome. It was easy to tell that there were problems: all the
dome lights were on. Normally at this time of night, just after sunset, the dome
would have been dark and the telescope beginning its night's work by looking at
several bright stars. Tonight, however, the dome aperture — or "slit" — was open
for "venting". This was the night assistant's first job each evening. It allowed the

air trapped in the dome to cool to the same temperature as the outside air — very necessary for good "seeing".

The air in the dome was already quite cold. The day had been hot, over 30 degrees Centigrade at noon, but now it was less than half that. During the night it would probably drop to only a few degrees above freezing.

From near the base of the telescope, the mutter of voices and the sounds of movement could be heard. The two astronomers walked across a small bridge of scaffolding-like steel girders to the very bottom of the telescope, which was now pointed straight up. Under the base of the telescope was slung a stout-looking steel cage, containing the IPCS detector and its associated computers. They popped their heads in through the door and said, "How's it going?" Their colleague, Dick, looked back. "Not good," he muttered, "We're only getting 5 kilovolts on the deflection coils. Should be nearer 25! Best leave these guys to it. We'll only be in the way!"

All three trooped glumly back into the control room, discussing what to do. Nothing seemed obvious until the equipment was either working or the engineers gave up — a thing they were not likely to do for several hours.

"I'm going to have a bite to eat," said Dick as he left. Peter shouted after him to bring back the "midnight lunches" when he came — packets of sandwiches and fruit to stave off the pangs of hunger in the middle of the night. Then he turned to John and muttered, "And I'll go and take a look at the weather." He passed out through the control room door, back into the cool air of the dome and out through its outer metal shell onto the "cat-walk" balcony slung precariously from the outer wall a hundred metres above the ground.

The view was superb. In the foreground the heavily wooded mountainside fell away quickly down to the plains of Central New South Wales. Peter walked around the dome. The town of Coonabarabran could easily be seen in the distance. A faint trace of smoke from a farmer "burning off" his stubble in a paddock 50 kilometres away could be discerned. He smiled as he saw there wasn't a cloud in the sky and strolled around the cat-walk to the west side of the dome. A blinding light revealed the last portion of the Sun just disappearing beneath the horizon. Nearby a flock of roseate parrots or "galahs" screamed their way overhead. A truly magnificent night, calm and still. It was very likely that the "seeing" — image quality — was going to be excellent: if there was any observing at all!

The astronomers re-met in the kitchen for a cup of coffee. They didn't really need one — but there wasn't much else to do. To add insult to injury, Dick had brought back a rumour from the dinner table that the "Yanks" had just discovered a record-breaking redshift 4 quasar. No further information, since the Americans were, perhaps understandably, playing their cards close to their chest. Gloom descended. There was little else for it but to sit and wait.

They pushed aside the salt, pepper and bottle of ketchup lying on the small kitchen table, wiped up some coffee stains and replaced them with a medium-sized wooden box. Opening the box, John dragged out several large cards with small photographs pasted on them. These were "finding-charts" that the observers hoped to be using later in the night to locate the quasars they had come to observe. These objects had been measured first using the large radiotelescope at Parkes, but the position determinations had then been improved to better than 2 seconds of arc using the radio interferometer at Tidbinbilla, near Canberra. This should be amply good enough to pinpoint the quasars, even among the many faint galactic stars in the field of view. But experience had taught the astronomers that things could —

and did — sometimes go wrong. This was why they had brought the boxes of finding charts.

Peter pulled out a small jewellers' magnifying glass and, putting it to his eye, looked keenly at the photo on one of the cards.

"You know," he said, "I think there's two of 'em on this one!"

The others bent over to see what he meant. One part of the photo showed two faint ink marks indicating the position of a radio source. In the middle of them was a faint, 18th magnitude star-like object. On the basis of its accurate position and flat radio spectrum, this was believed to be a quasar: and quite a bright one as quasars go. But, almost lying on top of it, was the hint of a second, fainter star. Was it just a star? — or could it be one of the infamous quasar "pairs"?

John put down his coffee mug, brushed the sandwich crumbs off his jumper and said, "I'll go out and have a look what they're doing." He was only gone a couple of minutes. "Still problems," he muttered as he returned. "I might go and start reducing that last lot of data."

This quarter of the year, these particular astronomers had been rather unfortunate. The scheduler who made up the observing programme had had to allocate the four nights allotted to the group in two bits. Almost four weeks ago they had been allocated two nights and the other two nights of their allocation had had to be delayed because of scheduling problems. There just weren't enough dark nights available in each month! The data John had mentioned had been obtained the previous month.

The process by which astronomers change their data from the form in which they collect it into the form in which it can be understood and, later, published, is called *reduction*. Sometimes, jokingly, observers feel that the data is so meagre that it shouldn't be "reduced" any more — particularly if it comes from an observing run affected by cloudy weather! But however apt or otherwise the choice of the term used, it is a job that has to be done.

John picked up a couple of circular plastic boxes each about the size of a thick LP record. Inside, through the transparent lid, could be seen reels of magnetic tape. This was the form in which the data was taken away from the telescopes at the end of an observing run. Normally no pretty pictures or spectra, but just a series of highly compacted, magnetized bits of iron dust on a long piece of thin plastic.

He walked out into the corridor, went down three floors in the red, dimly-lit lift and out into a warm, brightly lit room full of the hum of computer equipment. The main computer itself was half-hidden away behind a glass partition. It looked most unimpressive: just three small metal boxes occupying the size of a moderate-sized desk. Apart from a few ventilation holes in its top, a couple of small red lights and an on–off key, the computer was featureless. Its appearance certainly belied the half a million dollars that had been paid for it.

Behind the computer's main boxes and also in the partitioned glass room were the magnetic tape drives: taller boxes with two reel-holders mounted one above the other. It was onto these holders that John mounted his reels of tape. This was the cleanest room in the whole telescope. Great precautions were taken so that the minimum amount of dust should get in here and foul up the large whirring disc drives contained in the computer boxes or get into the reading heads of the magnetic tapes. A particle of dust in the wrong place could cause untold problems at a later stage, perhaps even making the data totally unreadable and eliminating a night's work.

The outer part of the computer room was much more interesting. It contained several large desks each with one or two television-like screens and keyboards on them. Some showed coloured displays while others were in black and white. At the moment, John was the only person in the room although, earlier in the day, it had been occupied by several people.

John sat down at one of the terminal screens and started to press a few keys. This was where the hard work was really done. While the crucial bit of an observing session was done at the telescope or, rather, in the control room, the hard slog was done in front of a terminal. In fact, the modern observational astronomer probably spends more than half of his working hours bent over one of these electronic video typewriters.

John was no expert. His typing was slow and careful, particularly as he logged on to the machine. One mistake here and the machine would snarl back at him a message such as, "User Account Not Recognized", or something similar. This was the way in which a dialogue was struck up with the machine. Only by typing in the correct password could the data reduction start. Passwords were used, as in many computer installations, in order to prevent unauthorized access by outsiders. This particular computer could be connected by telephone lines all over the world. Untold damage could be done to data and computer programs by "hacker-vandals" if they got into the system.

John was hoping to do several things with the data taken by the quasar observing team the previous month: for a start, the data had to be read from the magnetic tapes back into the "memory" of the machine where the necessary "number crunching" would take place. Secondly, calculations had to be made on the "arc line" data needed to put the real astronomical data in the correct form. Finally, the reduced data would be printed out and plotted on a graph plotter so that it could be easily seen and understood.

All of this would take time. To do it for just one quasar would take almost as long as to do it for many: once the computer program was written to process one object, it was fairly trivial to process several.

The first thing John displayed on the television-like screen in front of him was a set of "arc lines", a row of vertical lines stretching across and filling the screen from left to right. These lines had been recorded on the magnetic tape just before the first quasar had been observed for that night. The lines came from a tube containing helium and neon gas, rather like a fluorescent tube used in shop-window displays. It was needed in order to establish a wavelength scale for the data. All the data from the spectroscope had been recorded in channels numbered from 1 to 2000. Some contained more light — some contained less. There was no way directly of measuring the wavelength of the individual channels. So, to calibrate the channels it was necessary to record the spectrum of something for which the wavelengths *were* known.

John's hand moved to the side of the terminal to a joystick, rather like a small gear lever in a car. As he moved it up and down and from left to right, a pair of crossed lines moved in synchronization on the computer screen. Using the joystick, he indicated each of the 20 or 30 or so lines visible on the screen, following each resting point by typing in a wavelength for that particular line. At the end, he pressed another key and the screen blanked out for a few seconds: the computer was working hard establishing a "best-fit" relation between all the arc lines and their corresponding channel numbers.

The next job was to read into memory the spectrum of the first quasar. This looked quite different from the spectrum of the arc. For one thing it was much "noisier", or random looking: just a long line of up and down "scribble" with a few more prominent peaks sitting in it. A short burst of typing at the keys and John had the spectrum calibrated in wavelength. The computer had taken the channel numbers and used the best-fit from the arc lines to turn all the channel numbers into wavelength units, in this case, Ångstroms. John smiled as he saw this: actually physicists, including astronomers, had recently officially adopted the international convention of measuring all wavelengths in nanometres, or thousand-millionths of a metre, rather than Ångstroms. A few actually used these "new-fangled" units in their work, but the great majority of astronomers still used Ångstroms. As one of John's colleagues had said one night without much thought for historical veracity, "If it was good enough for Newton, it's good enough for me!"

Slowly John worked through the quasars observed the previous month. Although tiring in one way, in another it was fascinating — in essence, you were re-living a night from a few weeks ago. Frequently he had to reference a pad of pieces of paper by his side. This was the *observing log* that had been hand-written by the night assistant at the time of the observations. It recorded the times of each of the observations, so allowing them to be treated in the correct order. As well, it also contained valuable information about the status of the telescope at the time, data that would be required in order to finally put the quasar data in the best form.

In the previous observing session, many of the objects had been observed several times. The next job was to add all the observations of the same object together. In each individual spectrum, faint emission lines might be seen but they were difficult to discern properly and even harder to measure because of the presence of random noise caused by the motion of electrons in the receiving electronics of the spectrograph. By adding together several spectra, the data would be improved: the random noise would only add up slowly because it would typically have a high value on one spectrum while a lower one on the next. On the other hand, the real emission features in the spectrum would *always* add up, in direct proportion to the number of spectra. And so by adding many spectra, the real features would become easier to detect above the "grass" of the random noise.

Eventually the adding and calibration was finished. In all, last month's work had produced data on six quasars. Not too bad, since about two hours had been lost to bad weather. Two of the objects displayed on the screen didn't look too good: they showed no features at all — in fact, they might eventually turn out not to be quasars at all. But amongst the remaining four spectra, there was a real "goody": a very strong emission line near the dead centre of the spectrum at 5100 Ångstroms was almost certainly Lyman α. Since this line had a rest wavelength of about 1216 Ångstroms, the redshift would be quite a bit over 3. A very distant object indeed whose light had been emitted at a time when the universe was only a quarter the size that it is now!

John ripped the sheets of paper out of the plotter on which the results of the reduction were drawn. He "logged out", turned off the computer terminal and was preparing to go back upstairs when the door burst open.

"Jim's fixed it!!" yelled Peter as he came through the door."It was that bloody microprocessor chip on the video board." John knew this was no potato chip but a minute electronic part containing thousands of transistors. And essential for making the spectrograph run.

John showed Peter the plotter printouts as they got back in the lift and went upstairs. They were both very excited. But Peter became even more enthusiastic when he peered closely at one of the noisy plots. "Look at that," he breathed,"it could be Lyman α."

John looked closely at the plot. Near the right-hand end there was definitely a large "bump" of excess emission. Nothing else of note was visible in the spectrum. This supported Peter's suggestion: only Lyman α should be this strong without other lines being visible somewhere else on the spectrum. "You know," said Peter,"if we can just get another hour or so on this one, we might have a "winner".

As they passed back through the wooden door into the control room they threw the plot on the top of a desk and John pulled out a pocket calculator. A few seconds tapping at the keys and they had the suspected redshift. It would be a massive 4.2, much bigger than the highest redshift previously known.

Dick came back in from the cold of the dome accompanied by the two technicians. They looked tired and cold. They had been working on the equipment for the last six hours without pause except for a couple of minutes for a cup of tea. But now they had the problem fixed. On their faces was the look of men who had worked hard and knew that they had done a good job.

A quick glance at the clock showed the astronomers that so far only about two hours of the night had been lost to equipment failure. This was dutifully entered into the log by Fred who then went outside to turn off the dome lights and check the weather. The lost time was not good: but it could have been much worse. In a year, perhaps only 5% of time would be expected to be lost to equipment problems; but, to the astronomers scheduled, it was 5% too much!

The night assistant returned. From the smell of tobacco about him it was clear that he'd taken the opportunity to have a quick smoke, a thing expressly forbidden in the control room or dome itself where it would foul-up the computers. He reported that the night was perfectly clear and cold.

"Wonder what the seeing will be," muttered Dick. This was now the most important topic for the night. If the size of a star's image — or "seeing disc" — produced by the atmosphere was much bigger than a couple of seconds of arc, then too much light from faint objects would "splash" outside the instruments. On bad nights, the seeing got as large as 10 seconds of arc. These were the worst nights of all. Useless — and yet if the night was a clear one, the astronomers felt morally constrained to spend it observing. At a major optical observatory, a night's observing would be valued at around $10,000, not the sort of money to be squandered lightly.

If the seeing were bad, little could be done about it. The main cause of bad seeing was turbulence in the atmosphere lying above the telescope. Rather like the hot air "boiling" above a road on a very hot day. One local cause of bad seeing *could* be minimized: if the air in the dome was too hot as night began to fall, it would "boil out" of the dome aperture during the night. The solution that all major observatories used was to open the dome a couple of hours before the start of the observing night to allow the temperatures to equalize. The only time this was not done was if there were heavy clouds around. Boiling air might be bad, but water on the telescope or the high-voltage electronics would be a disaster!

The first object on tonight's observing list was an ordinary star. Not because the astronomers were interested in the star — in fact they were busy talking over a desk, and the observation was made solely by the night assistant — but in order to find if the telescope could be accurately positioned on an object. This was the so-called problem of "pointing". Later in the night, the telescope would be set on objects that could be barely seen, or even were completely invisible. A computer was given the job of allowing for all the imperfections in the telescope. Obviously it had to be doing its job properly.

Within seconds the faint stellar-like image appeared on the finding television screen. The astronomers groaned. The seeing was not the best — perhaps about 4 seconds of arc. Probably the aftermath of the hot day. It might get better later but, for the moment, only the brighter quasars could be observed.

These checks were soon over: Fred moved the telescope rapidly and skillfully from star to star, occasionally punching keys on the small computer terminal next to the large control desk. This was not the same computer that the astronomers had been reducing their data on downstairs, nor yet the same one that would shortly be used to take the new data from tonight. Rather it was a small machine whose sole task was to keep the telescope in the right place at the right time.

As well as position, time was important. Since the heavens appeared to rotate about the observatory because of the rotation of the Earth, the telescope had to move continuously just to allow for this motion and to keep the star or other object being observed in the field of view.

After the pointing stars, the night assistant turned his attention to another couple of stars. It could have seemed to the waiting astronomers that the exciting work of the night was never going to start! But they knew better. All the prior observations were crucial in being able to reduce the data properly. A spectrum without a wavelength scale would be valueless!

The new star whose image appeared on the small television screen was a "flux standard" star, an object whose absolute level of light emission was accurately known. If the colours of the quasars were going to be accurately calibrated, it was necessary that a standard star be measured. After what had seemed like hours but was, in fact, just a few minutes, all was ready.

The quasar that had excited the interest of the astronomers from the previous observing run was not yet visible. It wouldn't rise for another couple of hours. Before then they planned to look at three new objects. For each, there was a large white card containing a picture and a pair of coordinates giving a position on the sky that the telescope would be set to. The first quasar candidate was chosen and its position entered into the pointing computer. Only a "candidate" because no spectrum was yet available to confirm its true nature. A click of a switch and a faint whine was all that told the astronomers that the massive telescope out in the darkened dome was moving rapidly to the new position.

The night assistant made a rapid adjustment to the position to correct for the last fraction of a second of arc by the press of a button on the control console. The image disappeared. Almost at once it was replaced by another image of the star, but , this time, with a "slice" taken out of it. This was the view of the star "on the slit" of the spectrograph. The slice taken out of the centre was the light going down the slit and being fed to the spectrograph itself.

As the star disappeared from view, the astronomers swung round to look at a different sort of television display. This was called a VDU or visual display unit. It was one of Dick's standing jokes that he never knew what sort of display unit there could be other than a *visual* one! The words and pictures shown on these units were the main way the computer had of communicating with the astronomers. And the keyboard in front of the unit was the way the astronomers communicated with the computer.

The astronomers worked on into the night — or, rather, the early morning, since it was now well after midnight. They were all sitting down now — tiredness had set in. What John called "first-night-itis". After all, they'd been up at their usual time of 7.30 a.m., driven over 500 km and had stayed up all the night. Bed, if they were lucky, would come sometime around 8 o'clock in the morning.

But, although seated, they were still working hard. John was poring over the VDU screen. This terminal was controlling the way in which the spectrograph was taking the data. During exposures, though, it was possible to turn the computer's mind to something else — John was bringing back observations of objects made at the start of tonight's work and adding them together. Although final results would have to wait until the astronomers had more time to reduce the data properly, this "quick look" at the information would tell them if there were any potential "winners" in what had been done so far.

This sort of quick glance at the data was invaluable: this was the last "run" the astronomers would have on the telescope this season. In a few weeks the Sun would have moved into the particular part of the sky the astronomers were interested in — if anything important was missed, there would be no second chance for another year. If a real "goody" was found in the rough reduction, there might just still be time to return to it later tonight or tomorrow.

Peter was searching through the box of cards containing the pictures and identifications of the radio sources for which they wanted spectra. But it was clear there were far too many for just this run — even if tomorrow turned out to be a totally clear night. With luck, they could get another two or three quasars done tonight. If everything went right, perhaps another twenty tomorrow. The problem was that tomorrow might *not* be clear. If so, which three objects were most deserving of spending the very precious time on? This was the problem Peter was grappling with.

Peter finally pulled five cards out of the box and turned to Dick for his opinion. When the cards were shoved under his nose, it was clear that Dick had been dozing — not an uncommon occurrence at 2.00am in the morning. A discussion followed. While it was going on, Fred mentioned he was going outside to check the weather. No doubt he would: but the astronomers also suspected he would take his pipe with him. A walk around the cat-walk encircling the dome checking the weather was an excellent excuse not to be missed!

Fred reached to the back of the control desk and picked up his torch. It had a long loop of string attached to it at the handle, which he slipped over his neck. Pulling on a woolly "beanie" knitted cap, he passed out through the door of the control room into the dome. Of course, there would be no glimmer from his torch until he was well outside the dome wall itself and on the cat-walk. The slightest trace of light into the main instrument would totally ruin the exposure. It really would be a pity for light from the distant quasar to have travelled for over 1,000,000,000 years — and half way across the universe — only to be completely washed out by the glow from a 20 cent Ever-Ready battery!

Even worse, it might happen that the astronomers hadn't realized what had happened and the stray light would appear in the spectrum of the quasar as a possible emission line, giving either a wrong redshift or a totally incomprehensible result. Optical astronomers and night assistants were used to walking in the dark — just as radioastronomers became used to walking all over their massive telescopes, very often with only a few square metres of "chicken-wire" mesh between them and a 100-metre fall to the ground.

But, even though it was all in a night's work to Fred, he still shivered slightly as he passed through the pitch-black dome into the small doorway that led outside. It was in just such a situation that an American astronomer had been killed when the dome had moved round unexpectedly and crushed him.

It was a relief to be out in the clear night air. The very new Moon that had been visible as a thin crescent earlier in the night was now gone. The stars shone spectacularly above and, down in the western sky , the last parts of the Milky Way were visible. Even though the sky was clear, the air still smelt damp with the moist air rising laden with the scent of the pine trees in the valley below.

As Fred lighted his pipe, he paused for a minute, worried by some faint clouds in the far southern sky. But a moment later he smiled as he realized they were only the Large and Small Magellanic Galaxies, glowing unnaturally bright in the perfectly clear night air. He was sure there would be no more rain or cloud tonight.

Fred re-entered the control room, glanced at his watch and made a quick check with a chart hanging on the wall. It showed him that morning twilight would come a little after 4.30a.m., or in about another hour and a half. This would be *astronomical twilight* — a precisely defined time when the Sun was still 18 degrees beneath the horizon and when, to most people, it was still pitch-black. But, at the beginning of astronomical twilight, the first faint glow of the rising Sun would be sufficient to cause the astronomer's programme of observations to be abandoned. If not, just 15 minutes or so later and the strength of the Sun's light would be enough to cause permanent damage to the thousands of dollar's worth of spectrographic detectors.

As Fred walked round the control desk and looked at the three men, it was clear that something had happened. They were all wide awake, on their feet and bending over a screen showing the partially reduced results from the spectrograph. The main item of interest was a strong emission line, sticking up like a spike from the "grass" at the bottom of the screen. Its wavelength had been approximately measured by sticking a ruler on the screen and rapid calculations using a pocket calculator were in progress. If the line turned out to be Lyman α then this would be a record redshift. But *was* it Lyman α? If so, then there would not necessarily be any other strong lines visible in the spectrum. But if it were just an unusually strong CIV line, then it might be possible to see the real Lyman α line down at the blue end of the spectrum. One difficulty was that the astronomers had really "gone for broke" on this run, moving the grating in the spectroscope so that the wavelength range they were observing was strongly biased to the red part of the spectrum. There was not a lot of sensitivity in the blue end of the spectrum where the Lyman α would be expected if the redshift were rather more mundane.

What to do? One possibility would be to keep integrating, to see if any more lines appeared out of the noise "grass" as the data became more plentiful. On the other hand, it seemed a better plan to move the grating so that there was a much better "blue" coverage. The trouble with the latter idea was that it would take about 15 precious minutes to make the change — time that could be spent looking at another object.

In the end, they decided to move the grating. Fred had turned on the lights and Dick made a quick trip out into the dome. Far too dangerous to risk jumping onto the telescope structure itself in the pitch-dark. One false move and the astronomers would have crashed to the floor of the dome over 20 metres below. The telescope itself was pointing straight to the zenith to which it had been moved under telescope control to allow access. The grating took only a few minutes to move and they were back in the control room in well under the 15 minutes they had allowed. Lights off again, the telescope slewed back to the quasar's position and a new exposure was under way.

They soon had their answer: at the blue end of the spectrum a very strong emission line quickly "climbed up" out of the noise on the screen. Unfortunately, this was the real Lyman α. The other strong line had obviously been CIV. The quasar was an interesting object — but not one to establish a redshift record. The astronomers smiled wryly at each other. Fred grunted — he'd been looking forward to his bottle of Glenfiddich! They were not too disappointed — after all it had happened many times before. Perhaps the next observing run would turn up something more exciting: they felt sure that it would have to happen one day...!

As they turned back to the computer terminals, they could see the first traces of the sun lighting the screen. The night's observing was almost over. Almost, but not quite. There still had to be more observations of standard stars needed to calibrate the quasar spectra observed tonight. And a small light had to be turned on in the spectrograph itself to measure the irregularities of the observing screen. This so-called "flat field" would need to be exposed at a very, very faint level and for a long time in order not to damage the equipment. In fact, it would be exposing for the next 6 hours or so, long after the astronomers hoped to be in bed!

As they rode down in the lift to the ground floor, they took with them the remnants of their sandwiches and clutched the rest of the observing paraphernalia. They sleepily wished Fred goodnight as he got back into his car to drive down the mountain to his home for a sleep before the start of tonight's observing. It always *was* , "Goodnight" — even though it was technically morning! It just didn't seem quite right to wish somebody good morning as they were getting ready for sleep!

As Fred drove away and the astronomers trudged back to the Lodge, the first real glimpses of the sun shone brilliantly orange on the pure white of the massive telescope dome. Down in the valley these rays also caught unawares a few kangaroos feeding together on the dew-covered grass.

It had been a good night. Not a great one — no momentous discoveries had been made — but typical of many. The astronomers felt satisfied: they had got spectra for another 10 quasars in their sample. Only another few dozen to go to finish the project. Then they could perhaps understand whether the number of quasars really *did* drop off at redshifts around 4 — whether anything could be seen at all at such distances. Perhaps tomorrow they would indeed have found the edge of the universe.

Bibliography

The Astronomy Encyclopaedia, Patrick Moore (ed),Mitchell Beazley, 1987
An excellent reference book on all matters astronomical; contains some in-depth articles on particular subjects such as the Big Bang and galaxy superclusters.

Cosmology, Edward Harrison, Cambridge University Press, 1981
An authoritative and very readable account of cosmology from the earliest days to the present. The sections on the nature of the redshift and Olber's paradox are particularly good.

Quasars, Redshifts and Controversy, Halton Arp, Interstellar Media, 1987
A controversial but fascinating account of the long-standing argument over the non-cosmological nature of the quasar and galaxy redshifts by one of the world's best optical observational astronomers.

The Structure of the Universe, Jayant Narlikar, Oxford University Press, 1977
A rather mathematical but still quite readable book which looks at the universe on its largest scale in a somewhat unusual way. The treatment of the different cosmological models is particularly good.

The First Three Minutes, Steven Weinberg, Basic Books, 1977
A classic account of the crucial first three minutes after the Big Bang took place together with an excellent history of the discovery of the microwave background radiation.

The Hidden Universe, Michael Disney, Dent, 1984
Probably the best all-round book describing the problem of the "missing mass", from the scale of galaxies to that of the whole universe.

Essentials of Astronomy, Lloyd Motz & Anneta Duveen, Blackie and Sons, 1966
A very good general "background" book covering essentially the whole field of modern astronomy and astrophysics.

Relativity, the Special and General Theory, Albert Einstein, Methuen University Paperbacks, Fifteenth Edition, 1954
Although quite old, this is still one of the best introductions to the Special and General Theories of relativity from the "master".

Astrophysical Quantities, C. W. Allen, Athlone Press, University of London, 1973
A superb reference book on all sorts of astrophysical and astronomical data. Not, however, one to sit down and read from cover to cover!

The Red Limit, Timothy Ferris, Corgi Books, 1979
A book with some interesting insights into the people concerned with revealing mankind's growing conception of the universe.

Light from the Depths of Time, Rudolf Kippenhahn, Springer-Verlag, 1987
An excellent, up-to-the-minute book on cosmology. Particularly good is the exposition of the universes of the "Two-landers" or "Flatlanders", as Kippenhahn calls them.

Index